D1074366

ANALYSIS AND SIMULATION OF MULTIPORT SYSTEMS

ANALYSIS AND SIMULATION OF MULTIPORT SYSTEMS
The Bond Graph Approach to Physical System Dynamics

by

Dean Karnopp and Ronald C. Rosenberg

THE M.I.T. PRESS

Massachusetts Institute of Technology

Cambridge, Massachusetts, and London, England

Set in IBM Press Roman and
printed and bound in the United States of America
by The Maple Press Company.

Library of Congress catalog card number: 68-25381

Dedicated to H.M.P.,
who has never failed to amaze us;
and to C.R.K. and M.K.R.,
who have never failed us.

ACKNOWLEDGMENTS

The authors would like to acknowlege the support of Prof. James M. Austin, director of the M.I.T. Summer Session Office, who encouraged us to organize a special summer course on physical system dynamics in 1967, the notes from which have provided a basis for this book. The Summer Session Office also provided financial support for the typing of the manuscript of the book, which was accomplished by Miss Diane Mountain in record time.

The development of the ENPORT-1 programs for digital simulation, which are discussed in Chapter 7, was supported in part by Project MAC, an M.I.T. research program sponsored by the Advanced Research Projects Agency, Department of Defense under Office of Naval Research Contract Number Nonr-4102(01).

PREFACE

The present volume presents those aspects of bond graph techniques which have been thoroughly explored in a form intended to be useful for self-study. Since the concepts and notation of bond graphs are probably unfamiliar to the reader, it may be worthwhile to outline here the history of the development of bond graph techniques from their invention in 1959 by Professor Henry M. Paynter to the present. In an interesting historical note that follows this preface, Prof. Paynter discusses early scientific work that influenced him and the more philosophical underpinnings of bond graphs.

The most basic elements and notations for bond graphs were invented by Prof. Paynter after he had become concerned with power and energy interactions in physical systems. In two papers,[1,2] written in conventional notation for the most part, one can recognize his desire to represent power interactions with a single line, but the operating rules for the new graphical notation were not yet formulated.

By 1961, graduate students at M.I.T. had been exposed to bond graphs, and a book[3] from class notes became available. The book, although suited to supplementing Prof. Paynter's lectures, was not intended to be a self-contained textbook and was not devoted exclusively to bond graphs. Also, many of the implications of bond graphs had not been worked out at the time of its writing. Thus, although much interest was aroused by the book, both in this country and abroad, little progress in bond graph technology was made by those who were not physically present at M.I.T.

In the succeeding years, a number of graduate students and staff at M.I.T. were influenced by bond graphs but, because the notation was unfamiliar to the technical community, most of the references to bond graphs appeared in unpublished theses and notes, e.g., references 4-9. In other cases, workers sidestepped specific references to bond graphs in order to avoid the necessity of explaining the unfamiliar notation. Throughout the years since the invention of bond graphs, many of the students and staff at M.I.T. connected with the System Dynamics and Control Division of the Department of Mechanical Engineering have experimented with bond graphs and contributed to the development of bond graph techniques, although individual contributions are hard to document.

Despite the severe handicap of the lack of a standard reference on the bond graph notation, there are some specific references to bond graphs in the literature.[10-14] Also, two attempts to present bond graph techniques to professional engineers have been made;[15-16] the present volume is motivated by the success of the latest effort.[16]

The authors hope that this book will provide a stimulus to further work with bond graph methods by interesting a wider audience in the techniques and by providing a reference to those aspects of bond graphs that have been thoroughly studied. We recognize that many of the philosophical foundations of the methods that have been so intriguing to past workers are absent here, and some of the advanced work that has been accomplished in the field is not mentioned. These omissions are partly deliberate, in the interest of making the present volume as straightforward a presentation as possible, but also, no doubt, partly due to our own limitations. We hope, and indeed expect, that others will be encouraged by our effort to extend the concepts presented here into areas in which the new notation can make unique contributions to the analysis, simulation, and design of engineering systems.

Dean Karnopp
Ronald C. Rosenberg

January 1, 1968
Cambridge, Massachusetts

References

1. H. M. Paynter, "Generalizing the Concepts of Power Transport and Energy Ports for System Engineering," ASME Paper 58-A-296, presented at 1958 Annual Meeting, New York, N. Y.
2. H. M. Paynter, "Hydraulics by Analog - An Electronic Model of a Pumping Plant," *J. Boston Soc. of Civil Engineers,* July 1959, pp. 197-219.
3. H. M. Paynter, *Analysis and Design of Engineering Systems,* The M.I.T. Press, Cambridge, Mass., 1961.
4. D. R. Vaughan, *Speed Control in Hydro-Electric Power Systems,* Ph.D. Thesis, Dept. of Mechanical Engineering, M.I.T., Cambridge, Mass., Sept. 1962.
5. R. C. Rosenberg, *Computer-Aided Teaching of Dynamic System Behavior,* Sc.D. Thesis, Dept. of Mechanical Engineering, M.I.T., Cambridge, Mass., June 1965.
6. M. R. Weinberger, *Multi-Stage Random Search and Automatic Network Synthesis,* Ph.D. Thesis, Department of Mechanical Engineering, M.I.T., Cambridge, Mass., Jan. 1966.
7. J. C. Free, *Identification of Parameters for Nonlinear Lumped Models of Dynamic Systems from System Transient Response,* Ph.D. Thesis, Dept. of Mechanical Engineering, M.I.T., Cambridge, Mass., August 1967.
8. L. L. Evans, *Simulation Techniques for the Study of Non-Linear Magnetic Field Engineering Systems,* Sc.D. Thesis, Dept. of Mechanical Engineering, M.I.T., Cambridge, Mass., Aug. 1967.
9. A. G. J. MacFarlane, "Notes on the Multiport Approach to Systems Analysis and the Theory of Bond Graphs," Unpublished notes, Dept. of Mechanical Engineering, M.I.T., Cambridge, Mass., Aug. 1965, 67 pages.
10. H. M. Paynter, "Computer Representations of Polyphase Alternating Current Systems for Dynamic Analysis and Control," *Automatic and Remote Control, Proc. First International Congress of the International Federation of Automatic Control,* Moscow, 1960.
11. H. M. Paynter and D. C. Karnopp, "Design and Control of Engineering Multiport Systems," *Proc. IFAC Tokyo Symposium on Systems Engineering for Control System Design,* 1965, pp. 443-454.
12. F. T. Brown, "On the Future of Dynamic Analysis of Fluid Systems," in *Fluidics,* E. F. Humphrey and D. H. Tarumoto, eds., Fluid Amplifier Associates, Inc., Boston, Mass., 1965, pp. 262-268.
13. R. D. Gustafson, "A New Servovalve Concept - The Ball Valve," SAE Conf. Proc. Aerospace Fluid Power Systems and Equipment Conference, Los Angeles, Calif., May 18-20, 1965, pp. 458-470.
14. D. C. Karnopp, "Computer Representation of Continuous Vibratory Systems Using Normal Modes and Bond Graph Techniques," *Simulation,* v. 10, n. 3, Mar. 1968, pp. 129-135.
15. H. M. Paynter, Course Notes for Special Summer Course 2.75s, *Electronic Models for the Engineering of Multiport Systems,* M.I.T., July 1963.
16. D. C. Karnopp and R. C. Rosenberg, Course Notes for Special Summer Course 2.22s, *Physical System Dynamics,* M.I.T., July 1967.

HISTORICAL NOTE

The authors of this book have done me the honor of requesting a few words on the genesis of the bond graph. As this history has not been heretofore recorded, perhaps I can, in turn, honor by such an account this first book devoted exclusively to the study of physical system dynamics using bond graphs.

While yet a boy in high school, I was persuaded through the books of Steinmetz to adopt the rather curious viewpoint that voltage and current are mere mathematical fictions, product-factors of the real instantaneous power, taken proportional to the electric and magnetic field energies, respectively.[1] From that beginning, I have gradually become committed to the belief that energy and power alone are the fundamental dynamical variables, the ultimate currency of all physical interaction and transaction. So it was quite natural that my effort to develop a general theory of engineering systems, which began in 1950, should be preoccupied with energy flux and power flow.

The term "multiport," now standard in circuit theory, originated with Harold A. Wheeler[2] in 1949 in a conscious effort to extend energy-based network techniques to microwave bands and beyond. Generalizing on these ideas yet further, to extend their use to mechanical and other physical systems, my colleagues and I began to employ the terms "energy ports," "power bonds," and "multiport elements" as early as 1955.

But it was clear at the outset that conventional circuit graphing was inadequate for our purpose; for example, it was not possible to represent a 3-port gate valve as a circuit element. Until 1959, it was our custom to employ a form of duplex block diagram or signal flow graph as a system schematic (similar to those shown in Chapter 6 of the present book). Yet we were dissatisfied by the fact that, unlike circuit graphing, such diagrams forced an assignment of signal causality. Moreover, even esthetically, these graphs seemed needlessly confusing for complex systems. Clearly, we were searching for a new form of minimal or irreducible graph.

However, the requisite form of graph had already been available for just over a century, since its introduction by A.S. Couper[3] in 1858 in the form of structural formulas for chemistry. These structure graphs, upon further development by A. Crum Brown, were then expanded into a complete system, based upon a theory of valency, by Sir Edward Frankland in 1865-66.[4] It is also interesting that while Crum Brown's and Frankland's early graphs had circles around the letters representing elements, users found these circles superfluous, so that in the second (1870) edition of his book Frankland revised his structural formulas to the fashion used to this day.

About 1870, these structure graphs attracted the attention of the mathematician W.K. Clifford in England and the scientist-logician-philosopher C.S. Peirce in America. Clifford's interest led shortly before his death to the abstraction of a "linear graph" of "nodes" and "branches" as a mathematical system in its own right. Now it is conventional in modern graph theory to take *each undirected* branch as equivalent to a *duplex pair* of *oppositely directed* branches. Thus it was possible to graph each signal duplex representing a power flow as a single line – the power bond – to obtain the generalization of the power engineers' "one-line diagram."

On the other hand, Peirce was concerned throughout his career with the theory of systems of relations: his "theory of relatives." For him the *nodes* of a graph were taken to represent the *relations,* and the *branches,* the *terms.*[5] Moreover, Peirce stressed the singular role of the triadic (or 3-term) relation.[6] Finally, he insisted that every conjunction of two or more branches could itself be considered as a relation.[7] So it was that Peirce expressed systems of relations and of propositional functions as simple structural formulas.

Following Peirce, then, we adopted the convention of graphing each multiport as a *nodal* element, representing a particular constraint among the power bonds. But for circuits, then, this would require that we represent the two Kirchhoff Laws, themselves, as manifest multiport nodes!

Thus were devised on April 24, 1959, the two ideal 3-port energy junctions (0,1) to render the system of bond graphs a complete and formal discipline. The complete system was then first published in 1961.[8]

Henry M. Paynter

January 30, 1968
Cambridge, Massachusetts

References

1. C. P. Steinmetz, *Theory and Calculation of Transient Electric Phenomena and Oscillations,* McGraw Publishing Co., New York, 1909, p. 5.
2. H. A. Wheeler and D. Dettinger, "Measuring the efficiency of a superheterodyne converter by the input impedance circle diagram," *Wheeler Monograph No. 9,* Wheeler Laboratories, Great Neck, N. Y., 1949, p. 7.
3. A. S. Couper, "On a new chemical theory," *The Philosophical Magazine and Journal of Science,* [4], v. 16, pp. 104-116 (1858).
4. E. Frankland, *Lecture Notes for Chemical Students: Embracing Mineral and Organic Chemistry,* John Van Voorst, London, 1866.
5. C. S. Peirce, *Collected Papers,* Harvard University Press, Cambridge, Mass., 1931, 1933: 3:468-470; 3:479.
6. *Ibid.,* 1:347, 4:307-310.
7. *Ibid.,* 3:471.
8. H. M. Paynter, *Analysis and Design of Engineering Systems,* The M.I.T. Press, Cambridge, Mass., 1961.

CONTENTS

1. INTRODUCTION

1.1 Models of dynamic physical systems

The variety of dynamic systems of interest to engineers and scientists is very large and there is a natural tendency, in the educational process and in professional practice, to form special areas of interest and competence. A partial listing of the special fields relating to system dynamics of interest in engineering and applied science might include the following: *solid mechanics:* rigid body dynamics, vibration, physical acoustics; *fluid mechanics:* hydraulics, pneumatics; *electromagnetics:* circuits, electromechanics; *heat transfer:* energy conversion, thermal stresses; *automatic control; instrumentation, computation.* It is not reasonable to suppose that a single individual can become as competent in several of these specialties as he could in just one or two or, for that matter, that a single method of attack will be equally as fruitful for problems in all the fields as it may be for certain of the fields. This is because the significant problems in the various fields and hence the types of questions involved and decisions to be made vary widely from field to field.

On the other hand, if one looks with a critical eye at the dynamic models used in practice, one cannot help but be struck by the strong analogies that exist between the systems analyzed within the confines of single fields of specialization. This is all the more evident when one considers the dynamic models of composite systems, the parts of which fall into several areas of specialization. In order to make the analysis of a large system at all tractable, the models of the component parts must be rather simple, and it is usually the simpler models within fields of specialization that turn out to be closely analogous to models in other fields. These observations lead one to seek a uniform way to describe dynamic models of physical systems that traditionally fall into specialized categories but do have a great deal in common.

As the reader is probably aware, there have been many attempts to exploit analogies between various systems. Anyone exposed to a course on circuit theory, for example, can hardly fail to be impressed with the power of the circuit graph and its associated topological and operational techniques. There is therefore strong appeal in the idea of finding equivalent circuits for nonelectrical dynamic systems. In many cases one may be easily convinced that an electric circuit graph is preferable to the clumsy and nonstandard diagrams often used in other fields, but part of the advantages of circuit graphs for systems composed of simple elements is lost for more general systems. In fact, attempts to set up a structure for system analysis based on the electric circuit concept will prove severely limited in usefulness for significant problems in many other fields for several reasons. For example, the equivalent circuits for some systems would be so complex as to be no more subject to interpretation than the standard diagrams and equations used in a particular field. Further, circuit elements are nodic; that is, they react to potential differences only, while this property is not universal for elements in nominally analogous fields. While controlled sources may be included in circuits to model virtually any system that may be described by equations, a circuit graph dominated by controlled sources does not have any great advantage over other representations.

Perhaps the most universal method for representing dynamic systems is through differential equations, and it is entirely superfluous to point out the advantages of this method. On the other hand, anyone who has ploughed through page after page of equations describing an only moderately complex system will testify that despite the explicit nature of differential equations, or perhaps because of it, it may still be very hard to see just what the subsystem models are and whether some effect has been badly or incorrectly modeled. Also, unless some ingenuity is employed in notation, it is not clear whether all the required equations have been written nor is there any obvious route to a solution or simulation scheme. In fact, hardly any engineer of even modest experience can claim to have avoided the embarrassing experience of writing an equation set that subsequently was found to admit of no solution at all.

One reason for these difficulties may be that the problem formulation and solution are typically thought of as entirely separate operations. If all equations were written in a computer language such as FORTRAN, not as relations but as computable operations, the situation might be improved in a sense, but this will probably never be a popular method for analytical work.

Another reservation about using conventional mathematical symbolism as the only fundamental tool for systems analysis is that, just as the circuit idea is too restrictive for general physical systems, mathematical formulations are probably too general. Clearly, if we are only interested in physical systems, there must be some requirements on the formulation that could set physical systems apart from, say, economic systems or abstract dynamical systems. The distinction, which will be exploited in this book, will be based on the implications of power and energy flow in physical systems.

Thus the procedure to be followed will be to formulate problems in terms of power and energy variables first, and then to proceed to the general-purpose techniques involving the representation of the system in differential equation form, the drawing of signal flow graphs, or the implementation of a simulation procedure. The mechanism for the convenient and rigorous system of power flow will be the bond graph, and the main purpose of this study will be to present the rules and methods for working with bond graphs. Since the concepts and notation for bond graphs are still relatively new and there is a strong desire not to delimit prematurely the types of physical systems which may be described using bond graphs, what one might call the "theory of bond graphs" is not as complete or disciplined as, for example, the theory of electric circuits. It is, however, possible to give reasonably complete rules and operating procedures for generating and using bond graphs for most of the dynamic models used in practice in many of the separate fields which collectively comprise physical system dynamics. We intend that a specialist in the dynamics of a certain field should recognize the bond graph form for many of the models used in his field, and that dynamic systems outside his normal range of expertise will be made more understandable to him through the bond graph formalism.

1.2 Goals of bond graph methods

It may be useful here to outline the goals of bond graph methods as we see them. Many of these goals are, in large measure, met by presently known bond graph techniques applicable to restricted but useful and important classes of physical systems, and we optimistically expect that further research will be successful in extending these classes. The reader may judge for himself whether the goals we consider important are reasonable and, from the remainder of this book, how successful the bond graph techniques are in meeting these goals.

1. Certainly one of the fundamental goals for bond graphs is to provide a uniform mechanism for the description of a wide variety of physical systems. While there have been many attempts to do this in the past, one of the purposes of bond graphs is to do for systems involving mixed physical domains

what a device such as the circuit graph does for electromagnetic systems. We hope to exhibit the *structure* of rather complex mixed domain systems in a manner closely connected with what is often called the "physics" of the systems involved. In many cases, we wish to provide the means for direct physical modeling (i.e., the synthesis of a model of a system) by directly accounting for energy storage, supply, and dissipation effects throughout the system based on fundamental physical considerations.

2. We wish to focus attention on physical systems and power and energy exchanges. Although we will allow pure signal flows (i.e., zero power information transfer) in the scope of bond graph techniques, these signal flows will appear as special cases of general power interactions and will be used only as a result of a conscious act in the modeling process. By this means, some fairly common errors and inconsistencies that result from an inadvertent neglect of back effects may be avoided. Particularly, in low power electrical signal processing systems, the existence of isolating amplifiers and gross impedance mismatches often permits the use of methods that do not yield consistent results when finite power interactions are involved. For example, Fig. 1-1 shows a simple RC circuit and its "textbook" transfer function representation. A well-schooled student will assume without an explicit statement to the contrary that the current at the terminals associated with the voltage e_2 is always zero. However, if two RC networks are cascaded, he may well be tempted to multiply two transfer functions to find "the transfer function" for the combined network, leading to the paradox shown in the lower part of Fig. 1-1. While the source of the difficulty is quite evident in this example, in more complex situations transfer functions are often misused in a similar manner. Bond graphs should help the unwary avoid being trapped into false characterizations of dynamic systems because of neglected back effects.

3. A physically based sign convention is to be established and indicated in an explicit manner on the bond graphs. This seemingly trivial goal is actually quite important, as anyone who has attempted to extract numerical results

$$\frac{E_2(s)}{E_1(s)} \stackrel{?}{=} \frac{1}{\tau_1 s+1}, \quad \tau_1 = R_1 C_1 .$$

$$\frac{E_3(s)}{E_1(s)} \neq \frac{1}{(\tau_1 s+1)(\tau_2 s+1)}, \quad \tau_1 = R_1 C_1, \ \tau_2 = R_2 C_2 .$$

Fig. 1-1 A paradox in the prediction of transfer functions for circuits resulting from incomplete specification of the circuit.

from an analysis will testify. This is particularly true since we will not restrict the systems to be analyzed to be conservative or stable so that some standard means for checking signs will not be available in general. In addition, for linear systems and some nonlinear systems we desire a means for indicating parameter values for elements and initial conditions directly on the bond graph in an unambiguous fashion.

4. An important goal not usually mentioned for conventional systems analysis techniques involves obtaining an explicit indication of which variables for an element are to be considered independent and which are to be considered dependent or, said another way, which are the input and which are the output variables. In the context of bond graphs, these questions have become known as questions of *causality* or, to avoid conflicts with other related meanings of the word, *computing causality* or *experimental causality.* The problem of assigning a particular causality to a system model relates directly to the manner in which the system can be simulated or the manner in which the system equations can be solved. When all matters concerning the assignment of causality have been settled, then one is confident that the system has been well formulated in the sense that a recipe for finding the time history of all system variables, given the initial system state and the external inputs, is available.

Signal descriptions of elements are inherently causal in the described sense, but the form of the causality may not be appropriate for every system of which the element might be a part. Equation sets for systems elements are typically noncausal in form, and it is often not a trivial job to impose a causal structure on a large set of equations. The attempt to introduce causality in bond graphs is often revealing of the fundamental character of parts of the system, as will be demonstrated later.

5. It is important that bond graph techniques be compatible with standard analysis methods of proven usefulness. It is a purpose of the bond graph techniques to provide a framework for setting up analytical machinery in a manner disciplined to be physically consistent. The bond graph, quite apart from any philosophical implications of the study of power flow using linear graphs, may be regarded as a practical device for the generation of differential equations, block diagrams, signal flow graphs, transfer functions or the like, for for physical systems.

6. Another goal of the bond graph methods involves simulation, whether analog or digital. Some of the most interesting and important applications of bond graph techniques will certainly be in the simulation of complex dynamic systems in which the physical logic of the subsystem models is not lost because of the complexity of the system problem. In particular, one hopes for a certain flexibility in the choice of the subsystem models, so that a balanced system model may be formed and the effects of system design changes may

be readily exhibited. In many simulation programs, a rigidity is built in at an early stage for reasons of analytical convenience. For example, transfer functions may be formed in which many physical parameters are combined into the parameters actually appearing in the transfer functions. Assessing the effect of a single physical parameter change, or the introduction of a single nonlinearity in the model of an element may require a virtual reanalysis of the entire system. By relegating much of the manipulation of the bond graphs to a computer, one may pass from the physical system to the simulation in a very direct manner, avoiding the morass of detail that often accompanies the standard methods for setting up a simulation. Certain classes of problems have already been programmed for automated simulation using bond graph models and the ENPORT program, and it is our hope that further work in this direction will produce generally useful results.

1.3 Scope and intent of the present volume

This book is essentially a progress report on the theory and application of a relatively new notation for the study of physical system dynamics. As such, we do not intend to discuss the art of constructing models of physical devices which are valid in some specific sense. On the other hand, we hope to demonstrate the power of bond graph techniques to provide a variety of system models based on physical effects and with well-understood characteristics. We will assume that the reader has some experience in the modeling of dynamic systems in at least one field and will recognize the standard schematic diagrams that will be used in the examples to be discussed.

Although our intent is first of all to present the bond graph notation and to relate the techniques using bond graphs with standard techniques, we also hope that in the process the reader will gain experience in physical system analysis that will be of value whether or not bond graphs are used specifically. It would hardly be possible for one to follow the arguments regarding power, energy, sign conventions, computing causality and simulation without knowing or learning a great deal about system formulation.

In addition to stimulating interest in further research on bond graph methods, we hope this work will also prove of value to practicing system dynamicists and will be useful in the teaching of system dynamics to engineers and scientists in applied fields.

2. ENGINEERING MULTIPORTS

In this chapter we identify the types of physical systems that will be the concern of the remainder of the book. The term "engineering" in its title is meant to imply that our ultimate goal is to describe the systems in such a manner that manipulations of the component characteristics of interconnected systems to achieve a desired type of behavior may be carried out in a convenient way. For this reason our descriptions, which will follow established engineering practice in most cases, will not be the simplest, the most fundamental, or the most elegant ones in the sense that a theoretical physicist or mathematician might use these terms. We, in common with most of the engineering profession, will be concerned with efficient, useful, and verifiable approximate descriptions of systems. As we shall demonstrate, a wide variety of dynamic systems are, in fact, analyzed with the use of concepts and techniques that have a great deal in common, however different the various fields of engineering may appear to the narrowly trained specialist. It will suit our purposes to use a common descriptive and graphic language for all systems. Such a language is necessarily more abstract than a specialized language peculiar to a single field, but the benefits for an over-all system analysis of a common means of describing all the subsystems are very significant.

2.1 Graphical representations of dynamic systems

Some mathematicians, among them the great Lagrange, seem to have felt that it would be a virtue to be able to study dynamics without diagrams or other graphical notation. In engineering, on the other hand, the view that a picture is worth a thousand words has generally prevailed, and the starting point for the analysis of any dynamic system is usually a schematic diagram or other graphical or pictorial representation of the model of the physical system under study.

Since it is the purpose of this book to discuss the uses of a particular graphical notation, the bond graph, and since a variety of other graphical representation schemes are in common use, it is probably worthwhile to see whether there are deficiencies in the usual graphical methods that perhaps can be avoided by using bond graphs. At the outset, we should state that, within restricted physical domains, excellent graphical representations and corresponding analytical techniques already exist. It would be hard, for example, to generate any great enthusiasm for a new notation for electric circuits. The circuit graph with its topological and operational methods has certainly proved its usefulness within the domain of electric circuits. Similar statements could be made for the representations used in a number of other special fields of dynamics. When, however, we consider systems in which two or more physical domains are coupled, the situation is not so simple. The diagrams used to represent such systems typically are a hodgepodge of the diagrams used in the physical domains involved, and many of the techniques associated with the individual physical domains become invalid for the coupled system or must be applied with great circumspection.

In Fig. 2-1, three rather different types of graphical representation of dynamic physical systems are shown. Although the diagrams are not standardized to the extent that electric circuit graphs are, a specialist in the fields involved would undoubtedly understand roughly what the person who drew the diagram had in mind.

The point of considering these diagrams is to note that in many cases the attempt to represent interconnected subsystems leads to awkward combinations of words, equations, symbols, schematic diagrams, and semipictorial representations. Clearly, many system representations are incomplete in that there is not a single unambiguous meaning attached to each symbol. The diagrams of Fig. 2-1 are therefore really only the skeletons of the description of the system and must be supplemented by equations, or by engineering judgment, or by common sense, and unstated assumptions must be supplied. For example, in Fig. 2-1(a), the main motor is shown without any mechanical connection to anything, although there seems to be little point to a Ward-Leonard speed control system which does not drive some load. It is unfortunate that in many dynamic analyses so many assumptions are unstated and so many descriptions

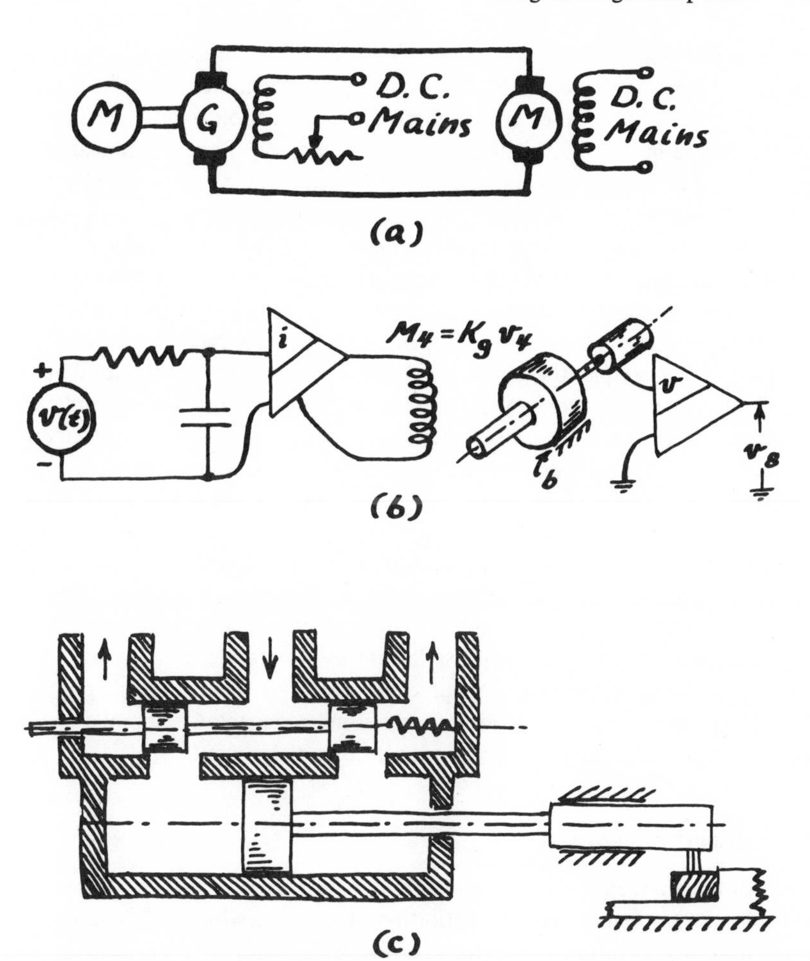

Fig. 2-1 Conventional representations of some simple dynamic systems. (a) Ward-Leonard system used for speed control of a D.C. motor, (b) Electromechanical system with amplification, (c) Hydraulic machine tool positioning system.

of systems are actually incomplete. One purpose of a unified and systematic approach to system dynamics is to make assumptions more explicit and to force system descriptions to be complete.

We may enquire, however, if there are some common features to system diagrams such as those shown in Fig. 2-1. One obvious feature of those diagrams is that certain system elements are regarded as *components.* For example, a motor, a shaft, an amplifier, and a hydraulic ram are clearly being thought of as single physical entities even though in every case one can argue that each component is itself a system which could be represented by a more fundamental set of elements. For example, an electric motor could be studied from the point of view of electromagnetic field interactions, and a shaft could be represented in the manner of continuum mechanics. The system analyst must choose at least an initial model of the system components which he hopes will provide a suitable basis for analysis and the subsequent engineering decisions to be made. If the component description proves inadequate for answering questions asked about system performance, it must be revised. At any stage in the analysis, however, a component description in terms of certain variables forces the system description to be made in a compatible set of variables. For example, the generator of Fig. 2-1(a) will in all likelihood be described in terms of a voltage and current in the armature, a voltage and current in the field, and a torque and speed of the rotor. The shaft connecting the motor with the generator must therefore be described in terms of a single torque and angular speed at the generator, even though one might argue somewhat pedantically that, considered as a three-dimensional continuum, a single rotational speed for the end of the shaft is difficult to define. Thus, although one is still free to model the shaft as a distributed system between the motor and the generator, the use of standard torque-speed characteristics for the generator seriously restricts the possible choices for a model of the shaft.

Since the dominant feature of graphical representations of dynamic physical systems involves the depiction of a set of interconnected components, we will now discuss, in more detail, the concept of a component.

2.2 Multiport components

One of the first, and often unrationalized, acts in system analysis is the isolation of components and the definition of variables which will be used to characterize the component. In the left side of Fig. 2-2, several system components are shown schematically and some typical variables are shown. As we have noted, the act of identifying variables does restrict the models of components that are to be interconnected. On the other hand, after the variables have been defined there still remains a great deal of flexibility in modeling the internal dynamics of the components. This flexibility in selecting compatible internal models for components will be discussed in later sections of the book. For the present we observe that in a great many cases the external variables selected for physical component description are directly related to power flow. In the typical situations shown in Fig. 2-2 we find variables defined in such a manner that the product of two variables is power (e.g. force times velocity, torque times angular velocity, pressure times volume flow, voltage times current). In most cases the identification of variables may be regarded as the identification of a *port* at which power interactions between

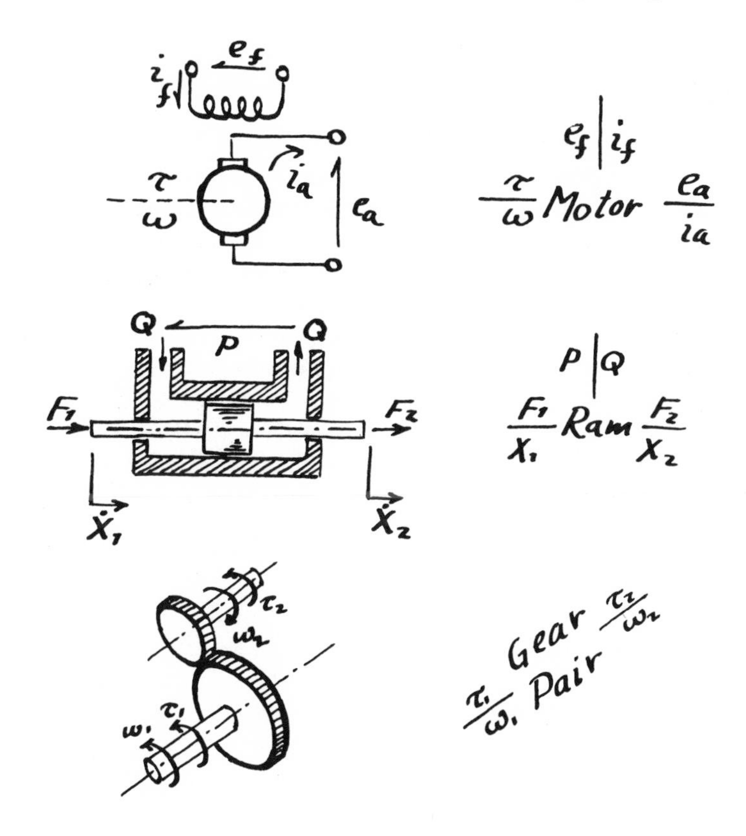

Fig. 2- 2 Some elementary systems considered as components and shown schematically on the left and as multiports on the right.

the component and its environment can occur. A way of describing a component is then to call it a *multiport,* i.e., a subsystem that may interact with other systems through one or more ports. Quite often the ports of the subsystems are separated spatially and are visible in the type of system diagram shown in Fig. 2-1, but later it will become evident that engineers do not hesitate to use ports (or to define power interactions) that are impossible to localize in space or to indicate on a semipictorial representation of the component. The bond graph will show all ports explicitly, whether or not the port is associated with a spatial location on a component.

In this text we consider the identification of the power interactions among elements as the fundamental partitioning process involved in modeling physical systems. While it is not necessary that power always be expressed as a product of two variables (for wave propagation problems, it is common to split up power flows into incident and reflected parts), it will simplify the presentation of bond graph techniques to restrict the discussion here to product representations of power. It will be our practice to represent components or multiports with words or letters and ports or power interactions with single lines or bonds. In the right side of Fig. 2-2, the physical components are represented as multiports with ports or free bonds indicated. Variables, such as voltage, current, force, and velocity, may be indicated as shown on the bonds. Actually, it is the ports and their bonds that are of primary interest since the expression of power flow could, in principle, take many forms, depending on just how variables were defined.

Now, although the internal description of each multiport is quite unrestricted, the reason for use of the word "bond" is evident when we consider that systems are made up of interconnected, or "bonded," multiports. When, for example, a motor is connected by a shaft to a generator, the bond graph for this system is as given in Fig. 2-3. The bond between the shaft and the motor indicates that a power interaction can occur. It also indicates that at the

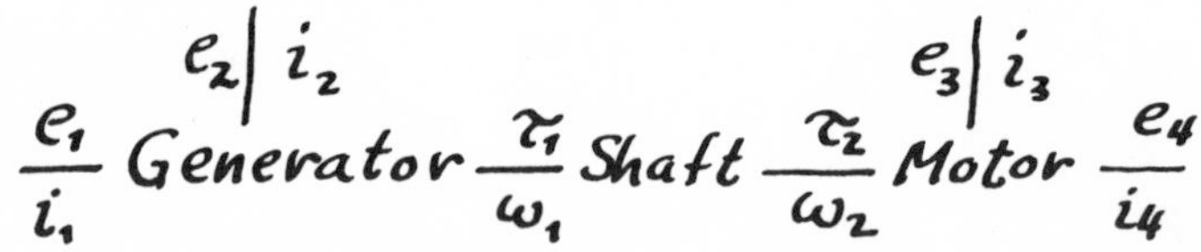

$$e_2 \,|\, i_2 \qquad\qquad\qquad\qquad e_3 \,|\, i_3$$

$$\frac{e_1}{i_1}\ \text{Generator}\ \frac{\tau_1}{\omega_1}\ \text{Shaft}\ \frac{\tau_2}{\omega_2}\ \text{Motor}\ \frac{e_4}{i_4}$$

Fig. 2-3 Three interconnected multiports shown in bond graph notation.

motor end of the shaft there is a single torque and angular speed that apply to both the motor and the motor end of the shaft. Note that at the generator end of the shaft another pair of power variables may be defined and another power interaction may take place. If the shaft were assumed to be rigid and massless, the two torques and the two angular velocities would be identical; thus the simplest model for the shaft is a simple bond. If elasticity, inertia, and/or bearing losses of the shaft were felt to be important, then the shaft would become a structured multiport itself.

2.3 Effort and flow variables

The class of multiports to be treated in this book has the property that each bond of a multiport is associated with a scalar power flow expressible as a product of two variables. It should be emphasized that power need not be expressed as a product in the actual analysis. For present purposes it is important merely that power can be so expressed. For this class of systems it is common practice to split the power into particular factors that are easily measured and that can be given physical interpretations. In general discussions,

convenient to give the names *effort,* e, and *flow,* f, to the two factors and to define the *power, P,* as follows:

$$P(t) = e(t) \cdot f(t), \qquad (2.1)$$

in which all the variables have been indicated as functions of time. In Table 2-1 some common physical variables are listed and it is indicated which variable will be considered to be an effort quantity and which will be taken to be the flow quantity.

Table 2-1. Some effort and flow quantities

Domain	*Effort, e(t)*	*Flow, f(t)*
Mechanical		
translation	Force component, F(t)	Velocity component, V(t)
rotation	Torque component, τ(t)	Angular velocity component, ω(t)
Hydraulic or pneumatic systems	Pressure, P(t) Head, H(t)	Volume flow rate, Q(t) Weight flow rate, W(t)
Electrical circuit	Voltage, e(t)	Current, i(t)

A number of comments on Table 2-1 are in order. First, note that we prefer to consider efforts and flows as scalar quantities. Although a vector force **F**(t) acting on a material point with vector velocity **V**(t) has an associated scalar power *P*(t) given by the scalar product

$$P(t) = \mathbf{F}(t) \cdot \mathbf{V}(t), \qquad (2.2)$$

we will refer to the vector quantities by means of components relative to a particular coordinate system. For example, if an orthogonal coordinate system were indicated by the coordinates x_1, x_2, x_3 and the vector components **F** and **V** were designated by corresponding subscripts, Eq. 2.2 could be expressed as follows:

$$P(t) = P_1(t) + P_2(t) + P_3(t),$$

$$P_i(t) = F_i(t) \cdot V_i(t); \quad i = 1, 2, 3, \qquad (2.3)$$

where the F_i and V_i would be efforts and flows and the *vector power port* would be considered as three separate *scalar ports.* In fact, this view is usually necessary when computation is to be done.

Second, while the first four entries in the effort and flow columns of Table 2-1 have a natural affinity based on concepts of force and velocity, it is not so obvious that both force and voltage should be considered as effort quantities and hence be treated in an analogous fashion. The reader may be aware of the many attempts to decide which pairs of mechanical and electrical variables are best treated analogously. In relating electrical circuits and mechanical systems the two possibilities were often called the "impedance analog" and the "mobility analog." Claims have been made that variables in several domains have certain natural similarities. For example, it has been argued that the power variables split naturally into intensive-extensive or across-through pairs and that this provides a rationale for considering one member of the pair as the equivalent of an effort and the other as a flow. The scheme of Table 2-1 is used here essentially for historical reasons. The choice seems natural in certain respects, but does result in series electrical circuit connections being considered as analogous to parallel mechanical system connections. In the bond graph approach, however, this causes no difficulty because the treatment of effort and flow is symmetrical and thus the selection of effort-flow pairs is quite arbitrary. None of the concepts and techniques discussed in this book would change in any essential way if the roles of effort and flow were interchanged in any domain. Thus we feel no need to provide any strong justification for our choice of effort and flow quantities.

The range of systems considered has been carefully restricted to include only those domains for which a pair of variables exist whose product is a power quantity. Thus heat flow problems will not be treated here, although the techniques developed can be extended to such problems if care is taken not to make invalid power-energy interpretations.

Another important class of problems that does not appear in Table 2-1 involves more complicated types of power bonds than we are presently considering. For example, the power flow associated with a steam line involves not only pressure and volume flow but also the temperature of the flowing steam. Although this type of problem has received some study in the past, it has an extra complexity best appreciated after the techniques suitable for systems of the type defined in Table 2-1 have been mastered; we will therefore not discuss such complex interactions in the present volume.

2.4 Classification of multiports

The two fundamental types of entities in bond graphs are the bonds themselves and multiports. Since a large number of multiports will be defined in succeeding chapters and bonded to other multiport components and systems, it is worthwhile at this point to begin to think of all physical devices as multiports. It is also of interest to try to classify the types of multiports that can exist.

The most obvious classification scheme for multiports is based on the number of ports through which the device interacts with the remainder of the system. A *1-port*, by definition, is assumed to interact at a single port with its environment. Internally, a 1-port may be either simple or complex. For example, a single electrical resistor may be taken to be a 1-port if the only power interaction that is considered involves the current through the resistor and the potential drop appearing across the terminals of the resistor. Similarly, an ordinary wall socket into which an appliance is plugged would probably be considered as a 1-port in predicting the dynamic response of the appliance, but whether the socket was considered to be a simple 60-cycle, 110-volt rms voltage source or the complex generating and distribution system that actually supplies the electric power to wall sockets is fundamentally a choice which the system dynamicist must make. For some purposes, the voltage source representation of the 1-port wall socket is clearly not adequate and a more sophisticated model would be in order.

A *2-port* has power interactions at two ports. A permanent magnet generator would typically be considered to have a mechanical port to which power in the form of a torque times a speed could be supplied and an electrical port from which power in the form of a voltage times a current could be obtained. A pump could be modeled as a similar 2-port as long as a suitable pressure difference and flow, and a torque and angular speed were sufficient to describe the operation of the pump. Another example of a 2-port is the gear pair in Fig. 2-2.

The electric motor and the hydraulic ram shown in Fig. 2-2 are clearly being modeled as *3-ports* with three distinct power interactions in each case. The classification scheme may be carried on to define *4-ports, 5-ports,* and so on. In general, one refers to an *n-port* to indicate a generic multiport.

While the classification of a multiport is unambiguous when the device is inserted into a system model, a physical device cannot be classified once and for all, and even a particular model of a device is sometimes hard to classify unambiguously. The hydraulic ram of Fig. 2-2, for example, might be used in a system in which F_1 was always identically zero. In such a case the ram would clearly be functioning as a 2-port, not a 3-port, although to make a point one could argue that the third port was simply bonded to a force source which happened to have $F_1 = 0$ as its characteristic.

A further classification of multiports is concerned with the physical domains involved with the ports of the device. A *1-type* n-port has only one type of energy flow at all of its n ports. The gear pair of Fig. 2-2 is a 1-type 2-port. All transducers are at least 2-type elements. The first two multiports of Fig. 2-2 are 2-type 3-ports, and one can imagine much more complex multiports composed of several transducers bonded together to form a subsystem.

A multiport that has ports involving more than a single type of power is of particular interest because the existence of such an element allows the formation of coupled multiple energy domain systems. Such systems often strain the traditional techniques of graphical representation, as illustrated by Fig. 2-2(b). From the point of view of bond graphs, however, all power transactions may be handled in a uniform manner, namely, by means of single lines or bonds representing power. Sometimes each energy domain is represented by a coded line (solid, dashed, dotted, etc.) for the bonds, but this device is merely a convenience for quick visual interpretation and is not necessary in using the general bond graph techniques. Often effort and flow variable symbols written next to the bonds as in Fig. 2-2 serve to identify the type of energy flow involved.

Another classification of multiports may be made on the basis of *reducibility*. Once a basic set of multiports has been defined, one may form composite multiports by bonding together multiports from the basic set. Such a composite multiport is then said to be *reducible* in terms of the basic set. It happens that some multiports are not reducible in terms of the given basic set. Such multiports then are said to be *irreducible*.

This concept of reducibility will be easier to appreciate after we have defined a particular basic set of multiports, but the concept is easily illustrated by means of an example. Consider a complex electrical network that is connected into a system only at two terminal pairs. Taken as a component the network is clearly a 2-port. If we are successful in representing all the network components as interconnected multiports from some basic set, then the network is a reducible 1-type 2-port. On the other hand, if a complex multiport is describable in terms of port variables, perhaps only in terms of experimental data, it may well be necessary to treat the multiport as an irreducible multiport. It might be best, for example, to use the data from performance maps of a turbine in a direct fashion rather than to try to find some combination of elements that, when interconnected, would exactly or approximately reproduce the maps.

Clearly, the concept of irreducibility is a relative one and depends on one's choice of the basic set of multiports. In Chapter 3 we shall consider one basic set of multiports that is generally useful, but it would be impossible to defend the contention that this set is *the* basic set, and hence we shall refrain from attempting to classify a given multiport as reducible or irreducible in an absolute sense.

2.5 Interconnected multiports

In Fig. 2-3 it has already been shown how the bonds of a multiport are used to form composite systems. When components share common power variables, e.g., common efforts and common flows, then we may show the components bonded together with a single line. When multiports are bonded together, power interactions can occur and hence energy may flow from one multiport to the other. A graph of the type of Fig. 2-3 is called a *word bond graph* and, although the models of the multiports are not yet explicit in this form of bond graph, the major power interactions and corresponding efforts and flows

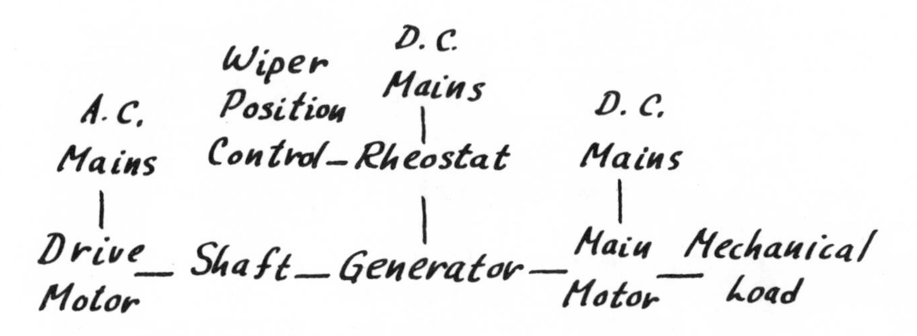

Fig. 2-4 Word bond graph for Ward-Leonard system of Fig. 2-1(a).

are clearly identified. When the components are reducible, a more explicit form of bond graph may be developed from a word bond graph, but for the present we are concerned with the overview of the system provided by the word bond graph.

Consider the bond graph shown in Fig. 2-4, a somewhat more complete version of the Ward-Leonard set shown in Fig. 2-1(a). The main motor has been shown connected to a load and the electrical terminals of the induction motor have been shown connected to an A.C. power supply. When forming a system from multiport components such as those shown at the right of Fig. 2-2, one is always aware of free bonds or ports that are not connected to anything, and it is reasonable to try to find a logical termination for the system. It is therefore not likely that the bond graph of a system will be as incomplete as the diagram of Fig. 2-1(a).

It should be evident that the bonds in Fig. 2-4 indicate power interactions in essentially the same manner as parts of the diagram of Fig. 2-1(a). Also, the words that represent the multiport components have the function of those symbols in Fig. 2-1(a) that serve as mnemonic devices for motors, generators, shafts, etc. without being specific about the detailed component models. However, the word bond graph is universal in that it can represent a wide variety of systems in various physical domains; after some basic multiports have been defined, we shall demonstrate how the word bond graph can be made specific when the detailed models of the system components have been decided upon.

2.6 Sign convention for power

A vexing problem in all system studies, which does not disappear when using bond graphs, is the question of sign conventions. We have split the power flow on a bond into the product of an effort and a flow quantity, but we must still consider the direction of power flow along the bond. Clearly if two multiports

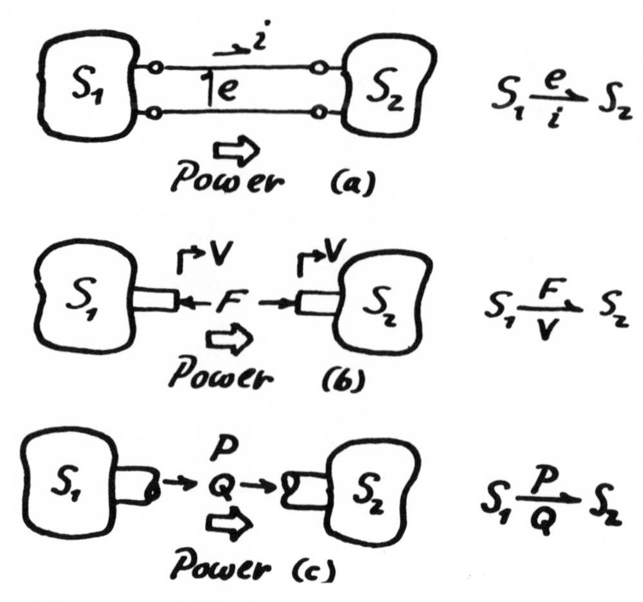

Fig. 2-5 Power flow convention for (a) electrical, (b) mechanical, and (c) hydraulic systems.

are bonded together, power flow out of one multiport is power flow into the other. In Fig. 2-5, several cases are shown in which two multiports are bonded together in such a way that common efforts and flows exist at the two ports. In each case, a convention for positive values of the effort and flow quantities is shown as clearly as possible with conventional notations. These have been so arranged that, if both effort and flow are positive, energy flows from left to right. On the bond graph this is indicated by a *half arrow* on the right end of the bond. This convention indicates that power *into* system 2 is given by the product $e(t) \cdot f(t)$, which is positive when both $e(t)$ and $f(t)$ have the same sign.

Since our major objective is to model physical systems, one may often begin by drawing conventional diagrams, such as those in Fig. 2-5, and then transfer the implied power directions to a bond graph, as shown on the right of the figure. With experience one may also use the sign conventions on the bond graph directly without bothering to make detailed definitions of all of the physical efforts and flows. A word bond graph may be *augmented* by choosing sign conventions for the power on the bonds and by indicating this by means of half arrows. This is equivalent on a circuit graph, for example, to the indication of sign conventions for voltages by plusses and minuses and for currents by arrows.

2.7 Causality convention for effort and flow signals

A bond graph model of a physical system, even when augmented to show sign conventions and with the effort and flow signals named, is still only an existential graph for the system. The graph may imply a number of dynamic relations that must be satisfied by the system variables, but there has been no decision about which of the variables for a component multiport are to be considered as independent and which as dependent. The assignment of input and output quantities for every multiport in a bond graph has come to be called the assignment of *causality* or, to avoid confusion with other related uses of the word, *computing causality* or *experimental causality.*

The basic idea behind the assignment of causality may be seen by descending from the single line representing a power bond to the effort-flow signal pair for each bond. In the following diagram the bond at the left is referred to as *acausal* and is of the type discussed previously. The corresponding acausal signal pair is represented by two lines of the type used in block diagrams, but the direction of the signal flow has not been established.

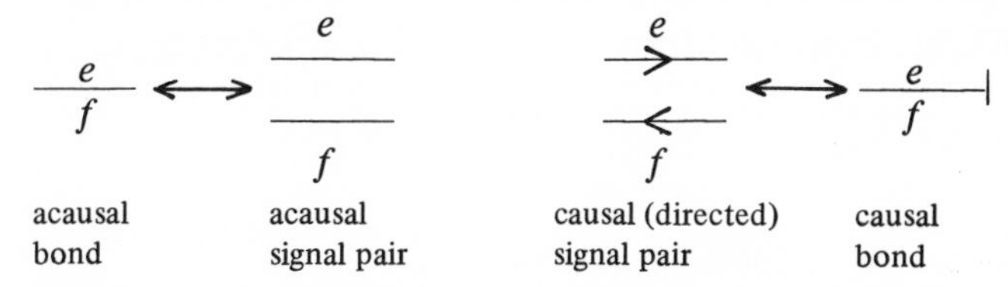

Both the causal signal pair and the causal bond are *augmented* to show the directedness of the two signals e and f. In the signal pair representation, the arrows on the lines have the significance of arrows on a block diagram. We shall uniformly assume that the effort and flow signals on a single bond are always oppositely directed. Thus a single crossline at one end of the bond, the so-called *causal stroke,* can serve to indicate simultaneously the direction of the effort signal and the direction of the flow signal.

As an example, consider two multiports, A and B, which are part of a system and share a common bond. If all parts of the system are ignored except A and B and their common bond, the graph fragment

$$\mathrm{A} \;\frac{\mathrm{e}}{\mathrm{f}}\; \mathrm{B}$$

merely states that e(t) and f(t) are the names of an effort and a flow that are common to a port of A and a port of B. If the graph fragment is augmented by a causal stroke in the following manner:

$$\mathrm{A} \;\frac{\mathrm{e}}{\mathrm{f}}\!\!\mid \mathrm{B},$$

the dual inplication is (1) that e(t) is determined by A and impressed on B; and (2) that f(t) is determined by B and impressed on A. If the causal stroke were placed on the other end of the common bond, the roles of e and f would simply be interchanged in (1) and (2). Note that the assignment of causality and that of a sign convention for power are independent and thus all four of the augmented bond graphs shown below are possible:

A —⇀| B, A ↽—| B, A |↽— B, A |—⇀ B.

The reader may already appreciate that a completely augmented bond graph with the bond variables named becomes rather dense with information; for this reason we shall typically not augment the bond graph until it proves necessary to do so. One of the most impressive features of bond graphs, however, is their ability to be transformed, from a rough existential statement about the sort of model of a physical system to be used, to a detailed graph that contains all the information required for a simulation of the system, by means of a series of operations on the original bond graph. This process will be easier to understand for the specific cases to be discussed in succeeding chapters.

The need and uses for the causality convention are often not clear to those first introduced to bond graphs. In the next section we shall try to show some of the causal implications of experimental testing of components, and in succeeding chapters the implications of causal considerations in analytical work and for the purposes of simulation will be discussed.

2.8 Measurement of multiport characteristics

The characteristics of multiport devices are typically determined by a combination of experimental and theoretical methods. In Chapter 3 a basic set of multiports will be studied which may be interconnected to form models of complex multiports. Included in this set will be abstracted versions of some traditional elements, such as springs, masses, electrical resistances, and levers, which are such a large part of the conceptual framework of any system study. There are, however, certain aspects of many engineering multiports that are difficult to predict with great accuracy before the component is actually built and that are typically checked by experiment in any case. For example, for the D.C. motor shown in Fig. 2-2 the relation between torque and speed for constant electrical excitation may be hard to predict in detail from analysis, but quite easily measured. The effects of magnetic saturation and windage would be especially difficult to predict. On the other hand it might not be necessary to measure the moment of inertia of the rotor if it has been calculated during the design of the motor. Thus the final model of a multiport may be a combination of physical insight, theoretical analysis, and experimental measurement.

In the case of the motor, one may be particularly interested in steady state characteristics, and the bond graph in Fig. 2-2 is useful in recognizing the variables to be controlled. One can imagine measuring the torque τ produced at various speeds, ω, with e_f and e_a held constant. Although the use of the bond graph cannot prevent one from failing to recognize and control some variable of interest (the temperature of the motor, for example), the graph does indicate certain functional relationships that were assumed to be valid when the ports were defined. In the case of the motor, the graph of Fig. 2-2 augmented to show causality (in Fig. 2-6) leads us to expect that experimentally we could find the torque for given values of ω, e_f, and e_a, and that a basic functional relation should exist for steady conditions, such as

$$\tau = \phi_1(\omega, e_f, e_a). \tag{2.4}$$

The bond graph of Fig. 2-6 also suggests that the formation of Eq. 2.4 is incomplete, since the currents i_a and i_f would also be related to the variables ω, e_f, e_a:

$$i_a = \phi_2(\omega, e_f, e_a); \tag{2.5}$$

$$i_f = \phi_3(\omega, e_f, e_a). \tag{2.6}$$

To one with no experience with electric motors, it would by no means be evident that an experiment could be devised in which the functions of Eqs. 2.4, 2.5, and 2.6 could be determined. Nor should it be taken for granted that the mere definition of a set of port variables for a real component will suffice to describe the component. It is fundamentally only through collective or individual engineering experience that useful descriptions of components are found.

Even for the most common components one is often surprised to find that the device is not described completely, and hence in some system studies the effect of the component cannot be evaluated for lack of data. For example, it would not be uncommon for a manufacturer to give only a torque-speed curve for a motor under the assumption that the voltages were constant, i.e.,

$$\tau = \phi_1'(\omega). \tag{2.7}$$

The relation of Eq. 2.7 is an incomplete description for the steady state in two

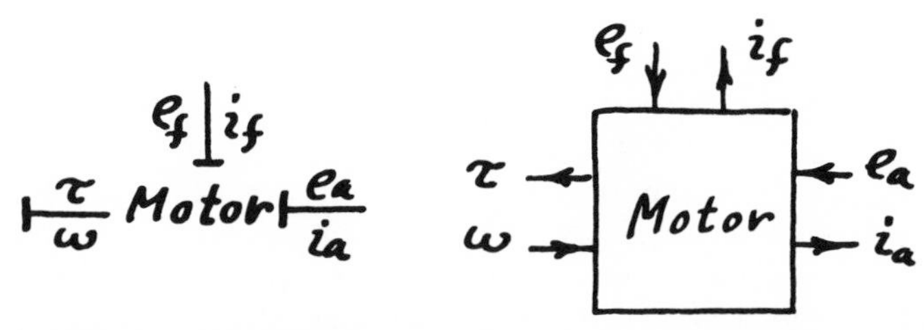

Fig. 2-6 Schematic representation of Eqs. 2.4, 2.5 and 2.6 as a causal bond graph and as a symbolic block diagram.

senses: (1) in many critical system studies, one will not be able to guarantee that the armature and field voltages will remain at the values assumed in finding Eq. 2.7, and (2) in most cases, one would need to find the current flowing in the armature and field to make sure that the motor is operating in a safe regime and to predict the interaction of the motor with the multiports to which it is connected.

It must also be clear that for multiports in general the proper causality for taking measurements and representing measured data requires considerable thought. For example, if the motor of Fig. 2-2 were always to be connected to voltage sources, then the characterization of Eqs. 2.4, 2.5, 2.6 (and the causality shown in Fig. 2-6) would be logical. However, it is quite possible that either a current source could be used on the field winding, or for reasons connected with the system in which the motor was to be used, it would be necessary that the torque be computed for given values of ω, i_f, and e_a:

$$\tau = \phi_4(\omega, i_f, e_a). \tag{2.8}$$

On paper, we can see that the function ϕ_4 is symbolically related to ϕ_1 and ϕ_3 as follows:

$$\phi_4(\omega, i_f, e_a) = \phi_1(\omega, \phi_3^{-1}(i_f, \omega, e_a), e_a), \tag{2.9}$$

where an inversion of Eq. 2.6 has been indicated by

$$e_f = \phi_3^{-1}(i_f, \omega, e_a) \tag{2.10}$$

and the result substituted into Eq. 2.4. Unless the functions ϕ_1 and ϕ_3 are very simple in form, one would not be well advised to try to find Eq. 2.8 by the method of Eq. 2.9. Also, if the functions are tabulated from an experiment, the process of Eq. 2.9 may be counted upon to reduce, perhaps drastically, the accuracy of the representation. It is even possible that for some sets of independent variables the functional relationship for the component will be multivalued and hence inversions of the type indicated by Eq. 2.10 will be impossible.

In summary then, the characteristics of a multiport are often rather complex when considered in complete form and there are several possible choices of an independent variable set, in both an analytic and experimental sense. Whenever possible, it is important to determine the multiport characteristics in the causal form that will be required for subsequent system analysis. For nonlinear systems these considerations are extremely important. One significant advantage to bond graphs is that the question of independent and dependent variables can be handled explicity for a system through the use of the causal stroke. In this way the preferred causal form for specifying characteristics when the multiport is to be inserted into a system can be studied. For system design purposes, therefore, the bond graph analysis can aid in determining the nature of experiments to be done on components or the form of characteristics to be provided the system analyst by the component supplier.

3. A SET OF BASIC MULTIPORTS

In Chapter 2 real devices were discussed from the point of view of power exchanges and external port variables. In this chapter we shall define a set of multiports that are highly idealized versions of physical elements and have proven useful in the modeling of real devices. Once any basic set of multiports has been defined, other multiports may be formed by combining the basic multiports; this is the typical procedure for representing engineering components. If it is found that a particular engineering device cannot be represented satisfactorily by combinations of the basic multiports, then one may say that the engineering multiport is an irreducible multiport relative to the basic set. The basic set of multiports to be discussed will suffice to model electric circuits including active sources, transformers, gyrators, and mutual inductance, mechanical systems involving linear motion and fixed axis rotational motion, and most hydraulic and pneumatic circuits. In Chapter 4, we shall turn to transducer models and show that many transducers also fall into the class of multiports that are reducible in terms of the basic set we have chosen. At the end of the present chapter, multiport fields will be discussed; if one wishes to consider general multiport fields as part of the basic set, then virtually all of the standard physical system dynamic models are reducible relative to this basic set. This fact is not of overwhelming practical significance, however, since a very complex system may be extremely difficult to represent in terms of the basic set of multiports even when some sort of system description is already known. Such is the case, for example, for systems involving large three-dimensional motions of interacting mechanical parts. Such systems may be very hard to describe in any manner, and bond graphs may not show any obvious benefits as compared with any other scheme. For systems that can be represented efficiently by bond graphs, the notation often allows one to visualize aspects of the system more easily than would be possible with equations or some other graphical notation specialized either for a single physical domain or for signals instead of power. The search for a bond graph representation of a complex system in terms of basic multiports frequently increases one's physical understanding of the system.

3.1 Basic 1-port elements

We shall now describe a set of elements that may be defined in terms of a single pair of energy variables at a port, the effort e(t) and flow f(t), and the time integrals of these quantities, the *generalized momentum,*

$$p(t) \equiv \int^t e(t)dt, \tag{3.1}$$

and the *generalized displacement,*

$$q(t) \equiv \int^t f(t)dt. \tag{3.2}$$

We shall consider, in order, 1-port elements which dissipate energy, store energy, and supply energy.

The 1-port *resistance element* is shown in Fig. 3-1. In terms of the abstract

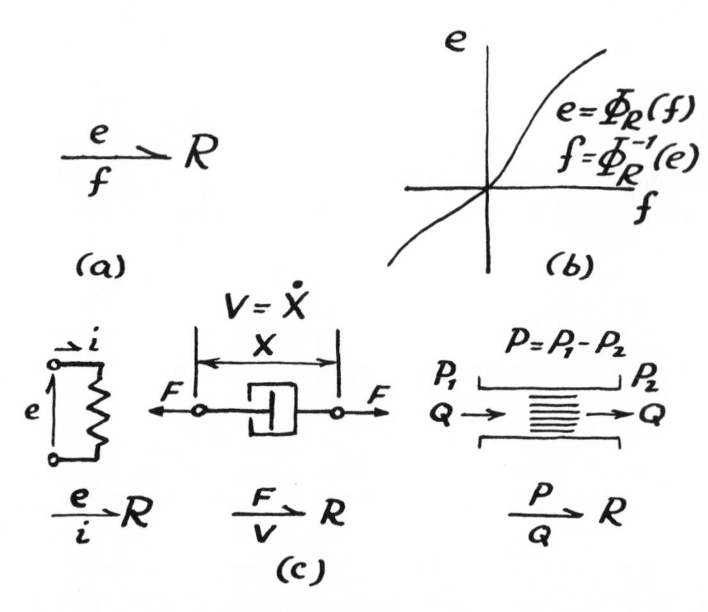

Fig. 3-1 1-port resistance elements. (a) abstract symbol, (b) defining relation, (c) representations in physical domains.

power variables e and f, the sign convention shown in Fig. 3-1(a) implies that the power, $e(t)\cdot f(t)$, represents power flowing into the resistance element. The element is assumed to provide a static relationship between e and f, as shown, for example, in Fig. 3-1(b). Note that if, on physical grounds, energy must always be dissipated, the graph of the relation between e and f with the power convention shown must lie in the first and third quadrants of the e-f space. Figure 3-1(c) shows several conventional schematic representations of the resistance element in particular physical domains.

Table 3-1. Summary of basic 1-port elements

Name	*Symbol*	*Defining Relations*	*Linear Relations*
Resistance	$\overset{e}{\underset{f}{\rightharpoonup}}$ R	$e = \Phi_R(f)$ $f = \Phi_R^{-1}(e)$	$e = Rf$ $f = Ge = e/R$
Capacitance	$\overset{e}{\underset{f}{\rightharpoonup}}$ C	$\dot{q} \equiv f$ $q = \Phi_C(e)$ $e = \Phi_C^{-1}(q)$	 $q = Ce$ $e = q/C$
Inertance	$\overset{e}{\underset{f}{\rightharpoonup}}$ I	$\dot{p} \equiv e$ $p = \Phi_I(f)$ $f = \Phi_I^{-1}(p)$	 $p = If$ $f = p/I$
Effort source	E $\overset{e}{\underset{f}{\rightharpoonup}}$ or $S_e \overset{e}{\underset{f}{\rightharpoonup}}$	$e = E(t)$ f arbitrary	$e = E(t)$
Flow source	E $\overset{e}{\underset{f}{\rightharpoonup}}$ or $S_f \overset{e}{\underset{f}{\rightharpoonup}}$	$f = F(t)$ e arbitrary	$f = F(t)$

The first line of Table 3-1 summarizes, in equation form, the characteristics of a 1-port resistance. If the resistance is to be passive in the sense that power cannot be supplied by the element, then the static function between e and f must be constrained such that $e\cdot f \geqslant 0$. In any case, the 1-port resistance with its static relation between effort and flow does not store energy, but two other 1-ports may be found in which energy can be stored.

The energy U supplied to any 1-port may be written as

$$U(t) = \int^t e(t)\cdot f(t)\cdot dt \tag{3.3}$$

if the sign convention of Fig. 3-1(a) is followed. Using the definitions of Eqs. 3.1 and 3.2, two alternative forms of Eq. 3.3 may be found:

$$U(t) = \int^t e(t)dq(t) = \int^t f(t)dp(t). \tag{3.4}$$

By consideration of Eq. 3.4, two forms of conservative, energy-storing elements can be determined.

First, suppose that a static relationship exists between e and q. Then Eq. 3.4 may be rewritten as

$$U_q(q) = \int^q e(q)dq, \tag{3.5}$$

and a conservative element has been found, since the net change in U_q is zero for any cycle in which q (or e) returns to its original value after an arbitrary excursion. The element shown in Fig. 3-2 exhibits these properties and is called a *capacitance element.* The relations defining capacitance elements are shown in the second entry of Table 3-1. The important feature of a capacitance element is the existence of a static relationship between e and q. The actual form of the relation depends on the definition of q which typically contains an integration constant that must be fixed either through initial conditions of the problem or through the fundamental physical description of the problem. In electrical circuits one often defines currents first, and charge variables are then defined as integrals of the currents starting from consistent initial

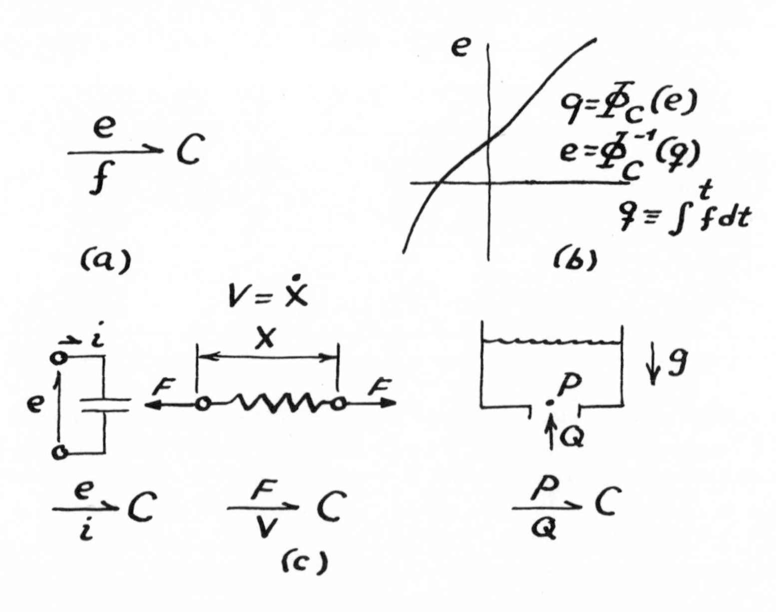

Fig. 3-2. 1-port capacitance element. (a) abstract symbol, (b) defining relations, (c) representation in physical domains.

conditions. In mechanical systems, it is more common to define positions first and to consider velocities as derivatives thereof. In either case, there are many possible proper time histories for q(t) that correspond to a single time history of f(t), and for this reason we have written q(t) as an indefinite integral of f(t). Typical capacitance elements are electrical capacitors, mechanical springs, and hydraulic accumulators, as shown in Fig. 3-2(c).

Returning to Eq. 3.4, if we suppose that a static relationship exists between f and p, then we may write

$$U_p(p) = \int^p f(p)dp, \tag{3.6}$$

and another conservative element has been found. Since the stored energy depends on p (or f), if p or f is cycled, no net change of U_p is involved. An element in which a static relationship holds between f and p is called an *inertance element* and is shown in Fig. 3-3. The third entry in Table 3-1 describes the properties of the inertance element.

As in the case of the definition of q, there is some freedom in the definition of p. The variable p, which is involved in the inertance element, is usually termed generalized momentum only for lack of a more representative name. In mechanical systems p represents the impulse of a force or torque; in electrical systems it represents a flux-linkage variable; and in hydraulic systems it is just the integral of a pressure or head, and is not

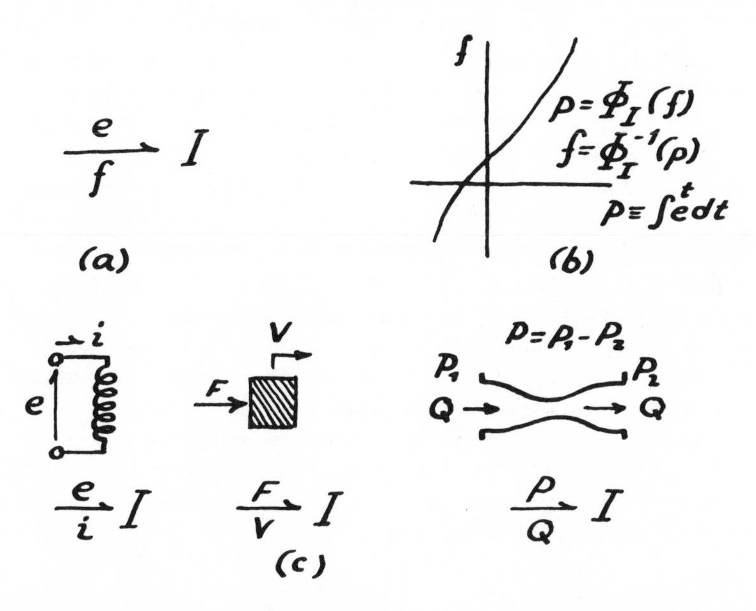

Fig 3-3 **1-port inertance element. (a) abstract symbol, (b) defining relation, (c) representation in physical domains.**

usually named.[1] There is an implied initial condition constraint in the relationship between f and p for an inertance element.

For the present there is no reason for restricting the functions Φ_C and Φ_I in Table 3-1 in the manner of Φ_R in order to assume that a passive element is intended. Even in the linear domain, the power convention that results in a positive coefficient for the resistance relation does not necessarily mean that a positive coefficient is required for the inertance and capacitance relation, although this is the usual situation. For example, mechanical springs with negative spring constants for a large range of displacement are often constructed and act like conservative elements as long as the system in which such elements are used does not become unstable and attempt to run to infinite values. Later, we shall see that functions Φ_R, Φ_C, and Φ_I that are not bi-unique in the sense that both the function and its inverse are unique will have to be treated with care for simulation purposes. If one is concerned with elements described in a manner valid only over a restricted range of the variables, then one should be prepared to consider quite general functions, and the elements –R, –C, –I may be distinguished only by the type of variables involved in the static relationships of the elements. From this point of view, the resistance may not appear to dissipate energy but will still relate an effort and a flow statically over finite ranges.

The final two 1-port devices to be defined here are the effort and flow sources listed in the last two entries in Table 3-1.

The notation E– and F– for effort and flow sources is useful in the abstract power domain, but the notation S_e– and S_f– is often more appropriate for physical domains in which the letters E or F may be conventionally used for certain variables that are not necessarily efforts or flows (e.g., F for force). These source devices are assumed to provide an effort as a function of time or a flow as a function of time without regard to the power delivered or absorbed. The power convention for these devices is typically as indicated in Table 3-1; i.e., $e \cdot f$ is power supplied by the source to the system to which it is connected. Since the sources are capable of infinite power generation, one must be concerned about the physical meaning of a system with sources. Real sources may be modeled by these basic sources and other elements which may account for the internal characteristics of real sources which prevent infinite power from being supplied.

Certain elementary systems are formed by interconnecting two of the basic 1-ports. Perhaps the most interesting is the oscillator shown in Fig. 3-4. We may write the equations of this system as follows:

By defining the variables q and p as

$$q(t) = q_o + \int_o^t f dt, \tag{3.7}$$

$$p(t) = p_o + \int_o^t e dt, \tag{3.8}$$

the element characteristics may be taken from Table 3-1. Note that the sign convention of Fig. 3-4(a) is the same for the capacitance element as that used in Table 3-1, but for the inertance element the sign conventions of Fig. 3-4(a) and Table 3-1 are in opposition. Therefore a minus sign must be included for the inertance relation:

$$e = \Phi_C^{-1}(q), \tag{3.9}$$

$$f = -\Phi_I(p) \tag{3.10}$$

Equations 3.7 to 3.10 describe the system, but one might prefer to rearrange the equations into state variable differential form as follows:

$$\dot{p}(t) = e = \Phi_C^{-1}(q) \tag{3.11}$$

$$\dot{q}(t) = f = -\Phi_I^{-1}(p) \tag{3.12}$$

with initial conditions related as follows:

$$e(o) = \dot{p}(o) = \Phi_C^{-1}\,[q(o)]. \tag{3.13}$$

$$f(o) = \dot{q}(o) = -\Phi_I^{-1}[p(o)]. \tag{3.14}$$

The reader may wish to rewrite Eqs. 3.7 to 3.14 using the variables of one of the physical examples of Fig. 3.4 in order to gain more understanding of the 1-port characteristics discussed at the abstract level. Note that all the relations are presented in a form suitable for the general nonlinear case, even though for some of the physical domains the 1-ports occur most frequently in a linear form.

3.2 Basic 2-port elements

Although the variety of possible 2-ports would seem to be much greater than the variety of 1-ports, only two basic 2-ports will be introduced here.

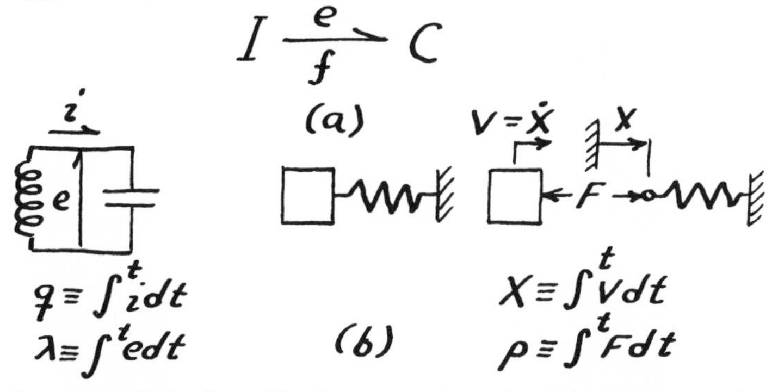

Fig. 3-4 An oscillator formed by interconnecting a 1-port inertance and a 1-port capacitance. (a) bond graph, (b) two physical interpretations.

Both of these elements will be *ideal* in the very specific sense of *conservation of power.* The sign convention used to write 2-port relations is shown in Fig. 3-5(a). The condition for power conservation is then

$$e_1(t) \cdot f_1(t) = e_2(t) \cdot f_2(t). \tag{3.15}$$

One way in which Eq. 3.15 can be satisfied is found in the ideal transformer of electric circuits. In generalized form, we write the characteristics of the 2-port *transformer* as

$$e_1 = me_2; \qquad mf_1 = f_2. \tag{3.16}$$

The bond graph of an ideal transformer is shown in Fig. 3-5(b), along with electrical and mechanical schematic diagrams for transformer elements. It is easy to see that idealized gear pairs and lever systems may fit Eq. 3.16; in later sections we shall encounter certain transducers and hydraulic elements that are often modeled by transformers. For the moment, however, we simply consider any element satisfying Eq. 3.16 to be a transformer.

Another way in which Eq. 3.15 may be satisfied is typified by the electrical 2-port called a *gyrator.* Writing the gyrator characteristics in effort-flow variables, we have

$$e_1 = rf_2; \qquad rf_1 = e_2. \tag{3.17}$$

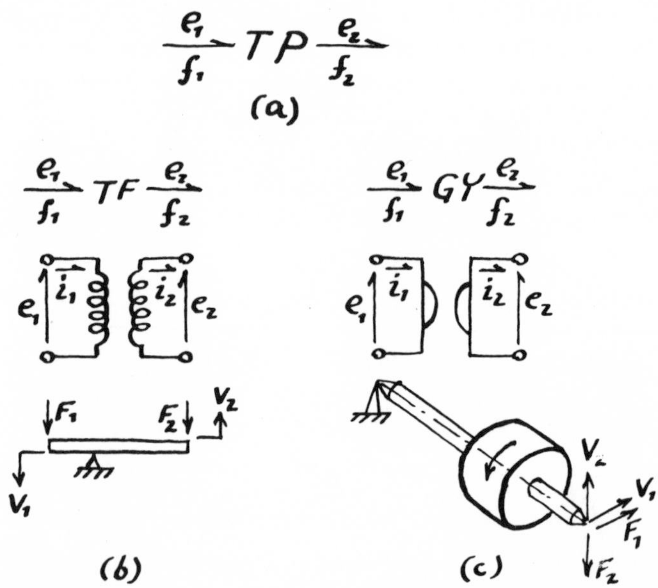

Fig. 3-5 Basic 2-port. (a) general bond graph with sign convention, (b) transformer, (c) gyrator.

The bond graph for the gyrator is shown in Fig. 3-5(c) together with its electric circuit graph symbol and a sketch of a mechanical system which at least approximately satisfies Eq. 3.17 for high rates of spin of the flywheel and low-frequency, small motions of the rigid shaft. Although the word gyrator was invented originally for the sort of gyrational coupling that exists in mechanical systems, the element is usually defined by the relations of the form of Eq. 3.17. Again, gyrators will be encountered later in connection with idealized transducers; in fact, these transducers may be represented as either transformers or gyrators, depending upon one's identification of efforts and flows in two physical domains. In any case, we shall need both the transformer and the gyrator in general and, although the gyrator may appear to be the more mysterious element of the two basic 2-ports, it is more fundamental an element than the transformer in bond graph terms.

To see this, consider first the cascade connection of two transformers shown below. The defining relations for the transformers appear below the bond graph and show that cascade combination is equivalent to another transformer.

$$\frac{e_1}{f_1} \rightharpoondown TF_1 \frac{e_2}{f_2} \rightharpoondown TF_2 \frac{e_3}{f_3} \rightharpoondown \quad ; \quad \frac{e_1}{f_1} \rightharpoondown TF_3 \frac{e_3}{f_3} \rightharpoondown$$

$$e_1 = m_1 e_2 \; ; \quad e_2 = m_2 e_3 \qquad\qquad e_1 = m_1 m_2 e_3$$

$$mf_1 = f_2 \quad ; \; m_2 f_2 = f_3 \qquad\qquad m_1 m_2 f_1 = f_3$$

In constrast, the cascade combination of two gyrators is equivalent to a transformer as the following bond graphs and equations demonstrate:

$$\frac{e_1}{f_1} \rightharpoondown GY_1 \frac{e_2}{f_2} \rightharpoondown GY_2 \frac{e_3}{f_3} \rightharpoondown \quad ; \quad \frac{e_1}{f_1} \rightharpoondown TF_3 \frac{e_3}{f_3} \rightharpoondown$$

$$e_1 = r_1 f_2 \quad ; \quad r_2 f_2 = e_3 \qquad\qquad e_1 = (r_1/r_2) e_3$$

$$r_1 f_1 = e_2 \quad ; \quad e_2 = r_2 f_3 \qquad\qquad (r_1/r_2) f_3 = f_3$$

Thus one could, in principle, consider every transformer as a cascade combination of two gyrators and dispense with the transformer as a basic element. Since certain physical systems occur naturally in a form that may be represented as a transformer, we shall include both 2-ports in our basic set.

It is important to realize that the gyrator reverses the roles of e and f in a system, as may be seen from Eq. 3.17. Thus the combination –GY–I acts, from the point of view of the free bond in exactly the same manner as the element –C, and –GY–C acts like –I. Thus both the systems I_1–GY–I_2 and C_1–GY–C_2 behave in a manner similar to the oscillator system I–C of Fig. 3-4. This property of the gyrator allows one to eliminate either –I or –C as a basic multiport, but as before physical considerations make it convenient to consider both –I and –C as basic 1-ports.

Table 3-2. Summary of basic 2-ports and 3-ports

Transformer	$\frac{e_1}{f_1}$ TF $\frac{e_2}{f_2}$	$e_1 = me_2$ $mf_1 = f_2$
Gyrator	$\frac{e_1}{f_1}$ GY $\frac{e_2}{f_2}$	$e_1 = rf_2$ $rf_1 = e_2$
Flow junction or 0-junction	$\frac{e_1}{f_1}$ 0 e_2, with bond e_3 | f_3	$e_1 = e_2 = e_3$ $f_1 + f_2 + f_3 = 0$
Effort junction or 1-junction	$\frac{e_1}{f_1}$ 1 $\frac{e_2}{f_2}$, with bond e_3 | f_3	$f_1 = f_2 = f_3$ $e_1 + e_2 + e_3 = 0$

For convenience, the bond graph notation and defining relations for the basic 2-ports are reproduced in Table 3-2. One curious feature of the transformer and the gyrator is that power is conserved even when the *modulus* m of the –TF– or the modulus r of the –GY– is not constant; in certain physical situations, elements arise naturally in which these moduli are variable. For example, in Fig. 3-6 a rigid bar is constrained to roll *without slip* on the surface of a circular cylinder. This is clearly a generalization of the fixed pivot lever, which may be described as a transformer in the idealized case.

From Fig. 3-6 the following relations may be derived:

$$F_1 = \frac{(l + R\theta)}{(l - R\theta)} \cdot F_2,$$
$$\frac{(l + R\theta)}{(l - R\theta)} \cdot V_1 = V_2. \quad (3.18)$$

Comparing Eqs. 3.16 with Eqs. 3.18 we see that this element may be regarded as a transformer with modulus

$$m = (l + R\theta)/(l - R\theta) \quad (3.19)$$

We define a *modulated transformer* by the symbol

$$\frac{F_1}{V_1}\text{MTF}\frac{F_2}{V_2} \quad (\theta \downarrow \text{ signal into MTF})$$

in which two power bonds and one signal flow are shown. A modulated trans-

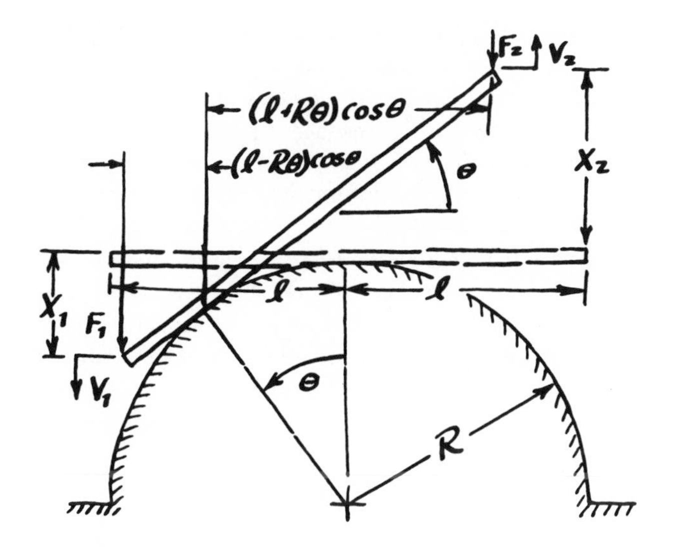

Fig. 3-6 Mechanical modulated transformer.

former is an element like a transformer but in which the modulus may vary as a function of some variable (θ in the example). In a similar way, a *modulated gyrator* is defined as an element that obeys the gyrator relations, Eq. 3.17, but in which the modulus r is a function of some variable. The symbol for a modulated gyrator is

$$\begin{array}{c}\downarrow\\ \text{—MGY—},\end{array}$$

in which again two power bonds and a signal appear. In both the MTF and MGY elements the signal quantity influences the power exchanges on the bonds but never changes the fact that power flowing into the element is instantaneously equal to the power flowing out of the element. Thus both elements are ideal in the power-conserving sense.

The modulus of an MTF or an MGY may depend on time or on other variables in a system. For example, in Fig. 3-5(c) the spin speed of the motor may be varied independently of the power variables F_1, F_2, V_1, V_2, and this will influence the modulus of the gyrator, which might then be considered to be an independent function of time. In Fig. 3-6 the variable θ which appears in the modulus, Eq. 3.19, is directly related to X_1 or X_2, the displacements corresponding to V_1 and V_2. When X_1 and X_2 are defined as shown in the figure, the relations between X_1, X_2, and θ are

$$X_1 = (l - R\theta)\sin\theta + R(1 - \cos\theta), \quad (3.20)$$

$$X_2 = (l + R\theta)\sin\theta - R(1 - \cos\theta). \quad (3.21)$$

Thus a knowledge of $X_1(t)$ or $X_2(t)$ should suffice to determine θ and hence m. The operations required to find m from a knowledge of $V_1(t)$ or $V_2(t)$ are, however, not trivial and therefore the occurrence of an MTF or of an MGY with the modulus dependent upon system variables is often a sign that a complex nonlinear system is involved and one should expect some difficulties in extracting the information necessary for a dynamic simulation of the system.

Although the MTF and MGY elements are very useful and will appear later in this book, a word of caution about the use of these elements is in order. These elements are at once very powerful and at the same time hard to discipline, because the nature of the signal input that sets the modulus appears to be quite arbitrary. It is possible to represent virtually any system using these modulated 2-ports and other elements in a variety of ways if the moduli are allowed to be dynamically related to system variables. When much of the dynamics of the system is put into the signals setting the moduli, the organizational structure which bond graph techniques usually brings to the study of physical system dynamics may be obscured. For this reason, we generally represent systems without the modulated 2-ports whenever possible and use these elements mainly when the physics of the problem suggests their use, as in the case of Fig. 3-6.

3.3 Basic 3-port elements

Evidently the only graph structures that may be constructed using 1-ports and 2-ports are long chains of 2-ports with 1-port terminations. Many more possibilities are available if 3-ports can be used, however, because two 3-ports bonded together form a 4-port, and the process can be continued indefinitely to form n-ports of any order. We shall now introduce two basic 3-ports that are ideal in the power-conserving sense and that allow bond graph representations for a large number of physical systems analyzed by conventional methods. These two ideal 3-ports form much of the basis for bond graph methods and largely set the bond graph apart from conventional representations. The fundamental idea is to represent as ideal multiports the connection structures typically known as "series" and "parallel."

First, we consider the *flow junction, 0-junction* or *common effort junction.* The symbol for this element is a zero with three bonds emanating from it:

$$—0— \quad , \quad \underset{1}{—}\overset{|3}{0}\underset{2}{—}, \quad \text{or} \quad \xrightarrow[f_1]{e_1} \overset{e_3 \downharpoonright f_3}{0} \xleftarrow[f_2]{e_2}$$

Using the power sign convention shown in the last version of the 0-junction, the relations for the element may be written as follows:

$$e_1(t) = e_2(t) = e_3(t), \tag{3.22}$$

$$f_1(t) + f_2(t) + f_3(t) = 0. \tag{3.23}$$

The 0-junction has a single effort on all its bonds (Eq. 3.22) and the sum of the flows to the element vanishes (Eq. 3.23). Taken together, these two properties imply that the 0-junction conserves power:

$$e_1(t)\cdot f_1(t) + e_2(t)\cdot f_2(t) + e_3(t)\cdot f_3(t) = 0. \tag{3.24}$$

The possible uses of the 0-junction are suggested by the example situations in Fig. 3-7(a). While it is fairly obvious that the structure of ideal electrical conductors and the ideal hydraulic TEE connection obey the same sort of equations as Eqs. 3.22 and 3.23, the mechanical example may seem contrived and, in a sense, it is. Only if the two forces on the massless carts happen to be equal and opposite do the equations of the system match those of a 0-junction. Note, however, that if F in the mechanical example originated in a massless spring connected to the two carts, then the condition for a 0-junction would indeed be fulfilled. Before considering some examples of systems in which 0-junctions appear, we define the dual of the 0-junction.

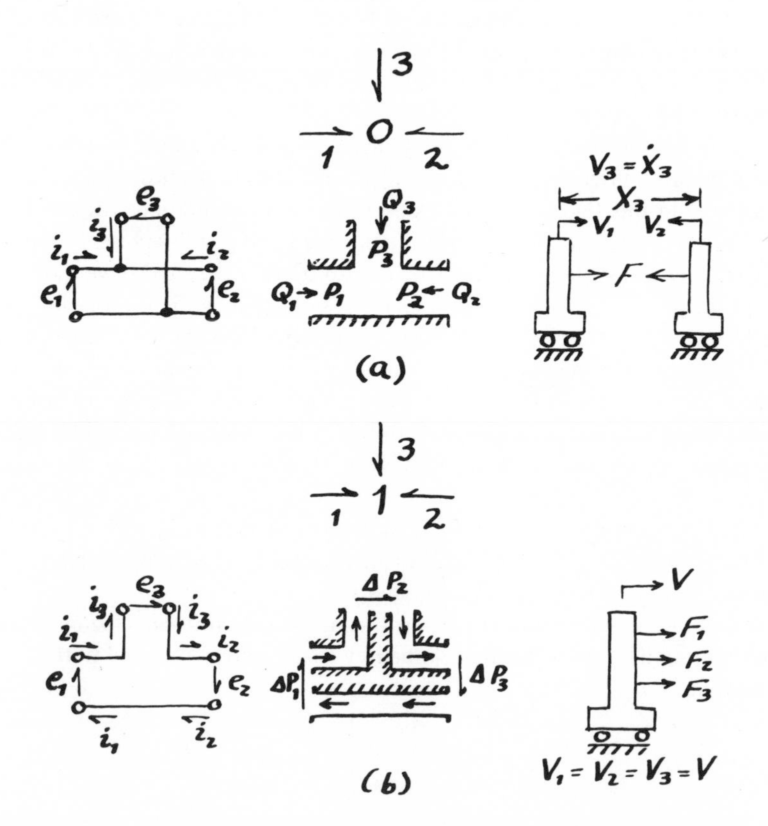

Fig 3-7 Basic 3-ports in various physical domains. (a) 0-junction, (b) 1-junction.

The *effort junction, 1-junction,* or *common flow junction* is represented by the symbol "1" with three attached bonds:

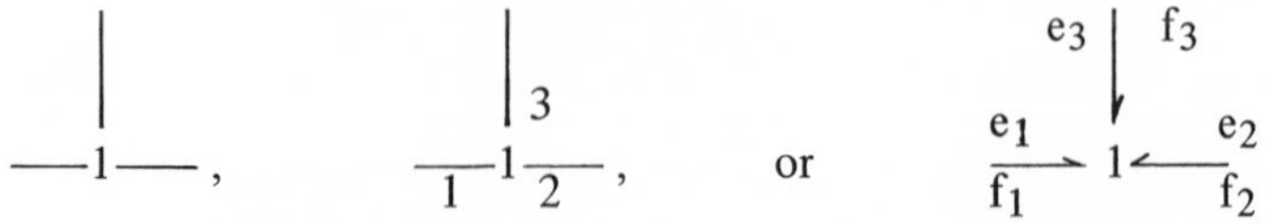

—1—, —1— (bonds 1, 2, 3), or $e_1, f_1 \rightharpoonup 1 \leftharpoondown e_2, f_2$; e_3, f_3 (bond 3 pointing into 1)

With the indicated power sign convention, the relations for this element are

$$f_1(t) = f_2(t) = f_3(t), \tag{3.25}$$

$$e_1(t) + e_2(t) + e_3(t) = 0. \tag{3.26}$$

These equations bear a dual relationship to Eqs. 3.22 and 3.23, but both the 0-junction and the 1-junction satisfy the power conservation relation, Eq. 3.24. A single flow exists for a 1-junction and the efforts on the bonds sum to zero. Several physical situations in which a 1-junction is involved are shown in Fig. 3-7(b). Note, for example, that if 1-port circuit elements were connected across the terminals of the ideal electrical conductor structure shown, the currents and voltages could be defined as shown, and the structure would behave as a 1-junction.

Figure 3-8 shows simple systems involving 0- and 1-junctions in terms of bond graphs and corresponding circuit graphs and mechanical schematics. Although in this figure we are seeking physical interpretations for bond graphs, it is more common by far to look for a bond graph representation of a given physical system and, in particular, to transfer the sign convention from the physical domain to the domain of bond graphs. This procedure will be followed in Chapter 4, in which standard procedures for the construction of bond graphs from circuit graphs and mechanical schematics are given. The reader should be aware that a bond graph constructed in an arbitrary fashion and with sign conventions imposed arbitrarily may not have a sensible interpretation in a physical domain. This is also true of electric circuit elements interconnected at random with ideal conductors–some elements might be shorted out completely with ideal conductors or left hanging with only one terminal connected. Such difficulties are avoided by the study of graphs derived from meaningful physical systems.

A slight generalization of the 3-port 0- and 1-junctions is possible by noting that two similar 3-port junctions joined by a single bond form a 4-port junction:

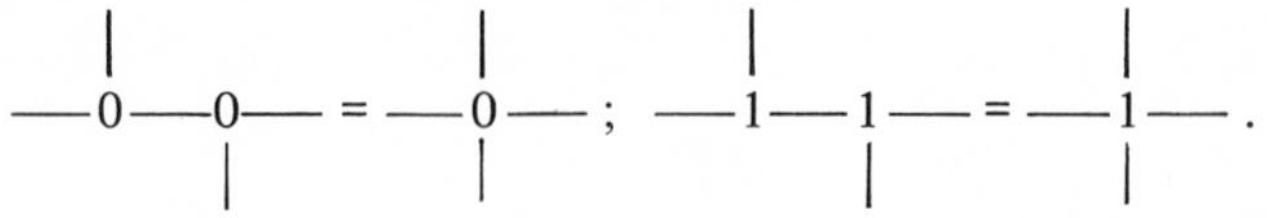

—0—0— = —0— ; —1—1— = —1— .

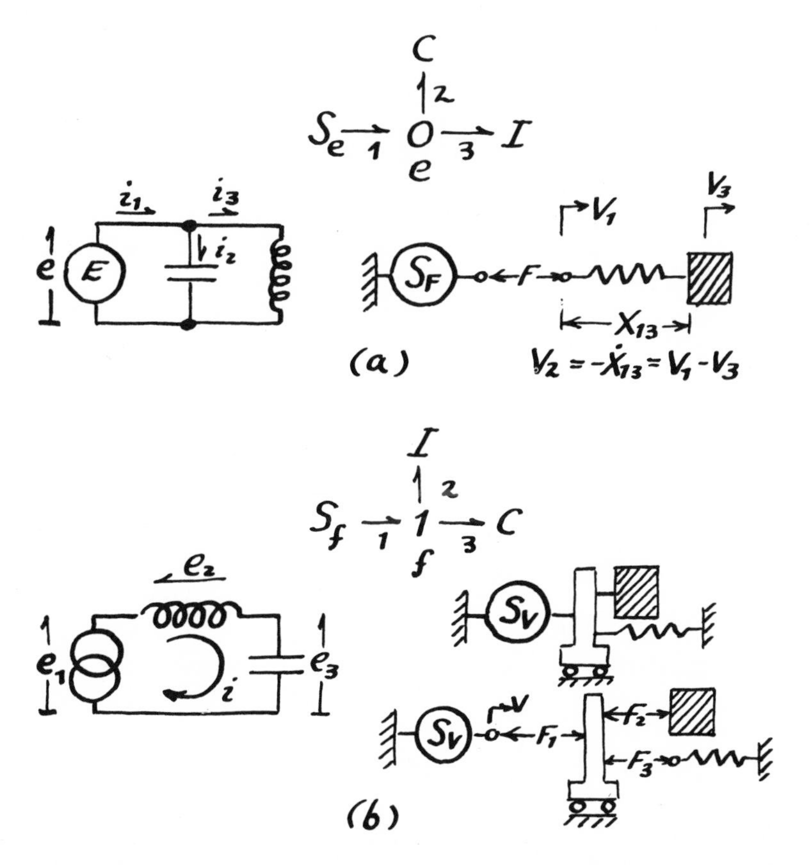

Fig 3-8. Example systems involving basic 3-ports. (a) systems using 0-junctions, (b) systems using 1-junctions.

It is sometimes convenient to define n-port 0- and 1-junctions in which a common effort or flow is communicated along n bonds and in which the complementary power variables on the n bonds sum to zero. As a very special case, note that the 2-port versions of the 0- and 1-junctions with certain sign conventions are entirely equivalent to a single bond:

—⇀0—⇀ = —⇀ ; —⇀1—⇀ = —⇀ .

However, for the cases —⇀0↽— , ↼—0—⇀ , —⇀1↽— , or ↼—1—⇀ , although there is a single effort magnitude and a single flow magnitude that appear at both ports of the 2-ports, there is a sign difference between these elements and a simple bond.

For easy reference, the ideal 3-port junction characteristics are summarized in Table 3-2.

3.4 Multiport fields

It is convenient to generalize the 1-port –R, –C, and –I elements that statically relate the variables e and f, e and $q = \int^t f dt$, and f and $p = \int^t e dt$, respectively. A multiport that can be described by static relations between the e's and f's of its external bonds is called an *R-field.* Similarly, a *C-field* is characterized by static relations between e's and q's on external bonds, and an *I-field* by static relations between f's and p's on external bonds. Let us write these definitions in a more precise manner.

If we adopt the first form for the characterization of the 1-port resistance from Table 3-1, $e = \Phi_R(f)$, then the generalization to an n-port R-field that is shown in bond graph form by the symbol

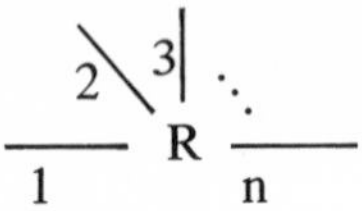

$$\overset{\;2\diagdown\; 3| \;\ddots}{\underset{1}{\text{———}}\;\mathrm{R}\;\underset{n}{\text{———}}}$$

is the set of static relations

$$\begin{aligned} e_1 &= \Phi_{R1}(f_1, f_2, \ldots, f_n) \\ e_2 &= \Phi_{R2}(f_1, f_2, \ldots, f_n) \\ &\vdots \\ e_n &= \Phi_{Rn}(f_1, f_2, \ldots, f_n). \end{aligned} \tag{3.27}$$

The important feature of the R-field is not the particular form Eq. 3.27 but rather the existence of a static relation between the e's and f's. Equation 3.27 is merely one of many conceivable ways to express the static relationship.

If we characterize the 1-port capacitance by the entry in Table 3-1, $q = \Phi_C(e)$, and use the symbol

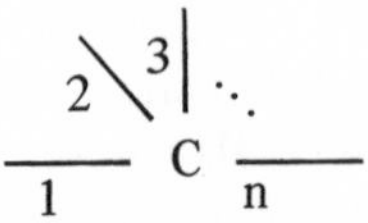

$$\overset{\;2\diagdown\; 3| \;\ddots}{\underset{1}{\text{———}}\;\mathrm{C}\;\underset{n}{\text{———}}}$$

for the n-port C-field, then the generalized relations would be written as follows:

$$\begin{aligned} q_1 &= \Phi_{C1}(e_1, e_2, \ldots, e_n) \\ q_2 &= \Phi_{C2}(e_1, e_2, \ldots, e_n) \\ &\vdots \\ q_n &= \Phi_{Cn}(e_1, e_2, \ldots, e_n). \end{aligned} \tag{3.28}$$

Once again it is the existence of a static relationship between efforts and displacements that is important and not the particular form of Eq. 3.28.

Finally, the multiport I-field may be represented by the generalization of $p = \Phi_I(f)$ and shown by the symbol

$$\begin{array}{ccc} & {}_2\diagdown \;{}^3| \;\; \ddots & \\ \underset{1}{\text{———}} & \text{I} & \underset{n}{\text{———}} \end{array}$$

The relations for the n-port I-field are then

$$\begin{aligned} p_1 &= \Phi_{I1}(f_1, f_2, \ldots, f_n) \\ p_2 &= \Phi_{I4}(f_1, f_2, \ldots, f_n) \\ &\vdots \\ p_n &= \Phi_{In}(f_1, f_2, \ldots, f_n). \end{aligned} \tag{3.29}$$

The multiport fields are important to bond graph techniques from a variety of points of view and will be encountered throughout the remainder of the book. They may appear directly in the form of relations, such as Eqs. 3.27, 3.28, and 3.29, or they may arise through interconnection of simpler elements in the construction of a system model. As an example of the first situation, it may be seen that the characterization of an elastic body by influence coefficients yields relations in the form of Eq. 3.28, and that of a rigid body by inertia coefficients yields relations in the form of Eq. 3.29.

To illustrate the latter situation, an interconnection of 1-port R's or C's or I's with 0-junctions, 1-junctions, and transformers (but not gyrators, generally) will produce a composite multiport with the character of an R–, or C–, or I-field. These notions will be discussed more fully in Chapter 4.

3.5 Causality for the basic multiports

The concept of causality was already discussed in general terms in Chapter 2, and we may now make some more specific uses of the idea with respect to the basic multiports. Some of the causal properties developed here will be applied in Chapters 5, 6, and 7. For now, we simply note that some of the basic multiports are heavily constrained with respect to possible causalities, some are relatively indifferent to causality, and some exhibit their characteristics in quite different forms for different causalities.

Causality for basic 1-ports

The effort and flow sources are the most easily discussed from a causal point of view since, by definition, a source impresses either an effort or flow time

Table 3-3. Causal forms for basic 1-ports

Element	Acausal Form	Causal Form	Causal Relation
Effort source	E ⇀ S_e ⇀	E ⇀| S_e ⇀|	$e(t) = E(t)$
Flow source	F ⇀ S_f ⇀	F |⇀ S_f |⇀	$f(t) = F(t)$
Resistance	R ↼	R ↼| R |↼	$e = \Phi_R(f)$ $f = \Phi_R^{-1}(e)$
Capacitance	C ↼	C ↼| C |↼	$e = \Phi_C^{-1}(\int^t f dt)$ $f = \frac{d}{dt}[\Phi_C(e)]$
Inertance	I ↼	I |↼ I ↼|	$f = \Phi_I^{-1}(\int^t e dt)$ $e = \frac{d}{dt}[\Phi_I(f)]$

history upon whatever system is connected to it. Thus, if we use the symbols E– and F– for the abstract effort and flow sources, the only permissible causalities for these elements are

E—| and F|—.

The causal forms for effort and flow sources are summarized in the first two rows of Table 3-3.

In contrast to the sources, the 1-port resistance is normally indifferent to the causality imposed upon it. The two possibilities may be represented in equation form as follows:

$$e = \Phi_R(f), \quad f = \Phi_R^{-1}(e), \tag{3.30}$$

where we use the convention that the variable on the left of the equality sign represents the *output* of the resistance or the *dependent variable,* and that appearing in the function of the right side is the *input* or *independent* variable for the element. This convention is used commonly, but not universally, in writing equations and corresponds to the notation used in computer programming, as, for example, in FORTRAN.

The correspondences between the causally interpreted characteristic equations and the causal strokes on the bond of the R– element are shown in the third row of Table 3-3. As long as both the functions Φ_R and Φ_R^{-1} exist and are known, there is no reason for preferring one causality over the other. It is possible, however, that the static relation between e and f shown in Fig. 3-1 might be multiple valued in one direction or the other; i.e., either Φ_R or Φ_R^{-1} might be multiple valued. In such a case the single-valued causality would be clearly preferable. In the linear case, with a finite slope of the e-f characteristic, the 1-port resistance is indifferent to the causality imposed upon it.

The characteristics of the C— and I— elements are expressed as static relations between e and $q = \int^t f dt$ and f and $p = \int^t e dt$ respectively. In expressing causal relations between e's and f's, we will find that the choice of causality has an important effect. Taking the capacitance element, we may rewrite the characteristics from Table 3-1 as follows:

$$e = \Phi_C^{-1}\left(\int^t f dt\right), \quad f = \frac{d}{dt}\left[\Phi_C(e)\right], \tag{3.31}$$

in which causality is implied by the form of the equation. Note that when f is the input to the C—, e is given by a static function of the time integral of f, but when e is the input, f is the time derivative of a static function of e. The correspondences between these causal equations and the causal stroke notation for the capacitance are shown in the fourth row of Table 3-3. The implications of the two types of causality, which are called *integral causality* and *derivative causality* respectively, will be discussed in some detail in later chapters.

Since the inertance element is the dual of the capacitance element, similar effects occur with the two choices of causality. Rewriting the inertance element characteristics from Table 3-1, we have

$$f = \Phi_I^{-1}\left(\int^t e dt\right), \quad e = \frac{d}{dt}\left[\Phi_I(f)\right]. \tag{3.32}$$

In this case, integral causality exists when e is the input to the inertance element, and derivative causality exists when f is the input. These observations are summarized in the fifth row of Table 3-3. Eqs. 3.31 and 3.32 are written in a form suitable for nonlinear C— and I— elements but the distinction between integral and derivative causality remains even for the special case of linear elements.

Causality for basic 2-ports and 3-ports

Proceeding now to the basic 2-ports, one might think initially that there would be a total of four possibilities for the assignment of causality of a transformer, viz., any combination of the two possible causalities for each of the two ports. However there are only two possible causality assignments, as the defining relations, Eq. 3.16, show. As soon as one of the e's or f's has been assigned as an input to the —TF—, the other e or f is constrained to be an output by Eq. 3.16. Thus, in fact, the only two possible

Table 3-4. Causal forms for basic 2-ports and 3-ports

Element	Acausal graph	Causal graph	Causal relations
Transformer	$\overset{1}{\rightharpoonup}$ TF $\overset{2}{\rightharpoonup}$	$\vdash\overset{1}{\rightharpoonup}$ TF $\vdash\overset{2}{\rightharpoonup}$	$e_1 = me_2$ $f_2 = mf_1$
		$\overset{1}{\rightharpoonup}\!\mid$ TF $\overset{2}{\rightharpoonup}\!\mid$	$f_1 = f_2/m$ $e_2 = e_1/m$
Gyrator	$\overset{1}{\rightharpoonup}$ GY $\overset{2}{\rightharpoonup}$	$\vdash\overset{1}{\rightharpoonup}$ GY $\overset{2}{\rightharpoonup}\!\mid$	$e_1 = rf_2$ $e_2 = rf_1$
		$\overset{1}{\rightharpoonup}\!\mid$ GY $\vdash\overset{2}{\rightharpoonup}$	$f_1 = e_2/r$ $f_2 = e_1/r$
0-junction	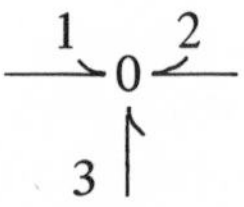 $\overset{1}{\rightharpoonup}$ 0 $\overset{2}{\leftharpoondown}$, 3 ↑	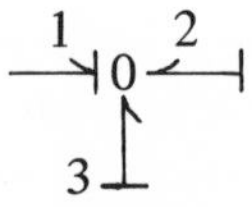 $\overset{1}{\rightharpoonup}\!\mid$ 0 $\overset{2}{\leftharpoondown}\!\mid$, 3 ↑ (stroke at 3)	$e_2 = e_1$ $e_3 = e_1$ $f_1 = -(f_2 + f_3)$
1-junction	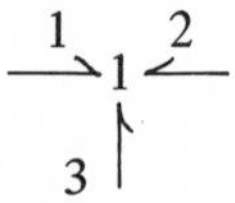 $\overset{1}{\rightharpoonup}$ 1 $\overset{2}{\leftharpoondown}$, 3 ↑	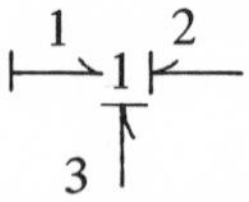 $\vdash\overset{1}{\rightharpoonup}$ 1 $\overset{2}{\leftharpoondown}\!\dashv$, 3 ↑ (stroke at 1)	$f_2 = f_1$ $f_3 = f_1$ $e_1 = -(e_2 + e_3)$

choices for causality for the transformer are |—TF|— and —|TF—|. The possible causalities are tabulated in the first row of Table 3-4, which should be compared to the entry for —TF— in Table 3-2. In Table 3-4, a simplified naming of the efforts and flows has been achieved by simply numbering the bonds. This technique will be explored in more detail in subsequent chapters, but for now, the correspondences between Table 3-2 and Table 3-4 should be evident. Again, causal equation equivalents to the causal stroke notation are given for all elements in Table 3-4.

For the gyrator, Eqs. 3.17 show that as soon as the causality for one bond has been determined, so is that for the other. Thus, the only permissible causal choices for the —GY— are —|GY|— and |—GY—|. The choices for the causality for the gyrator are summarized in the second row of Table 3-4, which may be compared to the corresponding entries in Table 3-2.

The causal properties of 3-port 0-junctions and 1-junctions are somewhat similar to those of the basic 2-ports. Although each bond of the 3-ports, if considered alone, could have either of the two possible causalities assigned, not all combinations of bond causalities are permitted by the characteristic relations of the element. For example, the relations for the 0-junction given in Table 3-2 or by Eqs. 3.22 and 3.23 indicate that all efforts on all the bonds are equal and the flows must sum to zero. Thus, if on any bond the effort is an input to a 0-junction, then all other efforts are determined and on all other bonds they must be outputs of the 0-junction. Conversely, if the flows on all bonds but one are inputs to the 0-junction, Eq. 3.23 states that the flow on the remaining bond is determined and must be an output of the junction. A typical permissible causality for a 0-junction is shown in the fourth row of Table 3-4. Here the causal stroke on the end of bond 1 nearest the 0 indicates that e_1 is an input to the junction and that all other bonds must have causal strokes at the end away from the 0. To interpret the diagram another way, the flows on bonds 2 and 3 are inputs to the 0-junction. These considerations are also expressed by the causal equations shown in Table 3-4. For a 3-port 0-junction, then, there are only three different permissible causalities in which each of the three bonds in succession plays the role assigned to bond 1 in the example shown in the table. For an n-port 0-junction this description of the constraints on causality is still valid and there are exactly n different permissible causal assignments.

For a 1-junction, the same considerations apply as for a 0-junction except that the roles of the efforts and flows are interchanged. Table 3-2 and Eqs. 3.25 and 3.26 indicate that all flows on the bonds are equal and the efforts sum to zero. Thus, if the flow on any single bond is an input to the 1-junction, then the flows on all other bonds are determined and must be considered outputs of the junction. On the other hand, when the efforts on all bonds but one are inputs to the 1-junction, the effort on the remaining bond is determined and must be an output of the junction. A typical permissible causality is shown in the fourth row of Table 3-4. In this example, bond 1 plays the special role of determining the common flow at the junction, and the remaining bonds supply effort inputs that suffice to determine the effort on bond 1. Clearly, there are three permissible causalities for a 3-port 1-junction, and there are n permissible different causal assignments for an n-port 1-junction.

Causality for multiport fields.

Since the multiport fields defined in Section 3.4 are generalizations of the 1-port resistance, capacitance, and inertance elements, the causality considerations for the fields are generalizations of the causal effects already discussed. For the fields, in distinction to the basic 2-ports and 3-ports, a wide variety of causality assignments may be permissible. For an n-port R-field, for example, we would expect that any causality at any bond would be permissible except

Table 3-5. Some special causal forms for multiport fields

Field type	Acausal Graph	Causal Graph	Comments and Relations
Resistance	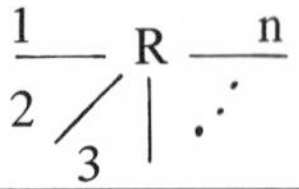 1 — R — n, 2, 3	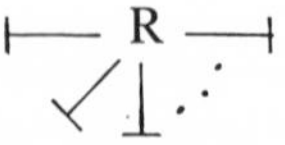 R	Resistance causality e $e_i = \Phi_{R_i}(f_1, f_2, \ldots f_n)$
		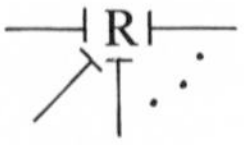 R	Conductance causality $f_i = \Phi_{R_i}^{-1}(e_1, e_2, \ldots e_n)$
Capacitance	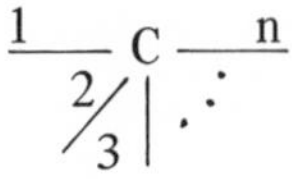 1 — C — n, 2, 3	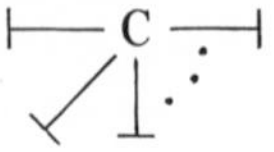 C	Integral causality $e_1 = \Phi_{C_i}^{-1}(q_1, q_2, \ldots q_n)$ $q_j = \int^t f_j dt$
		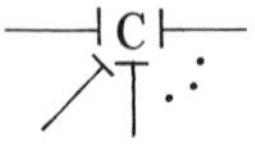 C	Derivative causality $f_1 = \frac{d}{dt}[\Phi_{C_i}(e_1 e_2, \ldots e_n)]$
Inertance	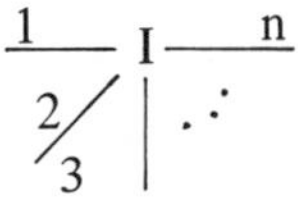 1 — I — n, 2, 3	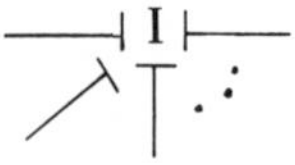 I	Integral causality $f_i = \Phi_I^{-1}(p_1, p_2, \ldots p_n)$ $p_j = \int^t e_j dt$
		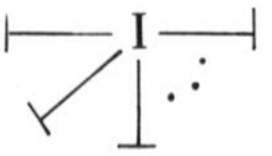 I	Derivative causality $e_i = \frac{d}{dt}[\Phi_{I_i}(f_1, f_2, \ldots f_n)]$

for the sort of problem with multiple-valued nonlinear functions that was discussed briefly for the 1-port resistance. Of all the possible combinations of causal assignments on the bonds of a multiport field, it is worth mentioning the two special cases in which the causality assignment at all bonds is identical, that is, efforts are inputs at all the bonds, or flows are inputs at all the bonds.

In Table 3-5 these two special forms of causal assignment are summarized for R,-C, and I-fields. For the R-field, shown in the first row of Table 3-5, we term the causality with all flow inputs *resistance causality* and that with all efforts inputs *conductance causality* in analogy with the descriptive terms used for 1-port resistance elements. In general, the indifference to causality of the 1-port R is carried over to the n-port R-fields.

For the multiport C-field and I-field, the two special cases of causal assignment shown in the second and third rows of Table 3-5 correspond to the cases of integral and derivative causality that were defined for the corresponding 1-port element. These two special forms of causality will be seen again in applications and will be studied more extensively in later chapters on analytical methods and simulation. We simply note here that mixed causalities for the C-fields and I-fields result in mixed integral-derivative relations.

Having defined and studied in some detail a basic set of bond graph elements and having made a preliminary examination of the methods of augmenting the elements to name the effort and flow quantities, to define sign conventions, and to indicate causality, it is appropriate to gain experience in the construction of bond graph models for physical systems in the next chapter. Then in Chapters 5, 6, and 7 analytical and computational techniques for bond graph models will be studied.

References

1. The need to define e, f, p, and q variables is not restricted to bond graph techniques, and modern works on dynamics are beginning to define all of these variables explicitly. See, for example, S. H. Crandall, D. C. Karnopp, E. F. Kurtz, and D. C. Pridmore-Brown, *Dynamics of Mechanical and Electromechanical Systems,* McGraw-Hill Book Co., New York, 1968.

4. BOND GRAPHS FOR INTERCONNECTED SYSTEMS

The aim of this chapter is to set forth the methods for finding valid bond graphs for common types of physical system models. In some cases this amounts to translating standard system representations, such as electric circuit graphs or mechanical schematic diagrams, into bond graphs using the basic set of multiports defined in Chapter 3. In other cases differential equation representations for physical systems will be restructured to show energy exchanges, and bond graph representations will then be sought. Since we will defer discussion of the manipulation and analysis of bond graph representations, and simulation programs based on bond graphs to later chapters, the bond graphs in this chapter will generally be existential statements about system models and will not necessarily require variable names, sign conventions or causality information. When the ideas and techniques of this chapter are mastered, it should become clear that bond graph methods provide a framework for synthesizing models of variable complexity for physical systems or components.

4.1 Single energy domain systems

To fix ideas, we begin with the most restrictive class of systems, namely, those systems that are composed of circuitlike elements in a single energy domain. In this class fall electric circuits, mechanical lumped parameter systems moving in one dimension, and simple hydraulic circuits. First, we consider systems composed of the 1-ports S_e–, S_f–, R–, C–, I–, and the two

3-port junctions $-\overset{|}{0}-$ and $-\overset{|}{1}-$. Later we will see that the 2-ports –TF– and –GY– may also be added without difficulty. In each case we pass from the physical system to the bond graph; this can always be done in an unambiguous fashion.

Electric circuits

Consider the problem of transforming an electric circuit diagram to an equivalent bond graph. The bond graph always pairs ideal circuit conductors such that a single current and voltage may be defined and such that the pro-

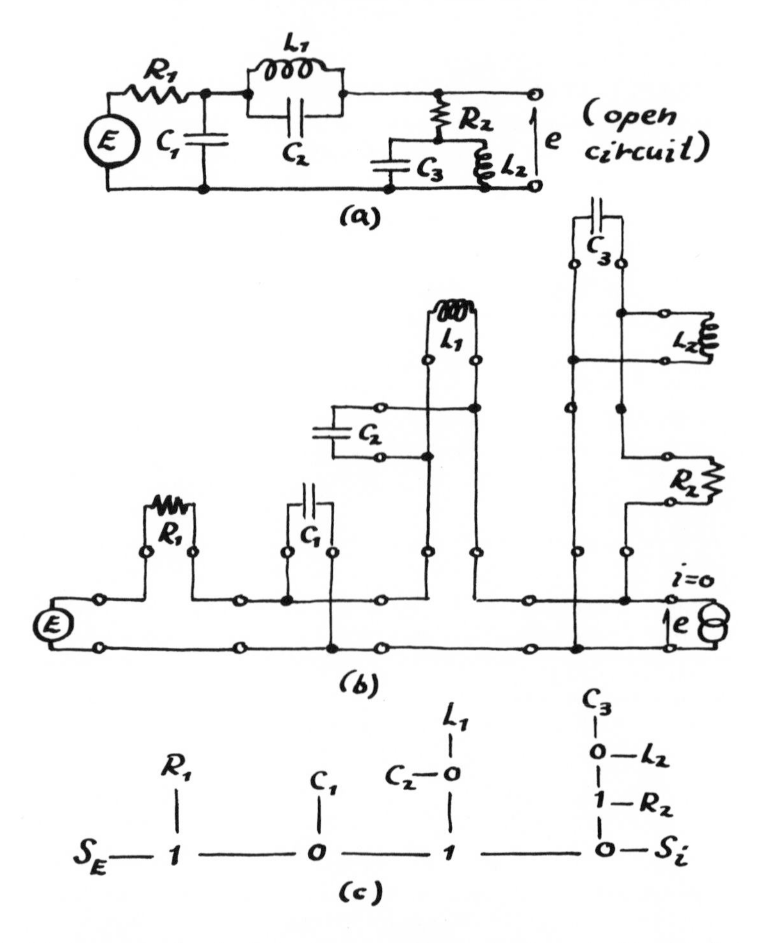

Fig. 4-1 Example of a circuit graph converted into a bond graph. (a) original circuit graph, (b) distorted circuit graph, (c) bond graph.

duct of the current and voltage is a power flow. For simple circuits this process can be done by inspection, but in other cases the return line for some of the currents is less than obvious and a systematic procedure is desirable. The circuit of Fig. 4-1 has a fairly obvious current return line and one may easily imagine the circuit distorted as in Fig 4-1(b) so as to make the 1-ports and the 0- and 1-junctions identifiable by comparing the bond graphs and circuits in Figs. 3-1, 3-2, 3-3, and 3-7 with Fig 4-1(b) The bond graph of Fig. 4-1(c) follows immediately from the distorted circuit graph of Fig 4-1(b) by simple identifications with the elements given in the last chapter. It should be evident that sign conventions can be transferred from the circuit graph to the bond graph, and named voltages and currents on the circuit graph can be transferred to the bond graph.

While the process of Fig. 4-1 underlies the conversion of any circuit to a bond graph, for many circuits the process becomes very involved because an obvious set of current return lines does not present itself and a more systematic and formal method is desirable. Observing that a node in a circuit defines a single voltage relative to a ground and that a 1-port circuit element is considered to pass a single current, it is natural to use the 0-junction with its single voltage and the 1-junction with its single current in a systematic fashion to satisfy the constraints implied by the circuit connections.

The following procedure will be illustrated by example:

(1) For each voltage of interest, and in particular for every node in the circuit, establish a 0-junction.

(2) Establish the current for each 1-port circuit element with a 1-junction bonded to the two 0-junctions that represent the two voltages at the ends of the 1-port elements and to the 1-port element itself.

While steps (1) and (2) suffice to define a bond graph, there are generally many possibilities for simplifying the graph. For example, if any 0-junction or 1-junction has only two bonds, the junction may usually be represented by a single bond. Further, several 3-port 0-junctions (or 1-junctions) with a set of common bonds may be combined to define n-port 0- (or 1-) junctions. Also, all the 0-junctions define voltages relative to an unspecified ground potential, and, for circuits, only differences in potential are significant. Therefore, one may pick any convenient 0-junction and define it to be at the ground potential. Since the bonds emanating from the ground 0-junction will then be at zero potential, no power can flow on these bonds and they may be eliminated. After the elimination of bonds to the ground 0-junction, the graph may often be simplified considerably.

These ideas are illustrated first for the very elementary circuit of Fig 4-2(a) for which the proper bond graph is evident by inspection. Three nodes, A, B, and G, are defined in Fig. 4-2(a) and the corresponding 0-junctions are shown

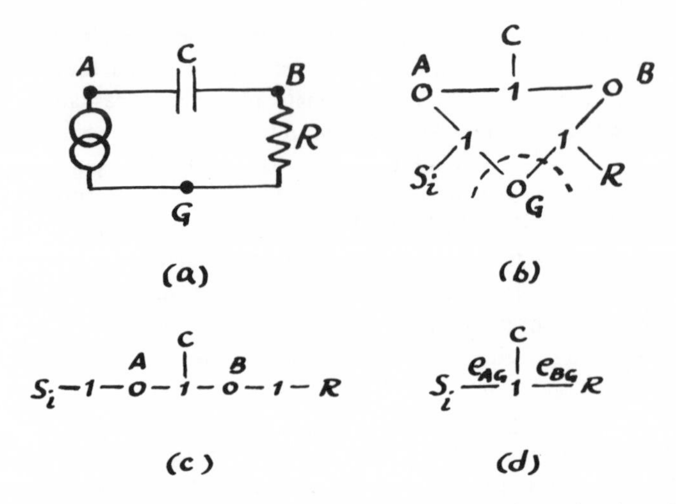

Fig. 4-2 Example of systematic conversion of circuit graph to a bond graph. (a) original circuit graph, (b) bond graph, (c), (d) simplified bond graphs.

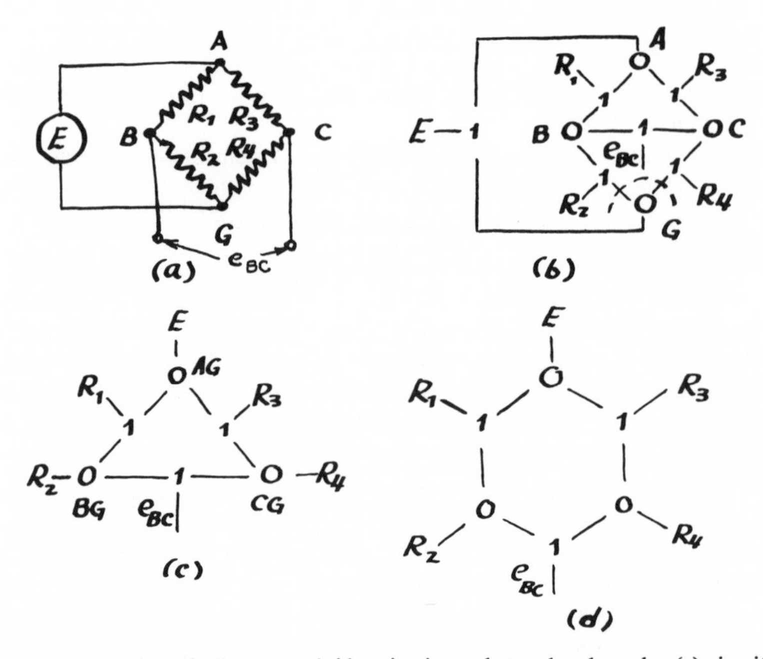

Fig. 4-3 Conversion of Wheatstone bridge circuit graph to a bond graph. (a) circuit graph, (b) bond graph, (c) simplified bond graph, (d) "benzene ring" structure.

in Fig. 4-2(b). The 1-junctions for each 1-port establish the current through the 1-port and apply to the 1-port the difference in voltage between the ends of the circuit element. By setting the voltage at G to zero some bonds are eliminated, resulting in the graph of Fig. 4-2(c). When the 2-port 0-junctions and 1-junctions of Fig 4-2(c) are considered as single bonds the result is the graph of Fig. 4-2 (d), which is readily identified with the original circuit and could have been found easily by the circuit distortion method shown in Fig. 4-1.

A more complex example is provided by the Wheatstone bridge of Fig. 4-3. The reader will probably find that the operation of drawing a "ground plane" or network of current return lines in order to discover the 0- and 1-junctions is a frustrating experience. On the other hand the procedure sketched in Fig. 4-3(b) and (c) is very straightforward. In Fig. 4-3(d), the simplified bond graph is more artistically drawn to show the hexagonally symmetric structure for the bridge circuit, which happens to be independent of the choice of ground node. This "benzene ring" configuration is typical of the structural information content of bond graphs and is invariant with respect to the nature of the 1-ports connected to the bridge. One should note that the voltage e_{BC} appears on a free bond and thus the system is not completely defined. If, for example, Fig. 4-3(a) is meant to imply that e_{BC} is an open circuit voltage, the free bond on which e_{BC} appears should be connected to a current source with zero current. On the other hand, if e_{BC} is supplied to an instrument or other system with finite impedance, the bridge port BC may be bonded to the instrument port by the bond having effort e_{BC}.

There are several possible bond graphs for a physical system and occasionally the systematic procedure may produce one that seems at variance with the bond graph obtained by distorting the circuit, as in Fig. 4-1. If no outright mistakes have been made, then a bond graph equivalence has been found. One should be cautioned, however, that since bond graphs may be constructed that admit no physical interpretation, one should refer back to the physical system for verification of a bond graph equivalence. In particular, as shall be demonstrated shortly, the physical system often restricts one to a limited set of the possible signs for the variables, and thus a bond graph with no sign convention indicated may be nonsensical from a physical point of view if an improper assignment of sign conventions is applied to it. This difficulty will not arise if sign conventions are properly transferred from the physical system.

To illustrate these points, let us consider again the example of Fig. 4-1. In Fig. 4-4 the systematic procedure is applied to the circuit in a fairly obvious fashion. Note that the current return line used in Fig. 4-1 appears as a logical choice for a ground node in Fig. 4-4, since many bonds may be eliminated when the node G is considered to be at zero voltage. As expected, the bond graph of Fig. 4-4(c) does closely resemble the graph of Fig. 4-1(e) when G is

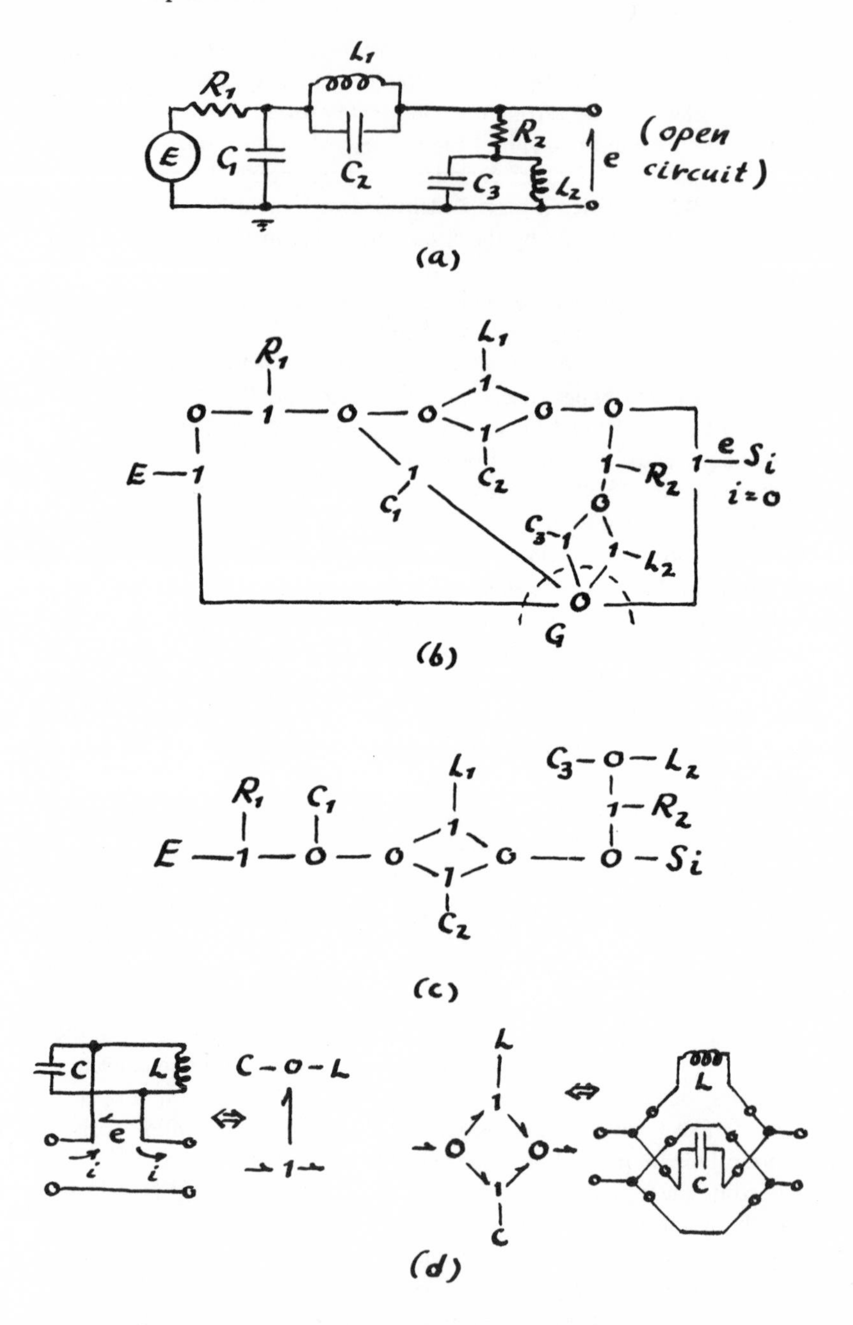

Fig. 4-4 Systematic procedure applied to the circuit of Fig. 4-1. (a) original circuit, (b) bond graph, (c) simplified bond graph, (d) bond graph equivalents.

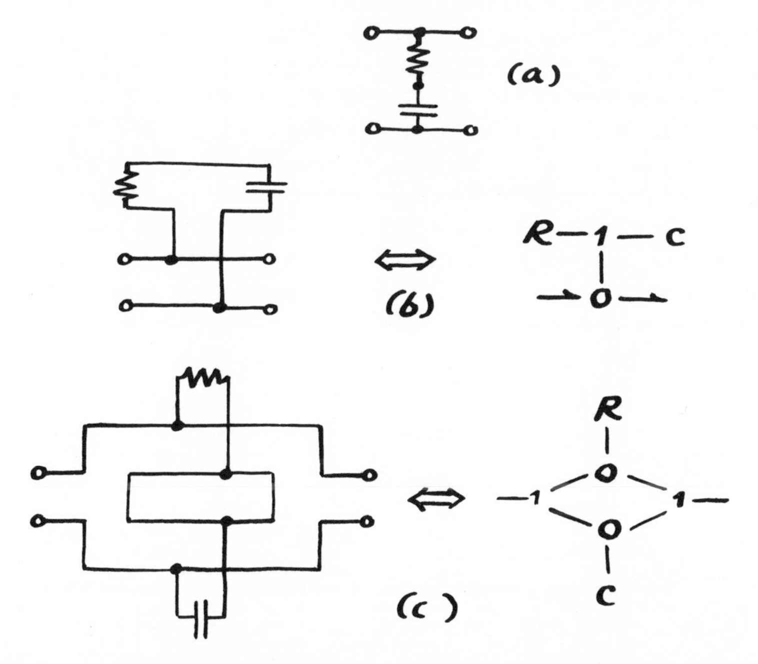

Fig. 4-5 Two bond graph equivalents. (a) original circuit, (b) distorted circuit and bond graph, (c) equivalent graphs.

used as the ground node. Only the part of the graphs that involve L_1 and C_2 appear to differ. In Fig. 4-4(d) the equivalence of the two bond graph representations is made evident by circuit graph distortions. There is no fundamental reason to prefer the bond graph of Fig. 4-1 over that of Fig. 4-4 and, indeed, there is some danger in attempting to convert from one bond graph to another. We may note, for example, that the circuit representation forced certain sign conventions on the bond graph. In the right-hand representation in Fig. 4-4(d), the definition of currents on the 1-junctions and voltages on the 0-junctions relative to a common ground means that only some of the possible power conventions on the loop in the bond graph are permissible. One set of consistent sign conventions is shown on the bonds in Fig. 4-4(d). If the powers are directed as shown, then the two bond graph representations do indeed represent the same circuit. With some of the other possible sign conventions on the bond graphs, the bond graphs would not represent the same circuit and hence might not be equivalent. It is safest first to assign power directions by appealing to the physical system and then to attempt a conversion to another form of bond graph. Figure 4-5 shows another commonly occurring pair of bond graph equivalents. This case is the structural dual of that appearing in Fig. 4-4.

The insertion of 2-ports such as –TF– or –GY– poses no particular problems, as the example in Fig. 4-6 indicates. In Fig. 4-6(a), the general procedure for making bond graphs from circuits is applied to an ideal transformer. If all four terminals of the transformer are given voltages by assignment of a 0-junction to each terminal, and it is observed that each winding acts like a 1-port in the sense that a single current flows in each winding, then the transformer may be connected to 1-junctions of each terminal pair to enforce this constraint. With the bond graph of Fig. 4-6(a), the circuit of Fig. 4-6(b) is converted to the bond graph of Fig. 4-6(c). One use of a transformer is to eliminate any D.C. voltage component between two parts of a circuit; this property of the

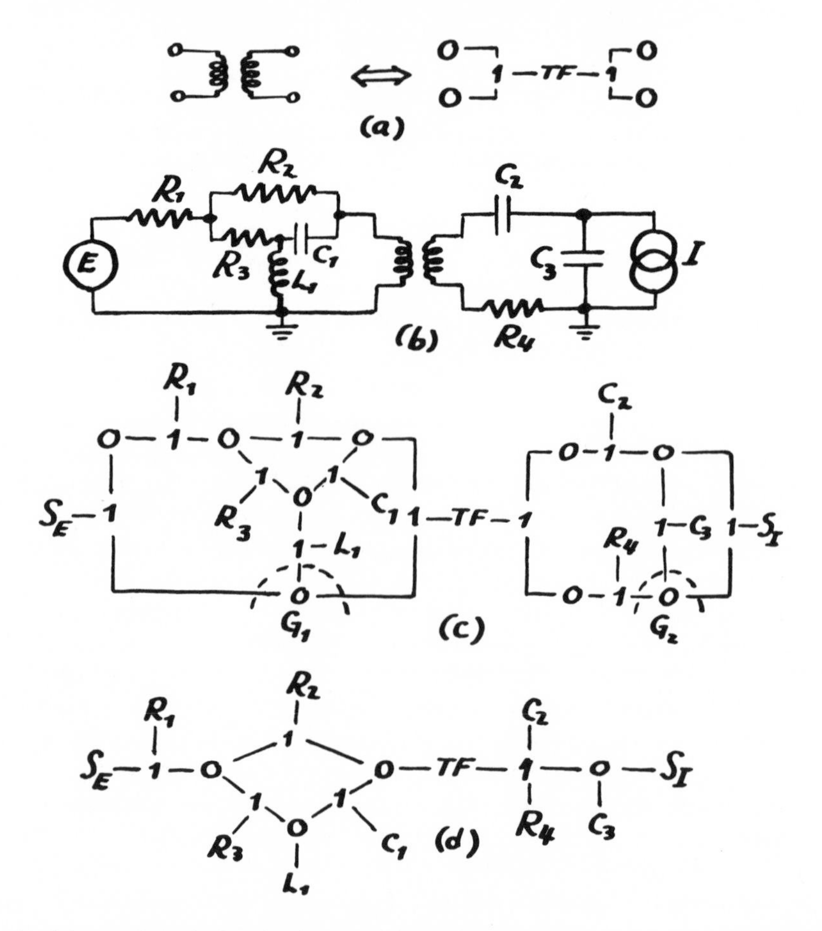

Fig. 4-6 **Bond graphs for circuits containing an ideal transformer. (a) bond graph for transformer, (b) circuit graph example, (c) bond graph of circuit, (d) simplified bond graph after choosing two ground nodes.**

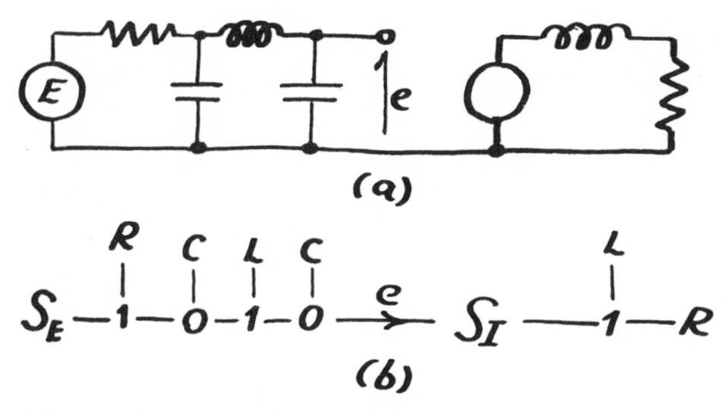

Fig. 4-7 Active elements in circuits and bond graphs. (a) circuit containing a voltage controlled current source, (b) bond graph incorporating an active bond.

transformer allows one to define independent grounds on the two sides of the transformer-coupled circuit. By use of this idea, the bond graph may be simplified, as shown in Fig. 4-6(d).

A further extension of circuit graphs involves their use in representing active elements like transistors and vacuum tubes. Such elements are used to isolate parts of circuits, and since part of the power supplied to them is neglected in the active representation some special techniques of representation in circuit graphs and bond graphs are necessary. The device of Fig. 4-7(a) is to be considered a voltage-controlled current source; i.e., the device injects a current into the right-hand part of the circuit dependent only on the voltage, e, appearing at the indicated terminal. The notation is also meant to imply that no current flows at the terminal. Most of the bond graph of Fig. 4-7(b) is found by straightforward application of the principles outlined above. The bond with the arrow is called an *active bond* and transmits a signal without power. When the bond emanates from a 0-junction as in the present example, the convention is that the single effort (voltage in the example) is measured and transmitted to some other element. The element $\overset{e}{\rightarrow} S_I \underset{i}{—}$ must then be described by a relation stating how the current supplied depends on the voltage, e. The active bond achieves an isolation of the two parts of the circuit, since none of the variables in the right-hand side can affect the left-hand side of the circuit. In the present case the active bond transmits a voltage signal, but no current flows. If the active bond emanates from a 1-junction in an electric circuit the dual situation is implied: A current is measured and transmitted as a signal with no voltage difference required for the measurement.

The controlled source characteristic need not be a simple static relation between the measured variable and the supplied power variables. It is often desirable to allow the elements with active bond inputs to incorporate transfer functions or other dynamic relationships to describe the element. Instruments and amplifiers are typically modeled using active bonds.

Hydraulic circuits

Let us now consider hydraulic systems composed of circuitlike elements. Despite the apparently severe limitation involved in using simple circuitlike elements, a surprising number of the dynamic analyses actually performed in practice use such elements to model real systems. One purpose here is merely to develop facility for describing systems in terms of bond graphs. Once this facility is attained, one still faces the problem of constructing models adequate to answer certain questions about the dynamics of practical systems.

Certain fluid systems, in idealized form, are quite obviously analogous to electric circuits; the extension of the methods discussed previously is thus very straightforward. Consider for example the circuit of Fig. 4-8(a), in which an incompressible fluid is assumed to flow through rigid, lossless lines in a configuration analogous to the electric circuit of Fig. 4-2 if the volume flow rate Q is considered to correspond to an electric current. An orifice plays the role of a nonlinear resistance, and a spring bellows may be taken to act like a capacitor. A bond graph is readily found by using the hydraulic analog of the general procedure for electric circuits. In Fig. 4-8(b), 0-junctions are established for pressures and 1-junctions for flows. The bond graph implies that for the orifice a single flow is related to a pressure difference and that the integral of a single flow through the bellows is related to a pressure difference. Also, the pump is considered to deliver a flow independent of pressures at the inlet and outlet of the pump. In a circuit, only voltage differences are important, and if one assumes only pressure differences to be important in the hydraulic circuit, then any pressure may be taken as a reference pressure and the graph is simplified in Fig. 4-8(c).

Clearly, once one has established the validity of circuitlike elements in a model of fluid devices, the problem of finding a bond graph for the system is not difficult. The validity of circuitlike elements is perhaps not so evident for fluid systems as for electric circuits, although in both cases we are dealing with idealizations and the ultimate verification of system models must rest in a comparison of predicted characteristics with the results of physical experiments. Although it is not the purpose of this book to discuss in any detail the problem of finding system models and ranges of validity for models of particular systems, a few obvious restrictions to circuitlike models for fluid systems should be mentioned. For example, most so-called positive displacement pumps are designed to operate properly only when inlet and outlet pressures remain within certain ranges. When inlet pressure falls below a certain value, cavitation will occur and the pump may not only fail to operate in the intended manner but may also suffer permanent damage. Thus one must keep in mind that preoccupation with pressure differences could result in invalid predictions when absolute pressures take on extreme values. Also,

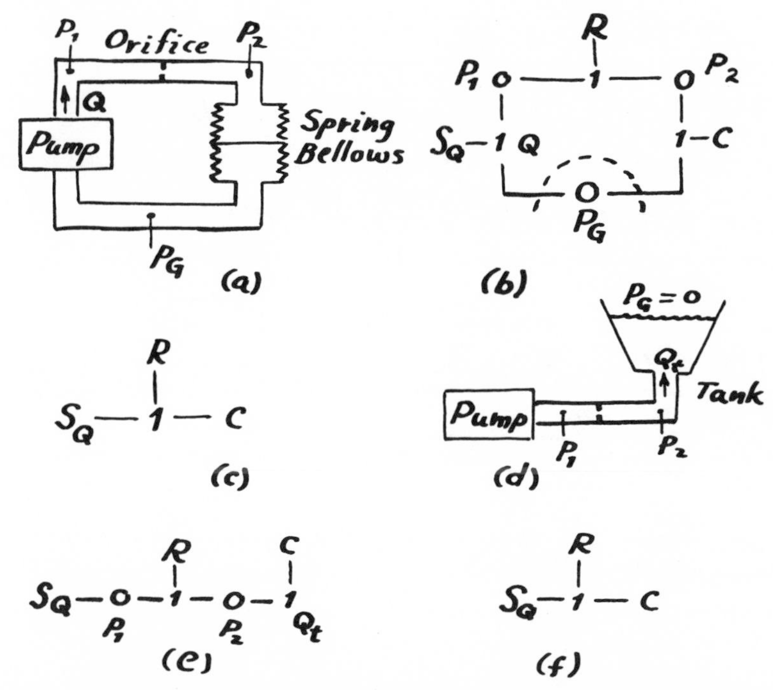

Fig. 4-8 Hydraulic circuits and bond graphs. (a) hydraulic circuit analogous to the electric circuit of Fig. 4-2, (b) bond graph, (c) simplified bond graph, (d) hydraulic system with gravity tank, (e) bond graph, (f) simplified bond graph.

in compressible flow an orifice does not provide a flow in response only to pressure differences; absolute pressures must also be known. Thus one must beware of the use of the 1-junction connected to the R for the orifice, since it carries the implication that only the pressure difference is supplied to a resistor modeling the orifice. Similarly, the graph simplification resulting in Fig. 4-8(c) is not always valid.

On the other hand, the bond graph approach, even using the circuitlike elements, is valuable in cases in which the analogy to electric circuits is less obvious than in Fig. 4-8(a). Consider the system sketched in Fig. 4-8(d), in which energy is stored in a tank via the gravity field. Since the pressure at the bottom of the tank depends on the height of fluid in the tank, and this in turn depends on the volume of fluid in the tank (or the time integral of the flow into the tank), it can be seen that the tank acts like a capacitor. Although one may be reluctant to define a flow *through* the tank in the sense of the spring bellows of Fig. 4-8(a) or of an electric capacitor, the bond graph

Fluid line segment including inertia, resistance, compressibility and pipe wall compliance

(a)

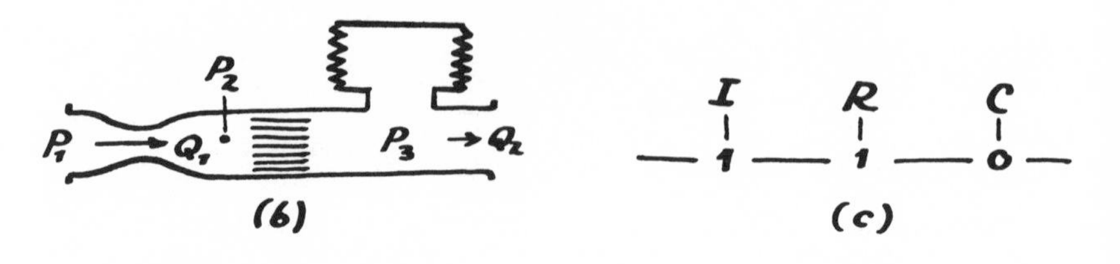

Fig. 4-9 Model of fluid line segment. (a) fluid line segment, (b) schematic of line segment, (c) bond graph.

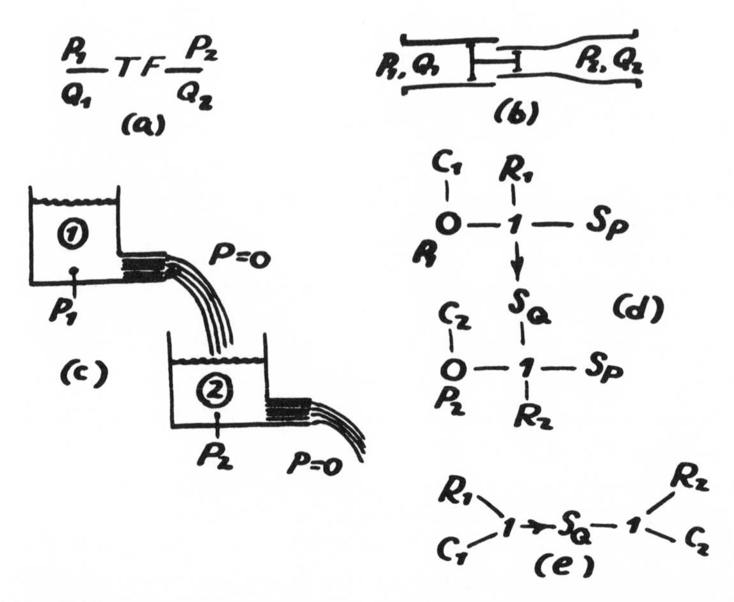

Fig. 4-10 Additional elements for hydraulic systems. (a) transformer bond graph, (b) transformer schematic, (c) cascaded hydraulic system, (d) bond graph for cascaded system, (e) simplified bond graph.

for the system is readily found, as shown in Figs. 4-8(e) and (f). With the ground node chosen as in Fig. 4-8(b), there is a close analogy between the two systems of Fig. 4-8 and this is reflected in the bond graphs of Figs. 4-8(e) and (f).

A typical use of circuitlike elements is shown in Fig. 4-9, in which a length of fluid constrained to flow in a pipelike passage is allowed to suffer a loss in pressure due to inertia and resistance effects and a loss of volume flow due to fluid compressibility and pipe compliance. The bond graph of Fig. 4-9(c) effectively conveys the type of model in question without becoming involved with the details of the relations used in a particular case. Obviously a long pipe may be modeled by a large number of such segments placed end to end, and one may proceed to a partial differential equation description of the line if the segments are allowed to become infinitesimal in length.

A number of other elements often encountered in electric circuits have their counterparts in fluid circuits. In Figs. 4-10(a) and (b) the fluid equivalent of the ideal electric transformer is shown, and Fig. 4-10(c) illustrates a cascaded fluid system that can modeled by an active bond and a controlled source. The active bond in Fig. 4-10(d) assures that the flow out of the higher tank is not affected by the variables in the lower tank. The controlled flow source indicates that energy is supplied to the lower tank by the flow. One may argue that the bond graph actually represents a system with a pump (the source), which under certain conditions behaves like the real system.

We shall encounter fluid systems again in the study of mixed electrical, mechanical, and fluid systems, but for now let us go on to consider some simple, all-mechanical systems.

Elementary mechanical systems

Fig. 4-11(a) shows a mechanical schematic diagram typical of the models often used to study vibration problems. Partly due to tradition, one typically attempts to describe the dynamics in terms of velocities and positions. Thus it may seem most natural to start the development of a bond graph by establishing 1-junctions for each velocity of interest and particularly for every mechanical node in the system. The forces on the nodes may then be found by using 0-junctions to find relative velocities across the 1-port elements. As in the case of gravity-tank capacitors in hydraulic circuits, the inertia elements do not seem to be quite as circuitlike as the corresponding elements in electric circuits. A force, for example, does not seem to pass through the mass element. Also, one must be careful to measure the velocities of masses with respect to an inertial frame. Despite these cautionary statements, the bond graph for mechanical circuits is easily found and verified. In Figs. 4-11(b) and (c) two bond graphs are given for the example system. The two versions

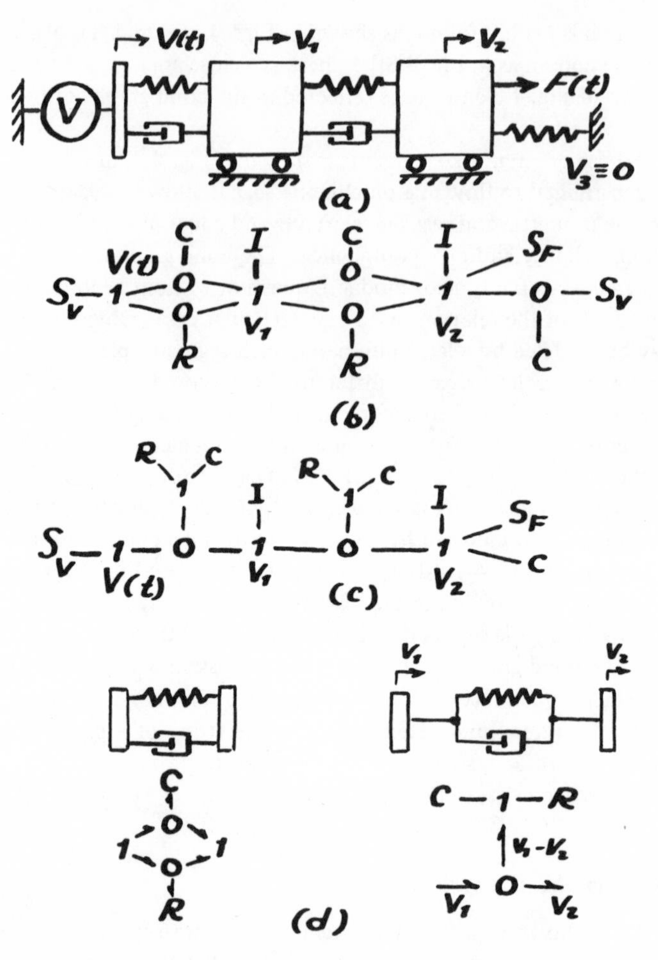

Fig. 4-11 Simple mechanical systems. (a) schematic diagram, (b), (c) bond graphs for system, (d) bond graph equivalents.

stem from two points of view in applying forces to the nodes. In Fig. 4-11 (b) each element force is related to the proper relative velocity and applied to the node (and thus to the inertia elements). In Fig. 4-11(c) two elements react to the same relative velocity and the sum of the forces is applied directly to the appropriate nodes. The appropriate bond graph and schematic equivalences are shown in Fig. 4-11(d). Note that the same sort of choice in electric circuits is shown in Fig. 4-5.

The techniques for representing simple rotational mechanical systems are very similar to those for the translational systems just discussed. As long as

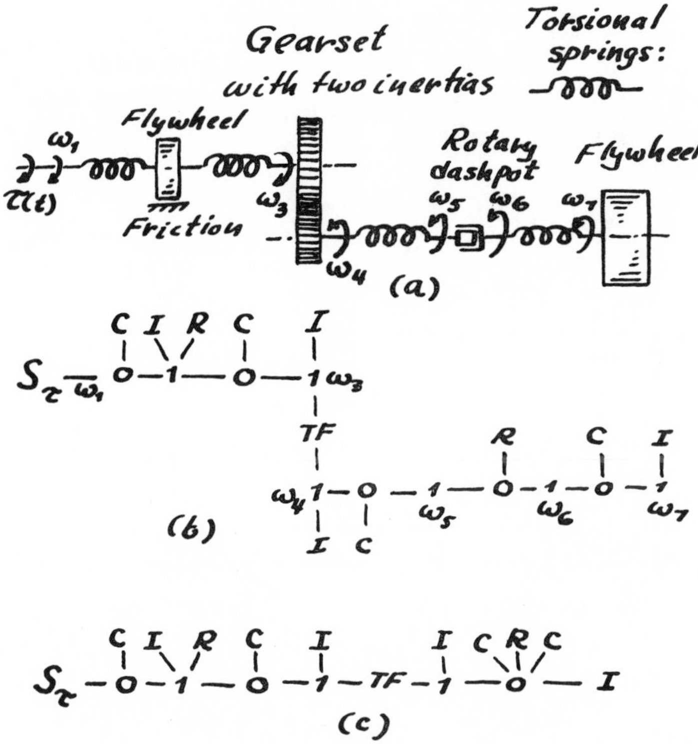

Fig. 4-12 **Rotational mechanical system. (a) schematic diagram, (b) bond graph, (c) simplified bond graph.**

only fixed axis rotation is involved, no new ideas need be introduced. In the example of Fig. 4-12, angular velocities are indicated by 1-junctions, and torques by 0-junctions. In this example, an ideal transformer is used to model a gear pair, and the rotational inertia of the gears is included. The transformer is useful for modeling levers or linkages in translational systems. Although the bond graph of Fig. 4-12(b) and (c) is easily written, there is no guarantee that subsequent analysis or simulation will not reveal some paradoxes in the system description. For example, the torque source clearly establishes a torque on the system at the first 0-junction of the system, independent of the properties of the capacitance (spring) attached to that 0-junction. If the spring constant were set to zero, however, no torque could actually be transmitted to the system. This is not a difficult paradox to resolve, and at this point we are concerned merely with finding bond graphs for systems, but subsequent chapters will show how manipulations on the bond graph will automatically reveal certain features of the problem

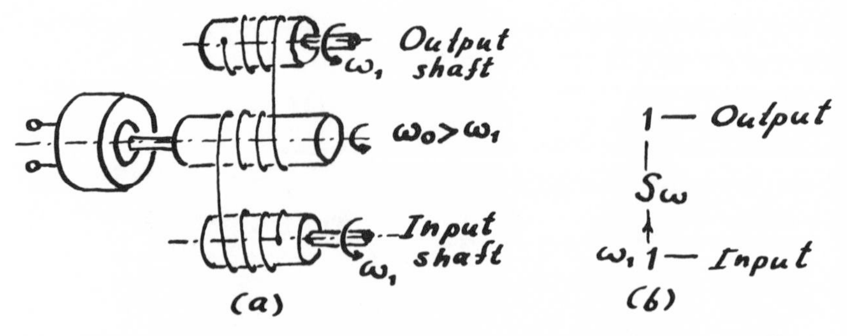

Fig. 4-13 **Capstan principle for amplification. (a) one-directional capstan amplifier, (b) bond graph.**

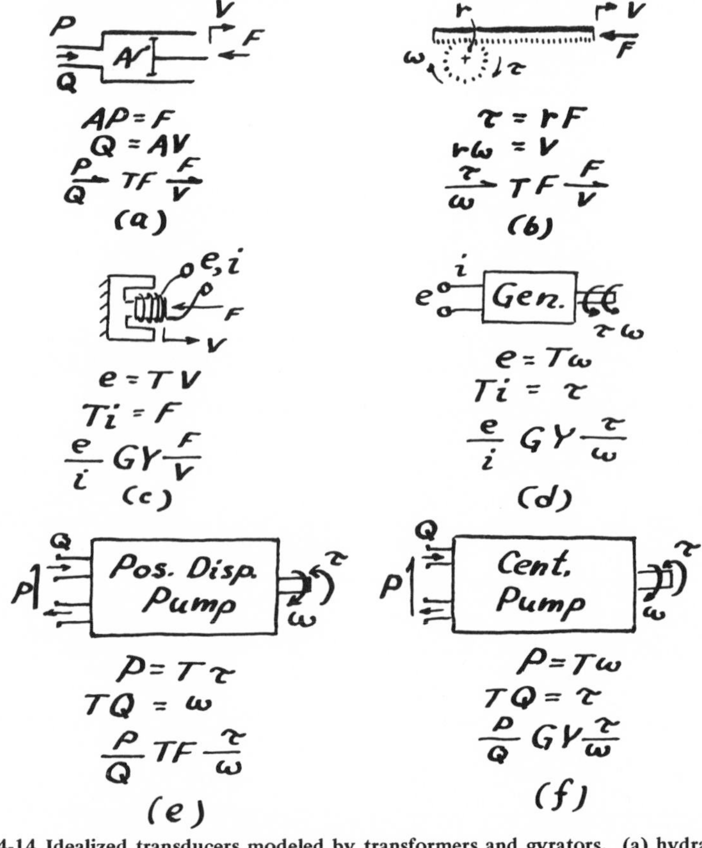

Fig. 4-14 **Idealized transducers modeled by transformers and gyrators. (a) hydraulic ram, (b) rack and pinion, (c) voice coil, (d) electric motor or generator, (e) positive displacement pump, (f) centrifugal pump.**

formulation that may lead to paradoxical results and may have been an inappropriate feature of the system model.

As a final example of simple elements in a single energy domain, Fig. 4-13 shows a schematic of a capstan drive that forms the basis of certain mechanical amplifiers and clutches. Although the device shown is unidirectional, actual devices may be constructed that are bidirectional. A simple bond graph for the device indicates transferrence of the speed from the input shaft to the output shaft through an active bond and a controlled angular velocity source. The active bond implies that the back torque on the input shaft has been neglected altogether.

4.2 Transducers and mixed domain systems

Transducers are devices that allow the coupling of subsystems of distinct energy domains and the forming of mixed domain systems. While they are often quite complex in detail, one can often idealize the inherent transduction phenomenon as a conservative process and model a real device by appending extra elements to account for energy loss and storage. Thus, parts of the real transducer model appear as parts of the subsystems that are coupled by an idealized transducer. Several examples of this common practice will be given. To set the stage for the description of mixed domain systems we first discuss ideal transducers.

Figure 4-14 shows several examples of a special class of transducers involving transformers and gyrators. In each case the 2-port device neither stores nor dissipates any energy; power in one domain is transferred instantaneously to another domain. Given any particular choice of the effort and flow variables in the various energy domains, the element appears as either transformerlike or gyratorlike. As shown by the two examples in Figs. 4-14(e) and (f), there seems to be little point in attempting to decide which variables should be efforts and which flows on the basis of avoiding gyrators since in a single pair of domains one may encounter both gyratorlike and transformerlike transducers.

In Fig. 4-15 typical models of two types of shakers used for vibration testing are shown. The equivalent circuits given are typical of those used before the gyrator element achieved the prominence it now enjoys. In order to use circuits with only transformers for transducers, the systems have to be analyzed by whatever analogy is necessary to put the transducer into transformer form. The source of the difficulty is easily seen from the bond graphs, which show that with a particular identification of efforts and flows one transducer appears as a gyrator and the other as a transformer. Thus the bond graph may be used as a substitute for equivalent circuits, with the advantage that a single procedure for analyzing the system components in each energy domain may be used.

The transduction parameters for the elements in Fig. 4-14 need not be constant; the transformers and gyrators are often modulated transformers and gyrators. In practical cases, the basic character of the transducer is often unaffected by variatious of the transducer parameter. The power balance feature is, for example, not affected by varying the transformer or gyrator modulus, although, as will be seen later, certain possible types of modulation may lead to an ill-defined problem or to computational difficulties.

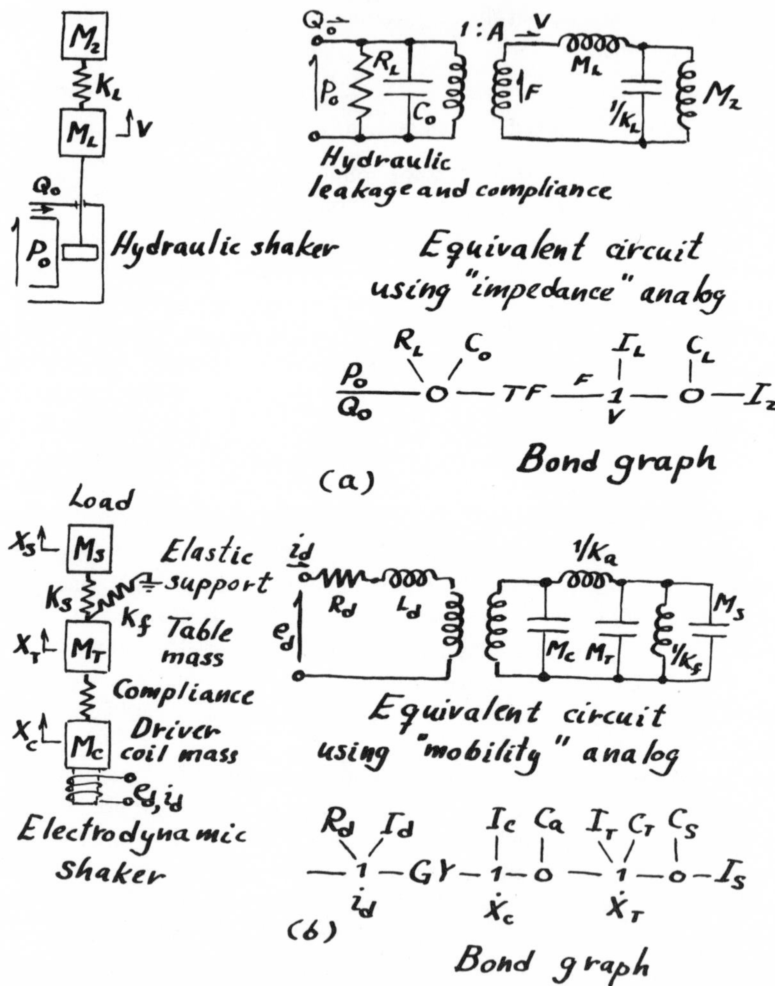

Fig. 4-15 Two shaker systems represented by equivalent circuits and bond graphs. (a) hydraulic shaker, (b) electrodynamic shaker.

While the transformer and gyrator transducers conserve energy, no energy is stored in them. Another class of idealized transducers is conservative but energy storing. As an introduction to such transducers, consider the two elements in Figs. 4-16(a) and (b). The lossless beam and rigid mass in plane motion would probably not be typically regarded as transducers, but these elements do provide a coupling between mechanical translation and rotation. Thus both elements could be represented, as shown, by a general 2-port transducer element, –TD–. On the other hand, it may be recognized immediately that both elements are conservative, store energy, and are 2-port fields, in the sense that multiport fields were previously defined in Chapter 3.

In the case of the beam, the stored energy U is expressed by the integral of the power supplied,

$$U = \int^t (F \cdot V dt + \tau \omega dt). \quad (4.1)$$

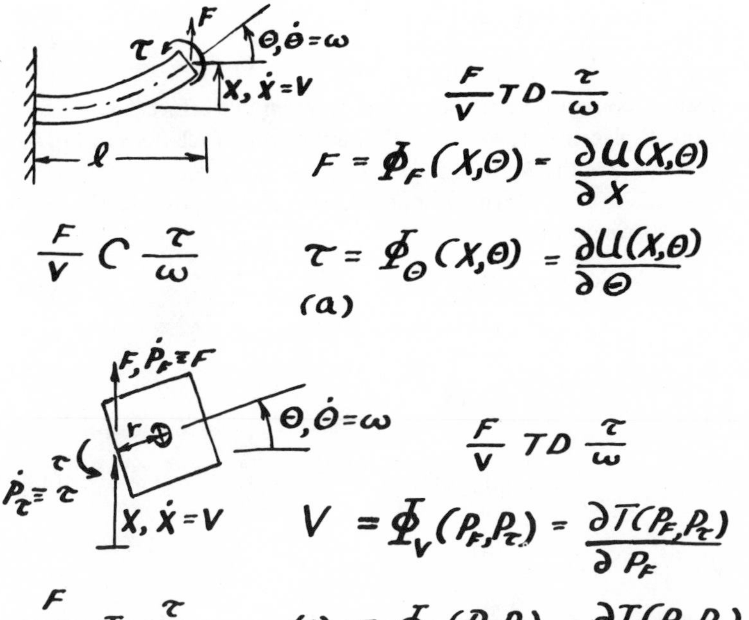

τ, F, $\theta, \dot{\theta} = \omega$, $X, \dot{X} = V$, ℓ

$\frac{F}{V}$ TD $\frac{\tau}{\omega}$

$$F = \Phi_F(X,\theta) = \frac{\partial U(X,\theta)}{\partial X}$$

$\frac{F}{V}$ C $\frac{\tau}{\omega}$

$$\tau = \Phi_\theta(X,\theta) = \frac{\partial U(X,\theta)}{\partial \theta}$$

(a)

$F, \dot{P}_F = F$, r, $\theta, \dot{\theta} = \omega$, τ, $\dot{P}_\tau = \tau$, $X, \dot{X} = V$

$\frac{F}{V}$ TD $\frac{\tau}{\omega}$

$$V = \Phi_V(P_F, P_\tau) = \frac{\partial T(P_F, P_\tau)}{\partial P_F}$$

$\frac{F}{V}$ I $\frac{\tau}{\omega}$

$$\omega = \Phi_\omega(P_F, P_\tau) = \frac{\partial T(P_F, P_\tau)}{\partial P_\tau}$$

(b)

Fig. 4-16 Beam and rigid body considered as energy-storing transducers between translation and rotation. (a) beam as a 2-port C-field, (b) rigid body as a 2-port I-field.

By use of the defined quantities,

$$dX \equiv Vdt, \text{ and } d\theta \equiv \omega dt, \tag{4.2}$$

U may be re-expressed in the following form:

$$U(X,\theta) = \int_{0,0}^{X,\theta} (F(X,\theta)\, dX + \tau(X,\theta)d\theta) \tag{4.3}$$

in which the integration path from the reference values 0,0 to the final values X,θ has no effect on the stored energy. From Eq. 4.3 the relations

$$F = \frac{\partial U}{\partial X}; \quad \tau = \frac{\partial U}{\partial \theta}, \tag{4.4}$$

are immediate. For the special case of a linear, uniform beam of length l, tension modulus E, and area moment of inertia I, undergoing small deflections, the explicit form of Eq. 4.4 is

$$\begin{bmatrix} F \\ \tau \end{bmatrix} = \left[\begin{array}{c|c} 12EI/l^3 & -6EI/l^2 \\ -6EI/l^2 & 4EI/l \end{array}\right] \begin{bmatrix} X \\ \theta \end{bmatrix}. \tag{4.5}$$

Since a static, conservative relation exists between two efforts and the corresponding displacements, we may indicate the type of relations of Eq. 4.4 or Eq. 4.5 by using the 2-port C-field, –C–.

For the mass of Fig. 4-16(b), a similar development is possible. Corresponding to Eq. 4.1 we now have

$$T = \int^t (V \cdot Fdt + \omega \cdot \tau dt). \tag{4.6}$$

Defining

$$dP_F \equiv Fdt, \; dP_\tau \equiv \tau dt, \tag{4.7}$$

we have

$$T(P_F,P_\tau) = \int_{0,0}^{P_F,P_\tau} (V(P_F,P_\tau)\, dP_F + \omega(P_F,P_\tau)dP_\tau). \tag{4.8}$$

Then

$$V = \frac{\partial T}{\partial P_F} \quad \text{and} \quad \omega = \frac{\partial T}{\partial P_\tau}. \tag{4.9}$$

If the rigid body of mass m, centroidal moment of inertia I_c, and distance r between the centroid and the point of application of F, undergoes plane motion with small θ, then the relationship between the flows and momenta is as follows:

$$\left[\begin{array}{c|c} m & mr \\ mr & I_c + mr^2 \end{array}\right] \begin{bmatrix} V \\ \omega \end{bmatrix} = \begin{bmatrix} P_F \\ P_\tau \end{bmatrix} \tag{4.10}$$

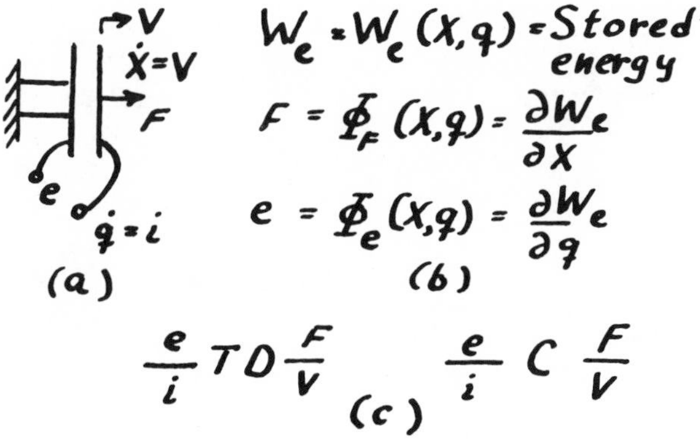

$\dot{X} = V$, F, e, $\dot{q} = i$

(a)

$W_e = W_e(X, q)$ = Stored energy

$$F = \Phi_F(X, q) = \frac{\partial W_e}{\partial X}$$

$$e = \Phi_e(X, q) = \frac{\partial W_e}{\partial q}$$

(b)

(c)

Fig 4-17 Idealized movable-plate capacitor. (a) schematic diagram, (b) defining relations, (c) bond graphs.

Taking a time derivative of both sides of Eq. 4.10 yields a more conventional version of the relations. Since Eqs. 4.9 and 4.10 represent static conservative relations between flows and momenta, the mass may be represented by the 2-port I-field, –I–.

Consider now the device shown in Fig. 4-17, which is obviously a transducer. Noting that the device in idealized form is conservative and that the state of the system is described by the charge on the capacitor and the position of the plates, one may follow the same sort of development as shown for the beam and the rigid body, resulting in the relations shown in Fig. 4-17(b). Since there is a static relationship between two efforts and two displacements, the device may be represented as a 2-port C-field.

The electrical dual of the moveable plate capacitor just discussed is the solenoid sketched in Fig. 4-18(a). Again the device is conservative, but now the state of the system depends on the mechanical displacement of the core and the generalized momentum, $\lambda \equiv \int^t e dt$, of the coil. Although the relations describing the element, see Fig. 4-18(b), bear a resemblance to those of the preceding three devices, we cannot represent the device as a simple C-field or I-field. From the electrical port, the system acts like an inductance (inertance), and from the mechanical port like a spring (capacitance). Thus, the character of the system may be illustrated by the last two bond graphs of Fig. 4-18(c). The device may be considered a 2-port I-field addressed through a gyrator on the mechanical side, or a 2-port C-field addressed through a gyrator on the electrical side. We may note parenthetically that the gyrator cannot be avoided in general by redefining efforts and flows. If the gyrator were eliminated in the solenoid, it would appear in the moveable plate capacitor, and both devices could appear in the same system. In fact, there may be no good reason for actually using the gyrator in the bond graph for the transducer

i e $\to V = \dot{X}$ F

$e = \dot{\lambda}$

(a)

$W_m = W_m(X, \lambda)$
$= \text{Stored energy}$

$F = \Phi_F(X, \lambda) = \dfrac{\partial W_m}{\partial X}$

$i = \Phi_i(X, \lambda) = \dfrac{\partial W_m}{\partial \lambda}$

(b)

$\frac{e}{i}$ TD $\frac{F}{V}$

$\frac{e}{i}$ I — GY $\frac{F}{V}$ $\qquad$ $\frac{e}{i}$ GY — C $\frac{F}{V}$

(c)

Fig. 4-18 Idealized movable core solenoid. (a) schematic diagram, (b) defining relations, (c) bond graphs.

except as an aid in interpreting the nature of the equations describing the device. In particular, the gyrator modulus is not defined by any physical parameter and thus the gyrator appears in this context as a more abstract construction than in the context of the gyrator transducers studied previously. For a more complete study of electromechanical transducers, see, for example, ref. 1.

As an example of a mixed system containing a transformerlike transducer, consider the pressure-controlled valve shown in Fig. 4-19. Here the schematic diagram is not as specific as an electric circuit diagram or a simple mechanical schematic diagram. Although certain assumptions about the dynamic model are implied by the schematic diagram, certain parts of the model have been left undefined in the diagram. We shall study a particular model of the system, the usefulness of which has been verified by experiment.[2]

In Fig. 4-19(b), a word bond graph has been made in which the more obvious assumptions inherent in the schematic diagram are made explicit but in which words are used to indicate elements that remain to be identified by experiment. In Fig. 4-19(c), the structure of a suitable model for the system is shown in bond graph form. By now the reader should be able to see clearly what sort of models are being used for the parts of the system. Any attempt to communicate this information in the standard ways will typically involve equations, block diagrams, equivalent circuits, and response plots, all of which were used in ref. 2. The bond graph lends clarity to the discussion of the component models, because the interrelation of the components is obvious even before the detailed characteristics of the components have been specified. In addition, the interconnections of the parts of the system are shown on a physical or power basis without requiring a sometimes premature commitment to input-output causality which accompanies the use of signal flow representations.

4.3 More complex systems

Before discussing some of the general features of interconnected systems, we pause briefly to examine some systems in both conventional and bond graph

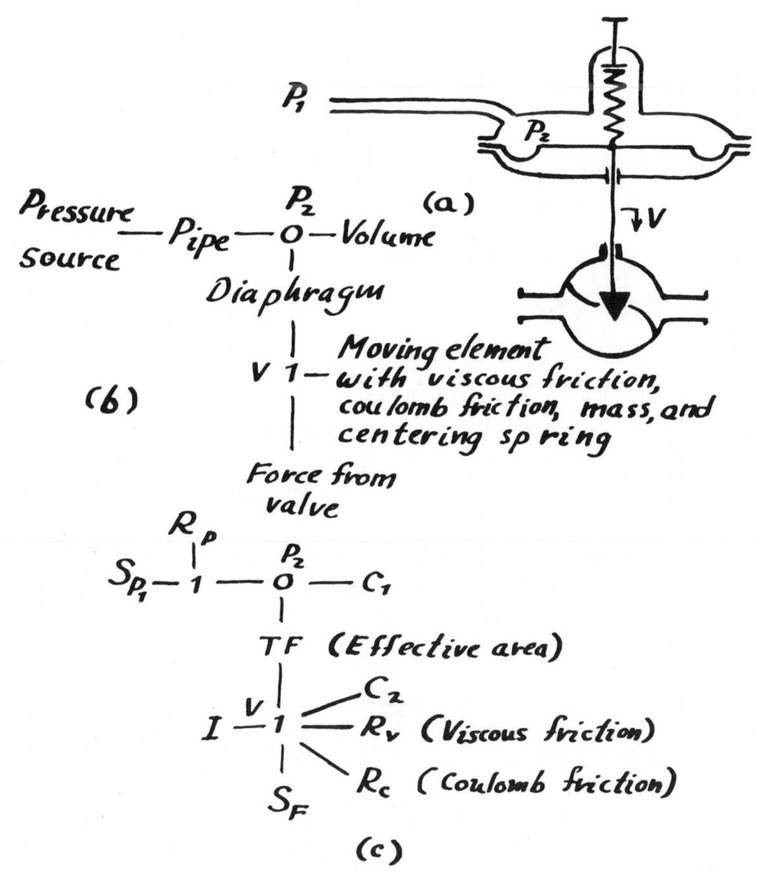

Fig. 4-19 Dynamic model of the moving elements of a pressure-controlled valve. (a) schematic diagram, (b) word bond graph, (c) bond graph.

representations. These examples will provide opportunity for the reader to test his ability to understand bond graphs and will show that in certain areas standard methods leave something to be desired. Some of them will also be used later in the chapters on analysis and simulation.

Electric circuits with mutual inductance

The first example is an electric circuit containing a controlled source and mutual inductance. In preparation, consider Fig. 4-20 which is typical of attempts to make mutual inductance phenomena fit into circuit graphs.[3] The dot-square-triangle notation is intended to represent the relative orientation of the three coils involved. The notation implies the following set of relations for the element:

$$\begin{bmatrix} \lambda_1 \\ \lambda_2 \\ \lambda_3 \end{bmatrix} = \begin{bmatrix} +L_1 & -M_{12} & -M_{13} \\ -M_{12} & +L_2 & +M_{23} \\ -M_{13} & +M_{23} & +L_3 \end{bmatrix} \begin{bmatrix} i_1 \\ i_2 \\ i_3 \end{bmatrix} , \tag{4.11}$$

where the flux linkage variables play the role of generalized momenta,

$$\begin{bmatrix} \lambda_1 \\ \lambda_2 \\ \lambda_3 \end{bmatrix} \equiv \int^t dt \begin{bmatrix} e_1(t) \\ e_2(t) \\ e_3(t) \end{bmatrix} , \tag{4.12}$$

and the system has been assumed to be linear. Note that the symmetry of the matrix in Eq. 4.11 is assured by an energy argument,[1] but the signs of the elements remain to be determined. A sketch of a physical system that would have the sign pattern of Eq. 4.11 is shown in Fig. 4-21(a). The directions for the e_j, i_j are uniformly chosen so that the self-inductance terms appear with positive sign as in Eq. 4.11, but the relative direction of the windings determines whether the contribution to the linking flux circulating in the toroid is positive or negative.

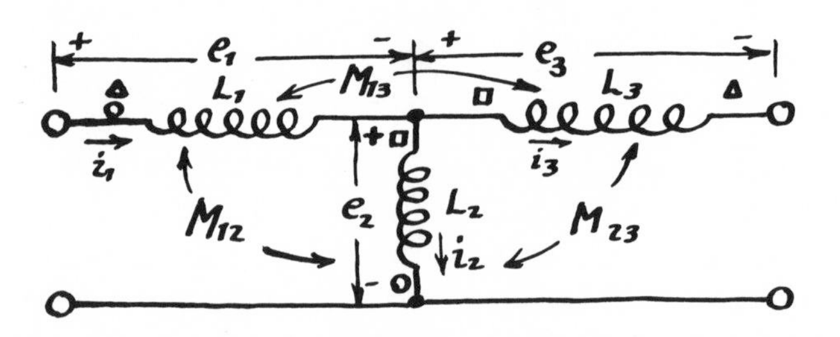

Fig. 4-20 Three inductively coupled elements.

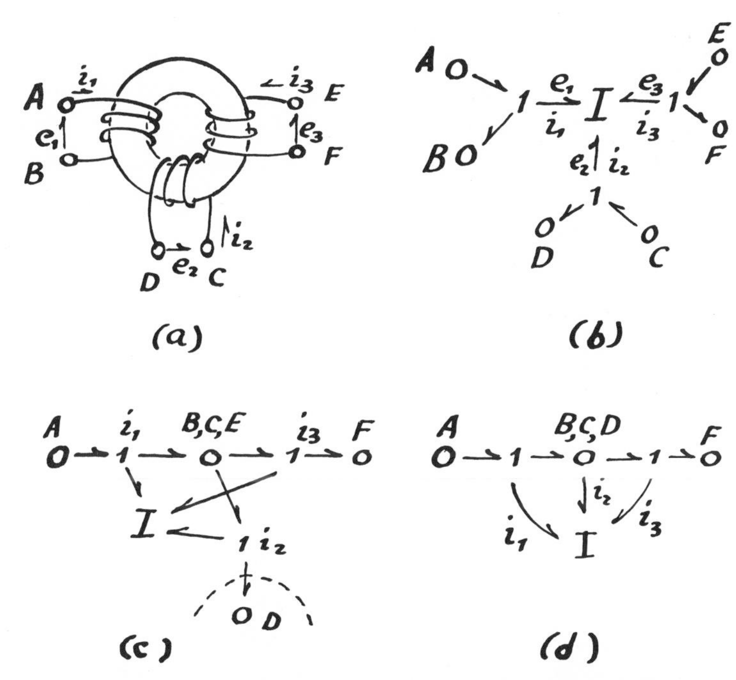

Fig. 4-21 Three coils with mutual inductance. (a) schematic diagram, (b) bond graphs, (c) coils in configuration of Fig. 4-20, (d) simplified bond graph when node D is grounded.

If we represent the element of Fig. 4-21(a) by a single symbol, –I–, defined by the relations of Eq. 4.11, the bond graph would appear as in Fig. 4.21(b) in which each terminal voltage with respect to an arbitrary ground is indicated. The sign conventions are carried over from Fig. 4-21(a) to Fig. 4-21(b).

Since the terminal connections of the circuit graph of Fig. 4-20 are not actually used in producing Eq. 4.11, it is of interest to form an actual bond graph for the circuit shown. Comparing Figs. 4-20 and 4-21, we see that nodes B, C, and D of Fig. 4-21 are common in Fig. 4-20 and there is at least an implication that node D will be grounded. In Figs. 4-21(c) and (d) the bond graph for Fig. 4-21 is developed. The 3-port I-field is still specified by the relation of Eq. 4.11 when the sign convention shown in Fig. 4-21 is used.

Although it is possible to construct a system of self inductances in series and parallel connections that has the relation of Eq. 4.11, and thus to form a 3-port I-field of –I elements and 0- and 1-junctions representing mutual induction, the self-inductance parameters are often the negative of the usual self-inductance parameters found for physical inductors. Therefore the sign convention for such "equivalent circuits" is at least as complicated as for the 3-port I-field representation.

In Fig. 4-22, a single-stage transistor amplifier model is shown in circuit graph form.[4] We are not interested in the range of validity of this circuit as a representation for the actual amplifier. It is our purpose to compare the circuit graph with the bond graph equivalent. The rather complicated set of symbols needed to represent the controlled source and the mutual inductance testifies that the circuit graph in such an application is not as self-contained a representation as might be desired. With the currents and voltages defined as shown, the 3-port I-field characteristics are as follows:

$$\begin{bmatrix} \lambda_3 \\ \lambda_4 \\ \lambda_5 \end{bmatrix} = \int^t dt \begin{bmatrix} e_3 \\ e_4 \\ e_5 \end{bmatrix} = \begin{bmatrix} +L_3 & +M_o & -M_\square \\ +M_o & +L_4 & +M_\triangle \\ -M_\square & +M_\triangle & +L_5 \end{bmatrix} \begin{bmatrix} i_3 \\ i_4 \\ i_5 \end{bmatrix} . \tag{4.13}$$

These characteristics describe the bond graph element with the sign convention shown in Fig. 4-22 (b). The bond graph in the form of Fig. 4-22(c) is a compact representation of the amplifier model. Both the source characteristic and the I-field must be specified independently of the graph, but the structure of the system is evident. It is also possible that a numbering of bonds rather than elements may prove beneficial (Fig. 4-23). Not only may the entire bond graph be given in a simple linear code formed by giving the type of element and the bonds incident upon it, but there is also very little possibility that the same name will be given to two elements by mistake. Note that the two resistors R10 and R1 in Fig. 4-23 were both numbered R_7 in Fig. 4-22.

Mechanical systems in general motion

We now consider some example systems involving mechanical elements. As has been mentioned, certain classes of mechanical systems are strictly analogous to electric circuits (see Fig. 4-11). It has also been shown that some mechanical systems are capable of representation as I- or C-fields (see Figs. 4-16 and 4-21). In fact, as large, three-dimensional motions are permitted for rigid bodies or massless elastic bodies, these elements are still I- or C-fields respectively, but the problem of describing the elements is greatly complicated by the nonlinear geometric relations involved. There are also situations in which one must consider distributed mass and compliance effects of a mechanical system, and for most purposes one must use approximate finite order representations for a system that in principle is of infinite order. Thus even simple-appearing mechanical elements are capable of very complex behavior, and any practical analysis or synthesis scheme must introduce a great many restrictions on the nature and allowed motions of the mechanical elements of the system.

As a beginning, let us consider the general motion of a rigid body. One way of looking at a rigid body is as a 6-port with three translational and

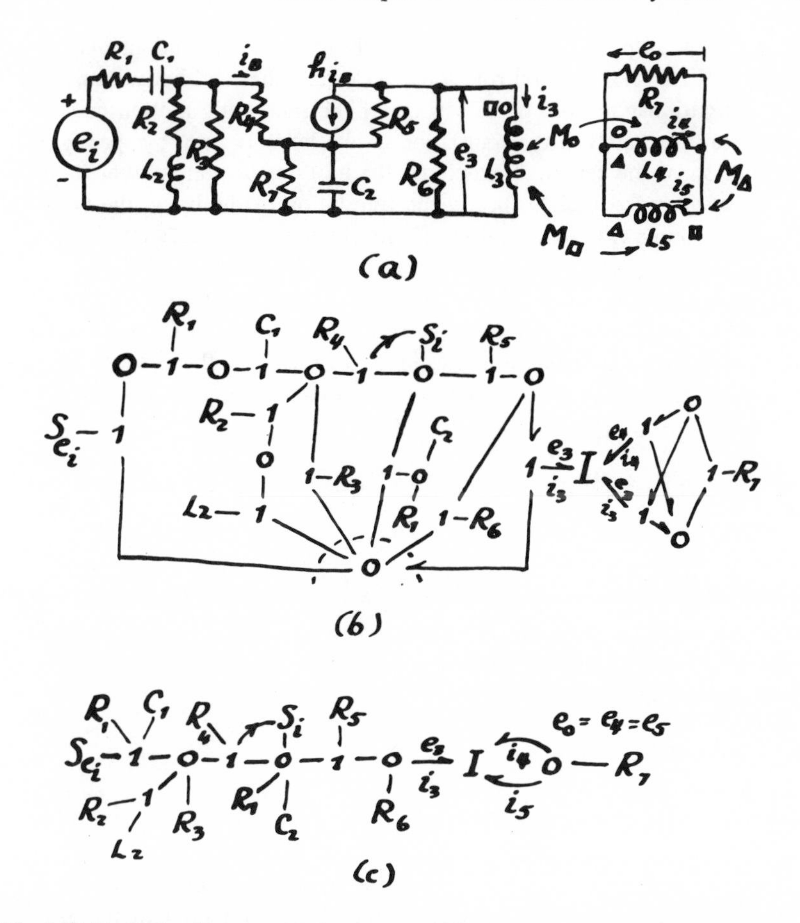

Fig. 4-22 Example with mutual inductance. (a) circuit graph, (b) bond graph, (c) simplified bond graph.

Fig. 4-23 System of Fig. 4-22 with bond numbering.

three rotational ports. Since the rigid body relates linear and angular momenta and translational and rotational velocities, the rigid body is an I-field. The translational and rotational aspects of the rigid body motion may be considered separately if the translation of the body is given by specifying the motion of the center of mass.[5] If the motions of points other than the center of mass are used to specify the translation of the body, the body will generally couple rotational and translational variables, as illustrated in Fig. 4-16.

If v_x, v_y, v_z represent the velocity components of the center of mass of a rigid body with respect to an inertial reference frame, and F_x, F_y, F_z represent net force components in corresponding directions, the constitutive relations for translation may be stated in vector or component form as

$$\mathbf{Mv} = \mathbf{P_F} = \int^t \mathbf{F}dt,$$

or

$$\begin{aligned} Mv_x &= P_x = \int^t F_y dt, \\ Mv_y &= P_y = \int^t F_y dt, \\ Mv_z &= P_z = \int^t F_z dt, \end{aligned} \tag{4.14}$$

in which bold-face lettering represents a vector quantity, M is the scalar mass of the body, and the velocity components may be expressed as the derivatives of displacement variables:

$$\mathbf{v} = \dot{\mathbf{x}} \quad \text{or} \quad \begin{aligned} v_x &= \dot{x}, \\ v_y &= \dot{y}, \\ v_z &= \dot{z} \end{aligned} \tag{4.15}$$

The constitutive relation for the rotation of the body may be stated in terms of the vector angular velocity ω, the vector torque about the center of mass, τ, and the moment of inertia tensor $\mathbf{I}_c$ as follows:

$$\mathbf{I}_c \boldsymbol{\omega} = \mathbf{P}_\tau = \int^t \boldsymbol{\tau} dt. \tag{4.16}$$

Although Eq. 4.16 exhibits some similarity to Eq. 4.14, rotation is basically a much more complicated phenomenon to describe than translation. In the first place the tensor $\mathbf{I}_c$ is a more complex entity than the scalar M. When the components of $\mathbf{I}_c$ are expressed in terms of a stationary coordinate frame, then the components change as the body moves. On the other hand, if $\mathbf{I}_c$ components are described in terms of a coordinate system that moves with the body, then the components remain constant, but it is often difficult to determine the motion of points on the body relative to a stationary frame from the time histories of variables in the moving frame. Also, although ω is a vector quantity, there is no vector quantity that plays a role analogous to x in Eq. 4.15. That is, one may *not* write an expression such as $\dot{\theta} = \omega$ or $\dot{\theta}_x = \omega_x$, except for very small motions. The rather complicated machinery of the Euler angles does provide a way to describe the rotational position of a body, but $\boldsymbol{\omega}$ is expressed in terms of derivatives of Euler angles and the angles themselves in a rather complex fashion. In many situations, large angle three-dimensional motion is not important and the problem of rotation is greatly simplified. Before going on to some examples in which rigid bodies play a restricted role, we give a bond graph interpretation of the well-known Euler equations.

Suppose that a coordinate system, x_1, x_2, x_3, is fixed within a moving body such that the inertia tensor with respect to this coordinate system assumes a principal form with only the principal moments of inertia I_1, I_2, I_3 appearing as components of $\mathbf{I}_c$. It is a standard exercise to express Eq. 4.16 in differentiated form in terms of components of $\boldsymbol{\omega}$, and τ relative to the x_1, x_2, x_3 coordinate system. The results are often called Euler's equations:

$$\begin{aligned} I_1\dot{\omega}_1 + (I_3 - I_2)\omega_2\omega_3 &= \tau_1(t), \\ I_2\dot{\omega}_2 + (I_1 - I_3)\omega_1\omega_3 &= \tau_2(t), \\ I_3\dot{\omega}_3 + (I_2 - I_1)\omega_1\omega_2 &= \tau_3(t). \end{aligned} \tag{4.17}$$

Rearranging these equations slightly, we may interpret some of the terms on the left-hand side of Eqs. 4.17 as torques:

$$\begin{aligned} I_1\dot{\omega}_1 &= -(I_3\omega_3)\omega_2 + (I_2\omega_2)\omega_3 + \tau_1(t), \\ I_2\dot{\omega}_2 &= -(I_1\omega_1)\omega_3 + (I_3\omega_3)\omega_1 + \tau_2(t), \\ I_3\dot{\omega}_3 &= -(I_2\omega_2)\omega_1 + (I_1\omega_1)\omega_2 + \tau_3(t). \end{aligned} \tag{4.18}$$

Figure 4-24 shows an interesting bond graph of Eq. 4.18. The two versions, Figs. 4-24(a) and (b), differ only in details, and both show power source elements (torques) and energy storing elements (inertances), coupled by an ideal junction structure composed of modulated gyrators and 1-junctions. In Fig. 4-24(b), the moduli are indicated adjacent to the gyrators. Energy is neither stored nor dissipated in the structure joining the inertances, and power simply circulates around the symmetrical, ringlike structure. The role of the gyrators may be investigated for a special case. Let $I_1 = I_2 \neq I_3$. Then Eq. 4.18 becomes

$$\begin{aligned} I_1\dot{\omega}_1 &= (I_1 - I_3)\omega_3 \cdot \omega_2 + \tau_1(t), \\ I_2\dot{\omega}_2 &= -(I_1 - I_3)\omega_3 \cdot \omega_1 + \tau_2(t), \\ I_3\dot{\omega}_3 &= \tau_3(t). \end{aligned} \tag{4.19}$$

The bond graph of Eq. 4.19 is shown in Fig. 4-24(c). The central feature of this graph is that two 1-port inertances are coupled through a gyrator.

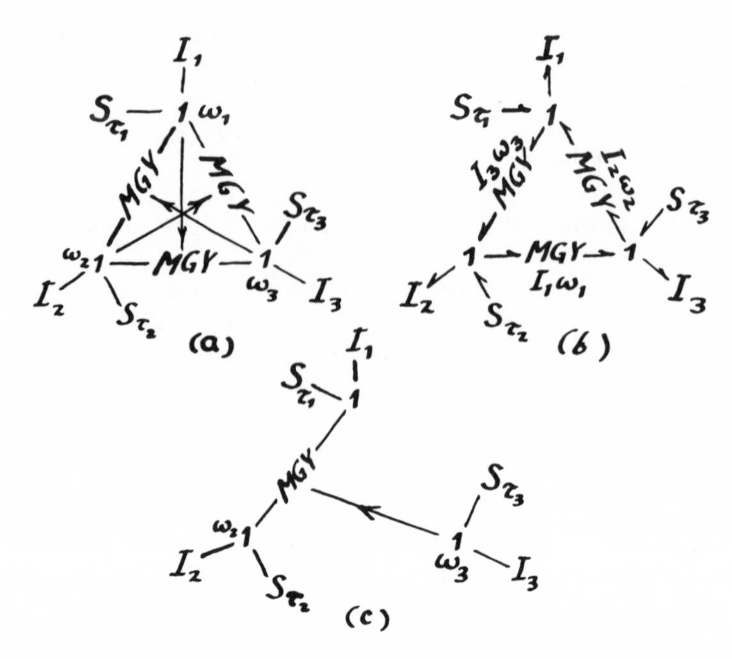

Fig. 4-24 Bond graph of Euler's equations for a rigid body. (a), (b) bond graphs, (c) bond graph when $I_2 = I_1$.

The system therefore has the character of an inertance coupled to a capacitance, an oscillator, as has been noted in Section 3.2. The graph of Fig. 4-24(c) models the precession of a symmetrical top. Unfortunately the variables ω_1 and ω_2 are measured in a moving reference frame, and it may be hard to find τ_1, τ_2, τ_3, which are torque components in the moving frame.

A common and useful special case of rigid body motion is that of plane motion. In this case only one component of angular velocity is nonzero and a rigid body may be considered to be a 3-port device. Note that the torques and forces necessary to ensure that the body does indeed execute plane motion are not considered here since they do no work, but such torques and forces may exist and may be important in designing a constraining mechanism. For the system shown in Fig. 4-25(a), the constitutive relations for the rigid body may be written as follows:

$$
\begin{aligned}
Mv_x &= P_x = \int^t F_x dt, \\
Mv_y &= P_y = \int^t F_y dt, \qquad (4.20) \\
I_c\omega &= P_\tau = \int^t \tau dt.
\end{aligned}
$$

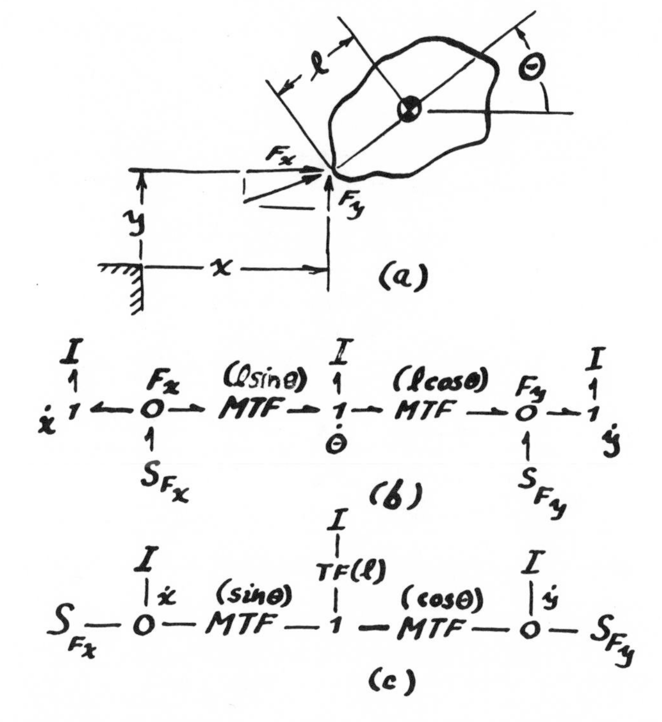

Fig. 4-25 Plane motion of a rigid body. (a) sketch of body, (b), (c) bond graphs.

In addition, the following relations are assumed to be valid:

$$v_x = \dot{x},\ v_y = \dot{y},\ \omega = \dot{\theta}, \tag{4.21}$$

$$\tau = F_x l\sin\theta - F_y l\cos\theta. \tag{4.22}$$

These relations are expressed by the bond graphs of Fig. 4-25(b) and (c).

With these preliminary results, we may analyze a simple finite element model of a flexible booster.[6] Figure 4-26(a) shows a sketch of the model. In Fig. 4.26(b) the two linked rigid bodies and the internal forces of constraint are shown. Note that the torsional spring of Fig. 4-26(a) is missing in Fig. 4-26(b). The equations for the system are similar to Eqs. 4.20 to 4.22. Writing them in the conventional form, we have

$$\begin{aligned} M_1\ddot{x}_1 &= -F_x, & M_1\ddot{y}_1 &= -F_y, \\ M_2\ddot{x}_2 &= +F_x, & M_2\ddot{y}_2 &= F_y, \\ I_{1c}\ddot{\theta}_1 &= \tau_1\ , & I_{2c}\ddot{\theta}_2 &= \tau_2, \end{aligned} \tag{4.23}$$

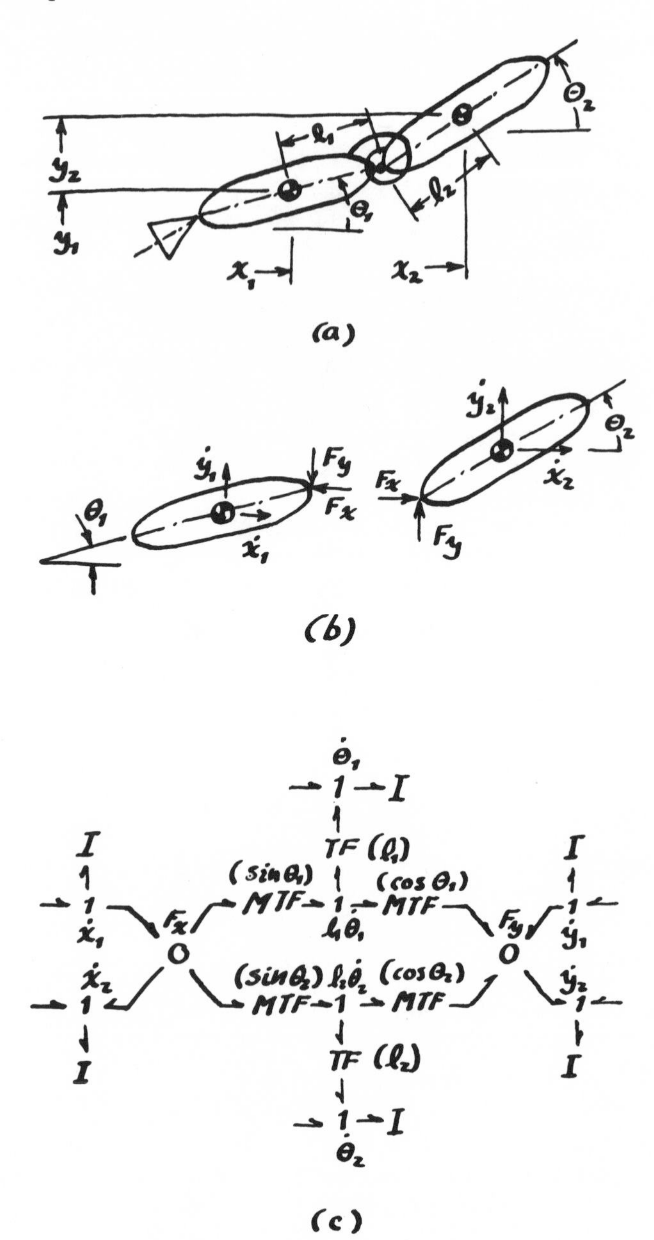

Fig. 4-26 Finite-element flexible booster model. (a) sketch of system, (b) linked rigid bodies, (c) bond graph.

with the kinematic constraints,

$$\begin{aligned} \dot{x}_1 - l_1\dot{\theta}_1 \sin\theta_1 &= \dot{x}_2 + l_2\dot{\theta}_2 \sin\theta_2, \\ \dot{y}_1 + l_1\dot{\theta}_1 \cos\theta_1 &= \dot{y}_2 - l_2\dot{\theta}_2 \cos\theta_2, \end{aligned} \tag{4.24}$$

and the dynamic relations

$$\begin{aligned} \tau_1 &= F_x l_1 \sin\theta_1 - F_y l_1 \cos\theta_1, \\ \tau_2 &= F_x l_2 \sin\theta_2 - F_y l_2 \cos\theta_2. \end{aligned} \tag{4.25}$$

The bond graph corresponding to Eqs. 4.23 to 4.25 are represented by the bond graph of Fig. 4-26(c). The free bonds in this graph are available for applying forces or torques. In Fig. 4-27(a) the forces due to the rocket engine thrust and the torsional spring are added to the bond graph of Fig. 4-26(c).

It is of interest to find a bond graph for a linearized version of the system when it is presumed in advance that θ_1 and θ_2 will be small. With this assumption, Eqs. 4.23 are unchanged but Eqs. 4.24 and 4.25 are modified to the following:

$$\begin{aligned} \dot{x}_1 &= \dot{x}_2, \\ y_1 + l_1\dot{\theta}_1 &= \dot{y}_2 - l_2\dot{\theta}_2, \end{aligned} \tag{4.26}$$

$$\begin{aligned} \tau_1 &= F_x l_1 \theta_1 - F_y l_1, \\ \tau_2 &= F_x l_2 \theta_2 - F_y l_2. \end{aligned} \tag{4.27}$$

The bond graph for the linearized system is shown in Fig. 4-27(b); it is interesting to note that one pair of MTF's disappears (i.e. becomes a pair of bonds) as $\cos\theta \to 1$, and another pair becomes coupled through an active bond because velocity terms of the form $l\dot{\theta}\sin\theta \to 0$, while terms of the form $F_x \sin\theta \to F_x\theta$ as the angles become small.

Figure 4-28 depicts an iterated structure composed of linked rigid bodies in plane motion. The bond graph for the system is readily constructed as in Fig. 4-28(b). This kind of iterated structure could be used to model the motion of long, flexible members and includes rotary inertia but not shear deflections. In the form shown, the model is capable of predicting the large angle motion of the system, because geometric nonlinearities are included. A linearized version of the system would represent an extension of the lumped "pi" or "tee" models that are commonly used for electrical and mechanical transmission lines. We see that bond graph techniques provide a framework for extending approximate lumped parameter circuit models for distributed parameter systems to cases in which the distributed system exhibits quite complicated behavior.

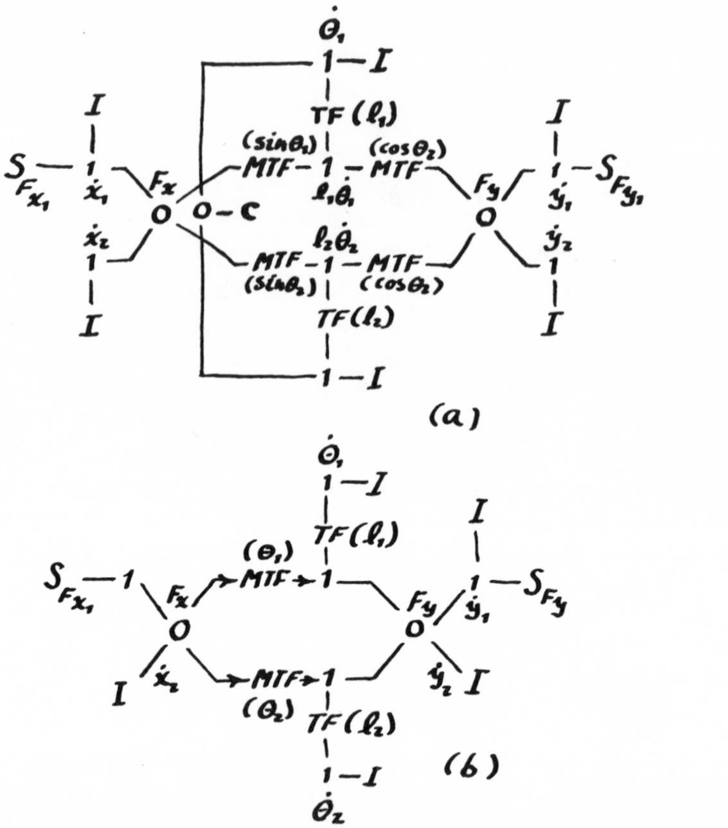

Fig. 4-27 **Bond graphs for flexible booster model. (a) bond graph for Fig. 4-26(a) including torsional spring, (b) bond graph for linearized version of model.**

Modal analysis for linear distributed parameter systems

For linear distributed systems quite a different approach to finding a lumped parameter representation may be based on the concept of normal modes. These ideas will be illustrated by considering some classical mechanical systems,[7] but the ideas in slightly modified form are applicable to a wide variety of systems described by separable partial differential equations.[8]

Consider the common introductory example for modal analysis shown in Fig. 4-29. If we agree that the force F(t) is to be supplied by some ex-

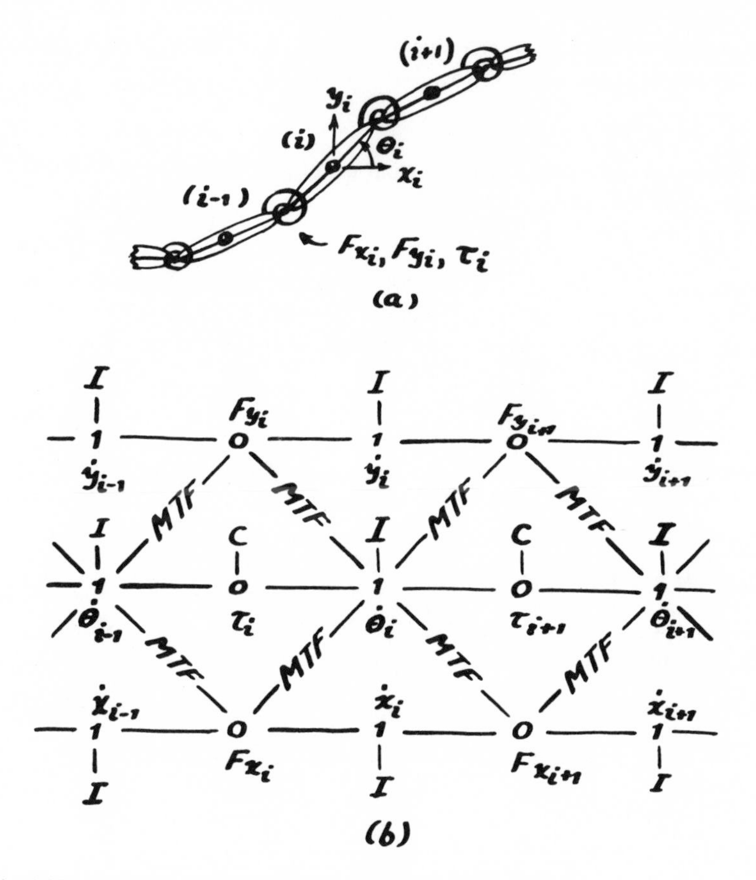

Fig. 4-28 Iterated structure. (a) sketch of system, (b) bond graph.

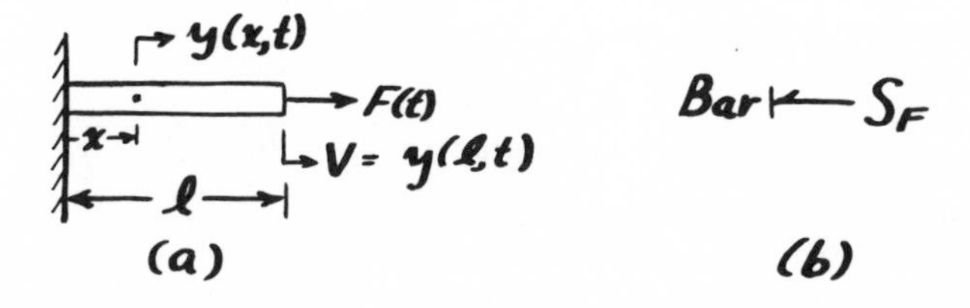

Fig. 4-29 Example for modal analysis. (a) schematic diagram, (b) bond graph.

ternal agent, then the beam is acting as a 1-port supplied with power from a force source, as indicated in Fig. 4-29(b). Using the notation

$$(\dot{\ }) \equiv \frac{\partial}{\partial t}, (\ ') \equiv \frac{\partial}{\partial x}, \qquad (4.28)$$

a conventional description of the system in terms of a partial differential equation is as follows:

$$\rho A\ddot{y} - EAy'' = F(t)\delta(x - l), \qquad (4.29)$$

in which ρ is the mass density, A the cross-sectional area, E the modulus of elasticity, and δ the Dirac delta function. Boundary conditions compatible with the causality (force as an input to the beam) and the use of δ in Eq. 4.29 are

$$y(0,t) = 0, \quad EAy'(l,t) = 0. \qquad (4.30)$$

The modal analysis for this system is very simple. It proceeds by eliminating the forcing term temporarily and separating the space and time parts of y(x,t),

$$y(x,t) = \sum_i Y_i(x)\eta_i(t). \qquad (4.31)$$

Substituting Eq. 4.31 into Eq. 4.29 with F = 0 yields a set of mode shapes determined to within an arbitrary amplitude,

$$Y_i(x) = \sin\left(\frac{2i-1}{2}\right)\frac{\pi}{l}\ ; i = 1, 2, 3, \ldots \qquad (4.32)$$

and a set of corresponding equations for the modal variables

$$\ddot{\eta}_i + \omega_i^2\eta_i = 0; \quad i = 1, 2, 3, \ldots, \qquad (4.33)$$

in which

$$\omega_i^2 = \frac{E}{\rho}\left[\left(\frac{2i-1}{2l}\right)\pi\right]^2. \qquad (4.34)$$

Upon substituting these results into the forced equation, Eq. 4.29, doing the standard multiplication by one mode shape, and integrating from x = 0 to x = l, the orthogonality of the mode shapes comes into play with the following result:

$$\frac{\rho Al}{2}\ddot{\eta}_i + EA\left[\left(\frac{2i-1}{2l}\right)\pi\right]^2\frac{l}{2}\eta_i = Y_i(l)F(t). \qquad (4.35)$$

Defining the total mass M and the static stiffness K by

$$M = \rho Al; \quad K = EA/l \qquad (4.36)$$

changes Eq. 4.35 to

$$\frac{M}{2}\ddot{\eta}_i + \frac{K}{8}(2i-1)^2\pi^2\eta_i = Y_i(l)F(t). \qquad (4.37)$$

An output quantity of interest is the end velocity

$$V(t) = \sum_{i=1}^{\infty} Y_i(l)\dot{\eta}_i(t). \tag{4.38}$$

In both Eqs. 4.37 and 4.38, the $Y_i(l)$ could be replaced by unity but this is a fortuitous result of the choice of modal amplitude employed in Eq. 4.32 and is not general.

Equations 4.37 and 4.38 are particular examples of the general situation when a continuous structure is forced by a single concentrated force. The bond graph of Fig. 4-30 represents these equations. Beginning at the force source, the 0-junction distributes the force through transformers to a group of oscillators. The modulus of the ith transformer is $Y_i(l)$, as seen in Eqs. 4.37 and 4.38. The oscillators have mass and spring constant parameters as defined by Eq. 4.37. One fact apparent from the graph is that the power flow from the source, S_F, to the individual oscillators takes place through a structure composed only of 0- and 1-junctions and transformers and that this *junction structure* can store no energy; thus all the power from the source is instantaneously distributed to all the oscillators or modes.

The causal strokes in Fig. 4-30 indicate the manner in which modal analysis is actually performed. The force is considered the given time function and is applied to the modes (Eq. 4.37). The resulting velocity is expressed as a scaled sum of the modal variables (Eq. 4.38). A simulation model based on the graph of Fig. 4-30 could be easily realized were it not for the infinite number of modes present. We shall shortly discuss the problem of reducing the model to a finite number of modes. Before considering the

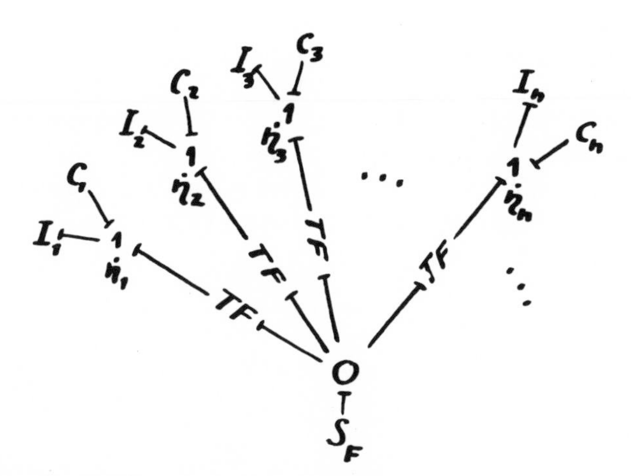

Fig. 4-30 Bond graph of modal analysis for example.

practical question of manipulation of the graph into convenient forms, let us note that one would generally wish to consider some energy dissipation in the system, even though it is well known that damped systems may not possess classical normal modes. In lightly damped systems it is common to assume a small amount of damping in each mode. In Eq. 4.38 this amounts to adding a term $B_i\dot{\eta}_i$ to the left-hand side; in the graph of Fig. 4-30 the equivalent operation is to join a dashpot to each oscillator. Representing the dashpot by the symbol R_i– and attaching one such element to each 1-junction simply means that an extra force proportional to $\dot{\eta}_i$ is applied. Since this procedure is not really part of the normal mode analysis per se, we shall leave off these energy loss elements in order to simplify the graphs. We shall assume, however, that for light damping all of our conclusions do remain valid.

To be useful for most practical purposes, the infinite graph of Fig. 4-30 must be reduced to a finite element graph. This is commonly done by using frequency domain ideas. For example, if it may be assumed that radian frequencies in the range $0 - \omega_o$ are of primary interest, one's first impulse is to include all modes with natural frequencies in this range and to neglect all others. This often produces satisfactory results since near any resonant frequency a single mode of a lightly damped system tends to dominate the motion. However, at off resonant conditions the infinite number of modes that are neglected may contribute significantly to the system response.

This effect is taken into account by observing that all modes with a natural frequency well above ω_o are "stiffness controlled" when forced by a signal with main frequency content in the range $0 - \omega_o$. That is, the response of these modes is not greatly affected by their inertance parameter. Thus as in Fig. 4-31(a), if $\omega_2 < \omega_o < \omega_3$, one may suppress the mass elements for all of the high-frequency modes (modes above the third mode). Then, observing that the infinite series of springs has the effect of a single equivalent spring, we may replace all high-frequency modes by a single *residual compliance*, as shown in Fig. 4-31(b).

The calculation of the value of the residual compliance is accomplished by consideration of the zero frequency, or steady-state response.

Let

$F(t) = F_o$ be constant,

and $X_o = y(l, t)$ be the static deflection under F_o.

Then, from static considerations and Eq. 4.36,

$$X_o = F_o/K. \tag{4.39}$$

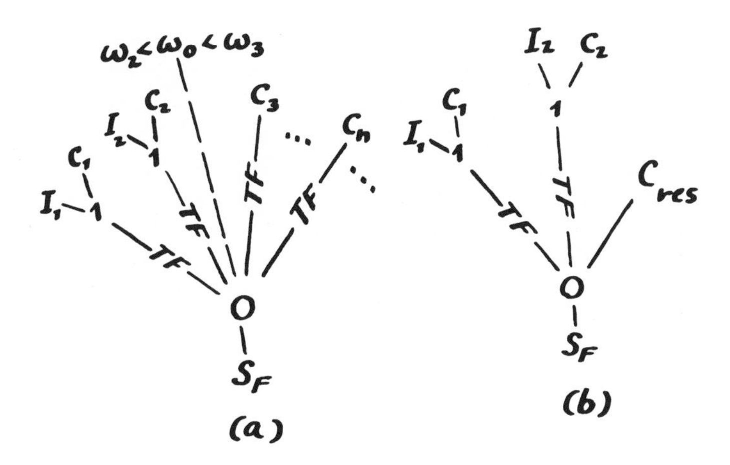

Fig. 4-31 Truncation of bond graph for modal analysis. (a) stiffness controlled modes, (b) residual compliance.

But, using Eqs. 4.37 and 4.38 or Eq. 4.31, we find

$$X_o = \frac{F_o}{K} \cdot \sum_{i=1}^{\infty} \frac{8}{\pi^2(2i-1)^2} \,. \tag{4.40}$$

Combining Eqs. 4.39 and 4.40 and defining a spring constant K_{res} for the residual compliance, we get

$$\frac{1}{K_{res}} = \frac{1}{K}\left[1 - \sum_{i=1}^{n} \frac{8}{\pi^2(2i-1)^2}\right] \tag{4.41}$$

whenever only the n lowest frequency modes are retained. For the case shown in Fig. 4-31, n = 2, and

$$K_{res} = 10.6K. \tag{4.42}$$

In use, the first two equations in the set Eq. 4.37, and the first two terms in Eq. 4.38 would be retained and, in addition, the residual compliance would add an equation of the form

$$K_{res}\eta_{res} = F(t), \tag{4.43}$$

and η_{res} would be added to the terms from Eq. 4.38. The residual compliance concept is easily generalized by using matrix representations.[9]

In Fig. 4-32 an interesting extension of the residual compliance idea is made evident by modifying the bond graph of Fig. 4-30 so that the model oscillators are spread out in a fan with increasing natural frequency running

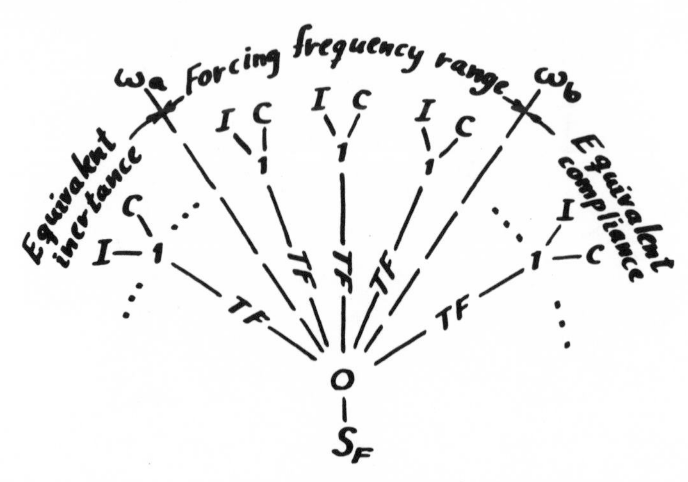

Fig. 4-32 "Frequency wedge" for limited range of forcing frequency components.

from left to right. If the input force contains frequency components in the range from ω_a to ω_b, there will be a certain number of modes with natural frequencies in that range and then two other groups with natural frequencies outside the range. For the high-frequency modes, we may argue that an equivalent compliance may be defined from static considerations. Now, the modes with natural frequency below ω_a will act in a "mass controlled" fashion when acted upon by the input force. That is, these modes will respond in a manner independent of their compliance parameters. Thus a *residual inertance* may be defined which represents the inertance of all the low-frequency neglected modes. This inertance is easily computed because the number of neglected low-frequency modes is finite. Using this idea, an excellent representation of the continuous system is obtained over a limited range with a minimum number of lumped parameter elements. Whenever the modes are available by calculation or measurement, this finite order representation is far superior to any other method of obtaining a lumped parameter representation over a limited frequency range.

Although it may appear that so far only $V(t) = \dot{y}(l, t)$ can be found from the bond graph, a slight modification will allow computation of the motion at any point. A way to show this is to consider that at a generic point x, zero force is applied. Thus, as shown in Fig. 4-33, an extension of Fig. 4-30 yields motion at the point x by the simple use of transformers with parameters $Y_i(x)$. At the same time it is clear from Fig. 4-33 that a concentrated force may be applied at any position x. Note that the 2-port residual compliance shown in Fig. 4-33 is a special case of a matrix com-

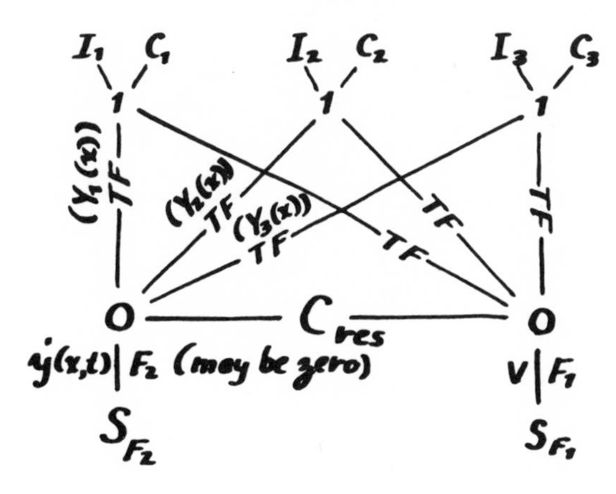

Fig. 4-33 Computation of motion or application of forcing at generic point x.

pliance of the type discussed in reference 9 and, in bond graph terms, is a 2-port C-field. If continuously distributed forces are present, then the standard decomposition into modal forces must be used.

It is clear from the discussion and the graphs so far developed that the natural inputs to the system, as described in the geometrical fashion starting with y(x, t), are all force terms. It may not be quite so clear that motion sources are allowable, although motion sources would appear as natural input quantities if the system were described in force-impulse rather than velocity-position variables.[10]

On the other hand, when many modes are retained in a representation such as that depicted in Fig. 4-30 or 4-31, the system itself should be well represented, independently of the nature of the external connections. That is, whether we regard the system to be supplied with a force and to respond with a velocity or to be supplied with a velocity and to respond with a force, the fundamental characterization of the system should remain valid. As a special case, in our example, if we changed the force source to a velocity source and set the velocity equal to zero at all times, this would appear to be a fundamental change in the boundary conditions at the right end of the rod. One's first impression would be that the modal analysis should be redone with fixed-fixed boundary conditions, but this is not really necessary. One of the often heard objections to modal analysis is that the boundary conditions enter in a very fundamental way and thus the method does not characterize the vibratory system independent of the causality of the forcing of the system. As we shall show, this objection to the use of modal analysis is not entirely valid.

As an example of the above considerations, let us write equations for the example problem for the representation involving the first two modes and residual compliance, as represented in Fig. 4-31(b) (see Eqs. 4.31, 4.37, 4.38 and 4.42):

$$\frac{M}{2}\ddot{\eta}_1 + \frac{\pi^2}{8} K\eta_1 = F(t), \tag{4.44}$$

$$\frac{M}{2}\ddot{\eta}_2 + \frac{9\pi^2}{8} K\eta_2 = F(t), \tag{4.45}$$

$$10.6K\eta_{res} = F(t), \tag{4.46}$$

$$X(t) = y(l, t) = \eta_1 + \eta_2 + \eta_{res}. \tag{4.47}$$

Suppose we require that X(t) and V(t) vanish. This is equivalent to considering the force source of Fig. 4-31(b) to be replaced by a velocity source in which velocity is always zero (Fig. 4.34). By adding causal strokes to the bonds of Fig. 4-34, the force at the zero junction may be determined using the residual compliance. Since $X = 0$, using Eq. 4.47 we get

$$\eta_{res} = -\eta_1 - \eta_2. \tag{4.48}$$

Then,

$$F(t) = 10.6K(-\eta_1 - \eta_2), \tag{4.49}$$

from Eq. 4.46.

Applying the force to the two modal oscillators, we have, from Eqs. 4.44 and 4.45,

$$\frac{M}{2}\ddot{\eta}_1 + \frac{\pi^2}{8} K\eta_1 = 10.6K(-\eta_1 - \eta_2), \tag{4.50}$$

$$\frac{M}{2}\ddot{\eta}_2 + \frac{9\pi^2}{8} K\eta_2 = 10.6K(-\eta_1 - \eta_2), \tag{4.51}$$

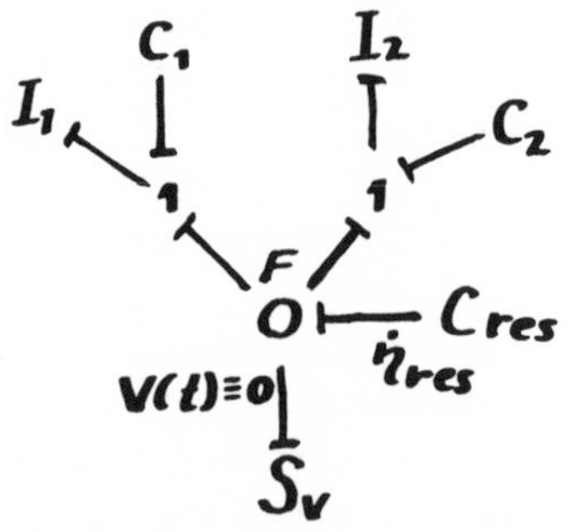

Fig.4-34 System of Fig. 4-31(a) with force source replaced by velocity source.

in which the effect of changing the boundary conditions (or changing causality of the system forcing) is simply to couple modes that were formerly uncoupled. It is of interest to compute the resonance frequencies of the coupled system. Denoting these two resonance frequencies by ω_1' and ω_2', respectively, we get:

$$\begin{aligned} \omega_1' &= 3.2\ E/\rho l, \\ \omega_2' &= 7.56\ E/\rho l, \end{aligned} \tag{4.52}$$

By computing the first two frequencies ω_1, ω_2 of the fixed-fixed system exactly, one finds

$$\omega_1 = \pi E/\rho l,\ \omega_2 = 2\pi E/\rho l, \tag{4.53}$$

and

$$\omega_1'/\omega_1 = 1.02, \quad \omega_2'/\omega_2 = 1.20. \tag{4.54}$$

Thus the first resonant frequency is accurate to within 2% and the second to within 20% when the two modes with the original boundary conditions are used to describe the case in which the bar is built in at both ends. It should be noted that if the residual compliance were not included, the causal inversion involved in changing from a force input to a velocity input would have eliminated the highest resonant frequency altogether. It must be admitted that a two-mode representation of the bar is rather crude and it is therefore not surprising that the change of a boundary condition from free to fixed resulted in a rather inaccurate representation. However, if a larger number of modes were retained, such a change would not cause the accuracy of the representation to deteriorate so drastically. Roughly speaking, if n modes were retained initially, n − 1 accurate resonant frequencies will be represented regardless of the causality of the forcing at one boundary point.

Although the use of coupled modes in analytical work is not particularly appealing because the resonant frequencies are not represented explicitly, for computer simulation purposes the important properties of the normal mode representation lie not in the "normality" of the modes but rather in the ability of the technique to make a very accurate system representation with a small number of elements over a limited frequency range.

As an example of the utility of the above ideas, consider the coupled system shown in Fig. 4-35(a). If both the bar and the beam are characterized by assuming that a force will act on the end of each, the boundary conditions for both will naturally be taken to be force-free at the end that will later be coupled. The characterizations are shown in Fig. 4-35(b). But

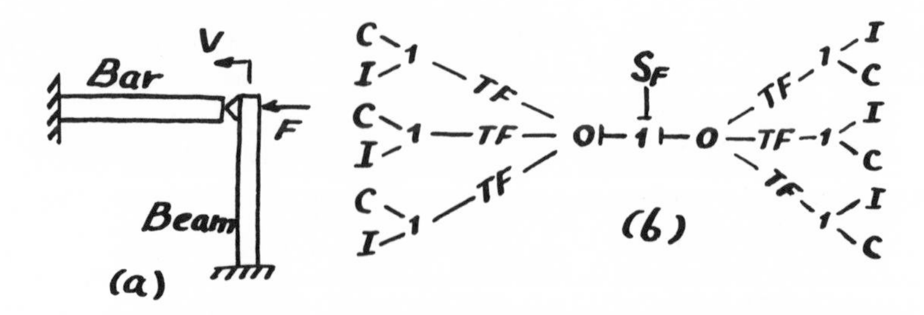

Fig. 4-35 Coupled vibratory system. (a) schematic diagram. (b) bond graph representation of modes.

after the systems are connected, the condition is that the lateral movement of the end of the bar must equal the transverse movement of the end of the beam. This is represented by the 1-junction in the center of Fig. 4-35(b). The external force acts on this common velocity junction, but any attempt to indicate the causality on the 1-junction will result in either the bar or the beam receiving a motion input and responding with a force. As we have seen above, this does not necessarily mean that one must find modes with new boundary conditions for one of the two subsystems; the bond graph of Fig. 4-35(b) or the equivalent equations may be used directly. One should only observe that whichever subsystem is chosen to accept the velocity input be represented over a somewhat broader frequency range than would otherwise be required, by including a few extra modes. This will assure an accurate representation. In a similar way, structural dynamics problems involving active systems may be more conveniently studied if the active systems can be considered to impart motions rather than forces to the vibratory systems. From a computer simulation point of view, this should not cause any particular difficulty even when the vibratory system is first represented in a form most suitable for force inputs.

We now consider some generalizations of our results. As a slightly more complicated example, we consider the beam shown in Fig. 4-36(a). It is a 4-port in that there are four distinct possibilities shown for exchanging power with external agents. Figure 4-36(b) shows the 4-port nature of the system with the representation of the beam left undefined for the time being. In finding modes for this system, one would typically let all external forces and moments go to zero; this would result in a so-called "free-free" configuration. Since the beam as a rigid body has two degrees of freedom, there will be two zero-frequency modes. Letting these two modes be translation of and rotation about the center of mass allows the zero-frequency modal variables to be uncoupled in the same manner as the oscillatory modes. Thus, if x_c is the coordinate of the center of mass, the small transverse motion of the beam, y(x, t), may be split up into modes as follows:

$$y(x,t) = 1\eta_1(t) + (x - x_c)\eta_2(t) + \sum_{i=3}^{\infty} Y_i(x)\eta_i(t), \tag{4.55}$$

where we have taken the two zero-frequency mode shapes to be

$$Y_1(x) = 1, \text{ and} \tag{4.56}$$

$$Y_2(x) = (x - x_c). \tag{4.57}$$

If the beam is uniform, it is a standard textbook exercise to find mode shapes and natural frequencies. When the forcings are applied to the system as represented by the modes, the result is as shown in Fig. 4-36(c), which is not a very simple graph except in comparison with the equivalent electrical or mechanical circuit or schematic which could be used to illustrate the model of the system.

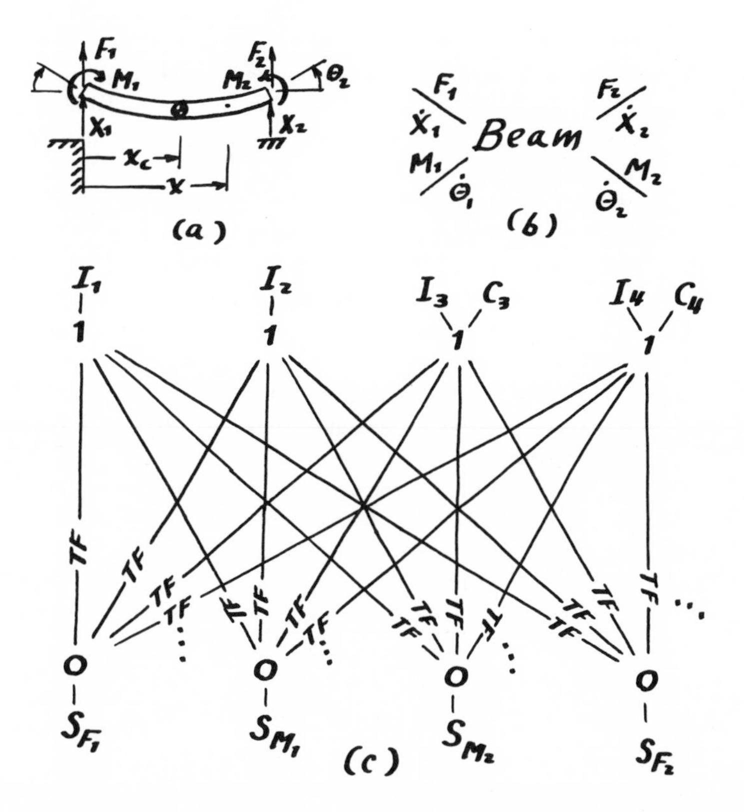

Fig. 4-36 Example of a 4-port beam. (a) schematic diagram, (b) word bond graph, (c) modal bond graph.

Any one of the force or moment sources could be exchanged for a velocity source in the same manner and with the same results as in previous sections. Starting with the free-free modes, we could derive representations for all other boundary conditions commonly studied as well as end conditions involving other dynamic elements. It is only necessary to keep in mind that the system, as described, accepts force and moment inputs naturally; the representation will lose something in accuracy with every motion input. To include a system built in at both ends, several extra free-free modes should be retained in order to achieve an accurate representation.

Finally, it is of interest to enquire whether modes derived from any set of boundary conditions may be used to characterize the system with any other set of boundary conditions. At least it is clear that our technique of merely exchanging force and velocity sources will not work in general. Consider, for example, the system of Fig. 4-29. With the usual geometric description, y(x, t), we see that at the right end a velocity exists in general and we may apply a force. Furthermore, if a velocity source is attached at this port, we have shown how the system representation may be changed into a "fixed-fixed" configuration. At the left end, however, no port exists because the velocity is always zero. In fact, all the modal shapes $Y_i(x)$ have a zero at $x = 0$, so that no sum of the modes can ever result in a velocity at the left end. Thus we may say in general that with the geometric description of the system, if all boundary conditions are of the force type (no constraints on geometric motion), the resulting modes may be used subsequently to model the system when motion constraints at the boundaries are added. Using the dual force-impulse characterization, the most general set of boundary conditions to start with are the completely fixed conditions, because subsequently certain force quantities at the boundaries may be made to vanish. On the other hand, any combination of fixed and free conditions, as for example pinned-pinned conditions, in the beam case, will somewhat restrict the combinations of boundary conditions that may be represented by the original modal decomposition regardless of whether a geometric or a force-impulse description is used.

It should be pointed out that certain problems are solved with fixed boundary conditions in which the boundaries are subsequently allowed to move, by using a form of D'Alembert's principle. This operation, which seems trivial in simple cases, is in fact quite awkward to apply in general and, since the problems handled by this method can also be handled by the methods outlined above, it will not be discussed here.

4.4 Some general features of physical system bond graphs

Since bond graphs provide a uniform mechanism for describing a variety of physical systems, it is natural to seek certain features of bond graphs that appear frequently and lend insight to the physical systems represented. We will first discuss the concept of a *junction structure.* There are a number of multiports that are ideal in the sense that power is transmitted with no loss or gain through the element and no storage of energy is possible. The list of such ideal elements includes 0, 1, TF, and GY. Any number of ideal multiports may be formed by bonding together primitive elements from this list, and we shall designate such multiports by the name *junction structure.* A junction structure that appears in a bond graph of a system performs the function of distributing power among its ports instantaneously and with no loss, just a network of ideal conductors distributes electric current or a network of ideal pipes distributes the flow of an incompressible fluid.

In the case of the simple systems with which we began this chapter, the reader will note that junction structures composed of 0- and 1-junctions are common. In Fig 4-15 junction structures involving TF and GY appear. A more interesting junction structure is shown in Fig. 4-24. In the absence of sources, it is clear that a rotating rigid body is a conservative element and one can see from Fig. 4-24 that any energy originally stored in the inertia elements may only be redistributed in time by the junction structure connecting the inertia elements. A similar observation may be made with regard to Figs. 4-26 to 4-28.

Other examples of junction structures occur in the normal mode representations shown in Figs. 4-30 to 4-36. In principle, the junction structure for normal mode analysis should have an infinite number of ports. The junction structure distributes power from a source into an infinite set of oscillators representing the time behavior of the normal modes. Since the junction structure for normal modes resulted from a separation of variables technique, the power flow quantities along the bonds of the junction structure do not seem to have an immediate interpretation with respect to the original physical problem. In spite of this, it does indicate, as do other junction structures, a conservation of power. For many problems, the finding of a junction structure for a system provides a satisfying check on the consistency of the formulation. When a system model contains a large number of active bonds or other signal flow descriptions, the system formulation may be correct in the sense that all power flows are correctly modeled, but this is not always easy to ascertain.

The expected form for the bond graph of the passive parts of a system is shown in Fig. 4-37. Generally, energy is stored in I-fields or C-fields, energy is dissipated in R-fields and energy is supplied through sources all of which are interconnected through ideal junction structures. This partitioning of the system, which is mainly of conceptual interest, leads us to re-examine the concept of a *field*, which has great practical significance particularly for automatic simulation, as will be seen in Chapter 7.

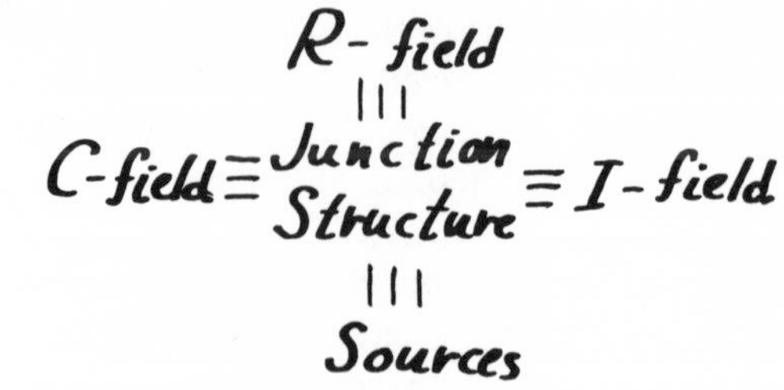

Fig. 4-37 General model of passive physical systems.

Fields are multiport versions of the –I, –C, –R elements, and these arise in essentially two ways. First, an engineering multiport may be modeled directly as a field. In Fig. 4-16(a) a 2-port C-field model of a beam is shown and in Fig. 4-16(b) a rigid body with restricted motion is shown as a a 2-port I-field. An example of an electrical subsystem modeled as an I-field is the mutual inductance in Figs. 4-20 to 4-23. Sometime a field is defined quite directly in terms of the port variables alone. This was the case in our treatment of mutual inductance. At other times it is useful to break up the field into simpler parts, such as a group of 1-ports and a junction structure. An example of this is shown in Fig. 4-25. For linear fields, in particular, there are a large variety of bond graphs that may represent the field, and it is partly a function of the task and the skill of the analyst which determines the final representation of the field. If the end result of the problem formulation is to be a simulation, it is probably safest to remain close to the original physical statement of the field characteristics and to avoid complicated changes of variables, unless a great deal of simplification results.

A second way in which fields arise is by connecting subsystems together into a complete system. Often problems in the attempt to assign causality so as to obtain integral causality may be traced to I- or C-fields. (R-fields usually cause no problems with causality, because the R-fields are indifferent causally). As a simple example of this effect of fields, let us consider a system in which two 1-port capacitances are joined by a 0- or 1-junction, as shown in Fig 4-38. In each case shown, a 1-port C-field is formed, and the causality at bond number 3 is assigned. In each case, the C-field acts in a sense like a 1-port capacitance element from a causality point of view. To get the equivalent 1-port characteristics shown in the figure from the relations of the components generally requires some algebraic manipulation of the static functions involved.

In the case of Fig. 4-38(a) there is no apparent difficulty in assigning integral causality, but since displacements q are involved, one must still be careful of initial conditions. The bond graph constrains e's and f's directly, but not p's and q's. In this example, the characteristics of the element may be written as follows:

$$e_1(t) = \phi_1[q_1(t)], \tag{4.58}$$

$$e_2(t) = \phi_2[q_2(t)], \tag{4.59}$$

$$e_3 = e_1 + e_2, \tag{4.60}$$

$$f_1 = f_3, \tag{4.61}$$

$$f_2 = f_3. \tag{4.62}$$

Since we are concerned with q's, we integrate Eqs. 4.61 and 4.62 to get the following relations:

$$q_1(t) = q_3(t) + q_{10}, \tag{4.63}$$

$$q_2(t) = q_3(t) + q_{20}, \tag{4.64}$$

where q_{10} and q_{20} are constants of integration that must be compatible

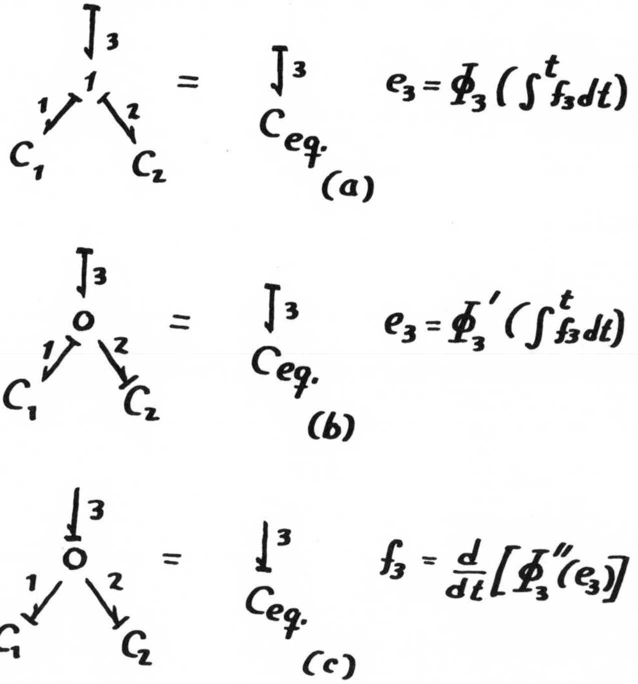

Fig. 4-38 Simple composite C-fields. (a) integral causality, (b) integral causality on external bond but mixed causality internally, (c) derivative causality.

with any assumed initial conditions. Now starting with Eq. 4.60, we may combine the relations to get an explicit representation of the field in terms of the component element characteristics.

$$\begin{aligned} e_2(t) &= \phi_1[q_1(t)] + \phi_2[q_2(t)] \\ &= \phi_1[q_3(t) + q_{10}] + \phi_2[q_3(t) + q_{20}] \\ &= \phi_3[q_3(t)] = \phi_3[\int^t f_3 dt]. \end{aligned} \tag{4.65}$$

When there is no difficulty in assigning integral causality within the field, as is the case in Fig. 4-38(a), results such as Eq. 4-65 are achieved in a straightforward manner. In the case of Fig. 4-38(b), we see that one of the 1-port C's must be assigned derivative causality if the causality of bond 3 is to be maintained. If we follow the causality shown, we will still be able to find a 1-port C equivalent of the field, but more algebraic manipulation will be required than was the case for Fig. 4-38(a). The relations for the system of Fig. 4-38(b) are

$$e_1 = \phi_1(q_1), \tag{4.66}$$

$$e_2 = \phi_2(q_2), \tag{4.67}$$

$$e_1 = e_3, \tag{4.68}$$

$$e_2 = e_3, \tag{4.69}$$

$$f_3 = f_1 + f_2, \tag{4.70}$$

Integrating Eq. 4.70, we have

$$q_3(t) + q_{30} = q_1(t) + q_2(t), \tag{4.71}$$

where q_{30} is a constant of integration compatible with initial conditions. Following the causality shown, we express e_3 in terms of q_1 from Eq. 4.66 and proceed with algebraic manipulation of the system relations,

$$\begin{aligned} e_3(t) &= \phi_1[q_1(t)] = \phi_1[q_3(t) + q_{30} - q_2(t)] \\ &= \phi_1[q_3(t) + q_{30} - \phi_2^{-1}(e_2)] \\ &= \phi_1[q_3(t) + q_{30} - \phi_2^{-1}(e_3)], \end{aligned} \tag{4.72}$$

in which ϕ_2^{-1} is the inverse of the relation Eq. 4.67. Now, if Eq. 4.72 can be solved for e_3 in terms of q_3, the desired result may be expressed as

$$e_3(t) = \phi_3'[q_3(t)] = \phi_3'[\int^t f_3 dt]. \tag{4.73}$$

When the ϕ's are nonlinear, these operations may not be simple or may even be impossible, but in principle the algebraic manipulations indicated for the static relations between e's and q's can be carried out.

In the case of Fig. 4-38(c), the causality at the field port is such that we expect the same sort of situation as occurs when a 1-port C is given an effort input; that is, we expect derivative causality. The relevant relations are the same as for the previous case except that we will not need Eq. 4.71. From Eqs. 4.66 and 4.67 we have

$$f_1 = \frac{d}{dt}\,\phi_1^{-1}(e_1), \tag{4.74}$$

$$f_2 = \frac{d}{dt}\,\phi_2^{-1}(e_2), \tag{4.75}$$

and upon using Eqs. 4.68 to 4.70 the result is

$$\begin{aligned} f_3 &= \frac{d}{dt}\,[\phi_1^{-1}(e_3)] + \frac{d}{dt}\,[\phi_2^{-1}(e_3)] \\ &\equiv \frac{d}{dt}\,[\phi_3''(e_3)]. \end{aligned} \tag{4.76}$$

Thus, the equivalence shown in Fig. 4-38(c) has been demonstrated.

Clearly, the same sort of considerations apply to I-fields as apply to C-fields, with f, p playing the role of e, q. Although for the purposes of analysis, the causality considerations of fields are not significant, for automatic simulation the question of causality is very important. Once a difficulty in assigning a desired causality has been identified with the existence of a field, the sort of manipulations that has been outlined may be undertaken to put the system into a form convenient for simulation. In many cases one can recognize a field in the physical domain (e.g. two springs in series or in parallel) and simplify the system by defining an equivalent element even before the bond graph is constructed. In other cases the bond graph may point out the existence of a previously unexpected field that arises in an interconnected system.

A final general feature of complex systems not previously emphasized involves the operations of measurement, amplification, and control. All of these operations, so important in modern applications, may be represented in bond graph terms using active bonds. Although in principle no measurement can take place without a power flow from the system measured, no signal can be transmitted without power flow, and no amplifier can be a perfect isolator, in typical macroscopic engineering applications the neglect of such power quantities may be quite obviously justified. In such cases, the active bond, by transmitting an effort or flow signal with no back effect from the complementary power variable does become a signal path in the sense of a block diagram, and signal flow methods are clearly applicable. When, as is sometimes the case, the physical system model is very simple and the signal conditioning is responsible for the important dynamics of the system, the bond graph is not a particularly efficient way to represent the system and one would perhaps be well advised to generate a block diagram for the physical system from the bond graph and then to continue the analysis in the signal domain. After a control system has been designed, based on a simplified model of the system, it may be appropriate to return to a more complete bond graph representation of the system to test the closed loop response of the system. In such a case active bonds will be useful, and a mixed signal-bond graph would be appropriate.

References

1. S. H. Crandall, D. C. Karnopp, E. F. Kurtz, and D. C. Pridmore-Brown, *Dynamics of Mechanical and Electromechanical Systems,* McGraw-Hill Book Co, New York, 1968, Chapter 6.
2. G. Hech, "Ein dynamisches Modell für das System 'Pneumatische Leitung–Membranventil," *Regelungstechnik,* v. 5, pp. 194-198 (1967).
3. J. B. Reswick and C. K. Taft, *Introduction to Dynamic Systems,* Prentice-Hall, Inc., Englewood Cliffs, N. J., 1967, p. 49.
4. Ref. 3., p. 90.
5. Ref. 1., Chapter 4.
6. A small angle version of this model is used in V. Cohen and B. Friedland, "Quasi-Optimum Control of a Flexible Vehicle," ASME Paper 66-WA/ Aut 2.
7. K. N. Tong, *Theory of Mechanical Vibration,* New York: John Wiley & Sons, New York, 1960.
8. L. A. Gould and M. A. Murray-Lasso, "On the Modal Control of Distributed Systems with Distributed Feedback," *IEEE Trans. on Automatic Control,* v. AC-11, Oct. 1966, pp. 729-736.
9. R. G. Schwendler and R. H. MacNeal, *Optimum Structural Representation in Aeroelastic Analysis,* Technical Report ASD-TR-61-680, Flight Control Laboratory, Wright-Patterson Air Force Base, Dayton, Ohio, March 1962.
10. D. C. Karnopp, "Coupled Vibratory System Analysis Using the Dual Formulation," *J. Acous. Soc. Am.,* v. 40, Aug. 1966, pp. 380-384.

5. ANALYSIS OF MULTIPORT SYSTEMS

In this chapter we present a systematic procedure for formulating a set of differential equations for a given bond graph. There are many aspects to be considered in choosing variables, organizing system constraints and characteristic relations, and developing a set of interrelated equations in a form amenable to treatment with standard solution techniques.

The set of bond graph elements encompassed by the formulation procedure includes C, I, R, E, F, TF, GY, 0, and 1. Certain restrictions will be placed on the form of characteristics for the C, I, and R elements, as well as on the nature of the MGY and MTF (modulated) two-ports. The elements 0 and 1 are of course strictly linear in both e and f by definition. Multiports that have not been (or cannot be) reduced to an equivalent model in terms of the elements listed may still be handled satisfactorily by the formulation procedure in many cases.

The overall procedure involves several main steps, which are described very briefly as follows:

(1) Name all quantities in the bond graph;

(2) augment the information on the bond graph by assigning signal directedness;

(3) select a suitable set of state variables for the formulation of relations;

(4) formulate the governing relations in terms of the state variables selected above and the sources.

We shall not attempt to describe methods of solution but be satisfied to indicate references that explain how to proceed from certain formulations.

Generally, we consider a system to be adequately formulated when it is expressed as a set of first-order integral or differential equations. This form is the one adopted by most modern control systems analysis theorists and is also useful to those concerned with implementing the relations on analog or digital computers. In fact, Section 6.1 presents a direct conversion method from bond graph to block diagrams, and the form of the block diagrams is almost the same as if equations were first derived using the procedure of this chapter, and the relations then expressed in block diagram form. Section 7.1 discusses a particular digital computing scheme (ENPORT) which directly implements the procedure described in this section.

Before actually describing the formulation procedure let us consider a typical approach to deriving a set of equations in the absence of a systematic method.

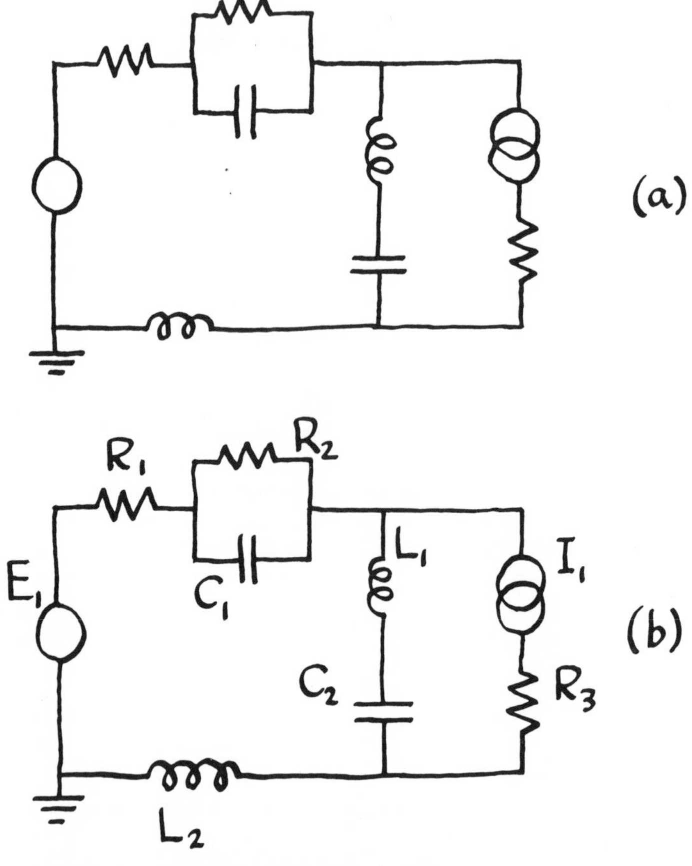

Fig. 5-1 Naming quantities in an electric circuit diagram. (a) an electric circuit diagram, (b) names added to the elements,

Fig. 5-1(a) shows a simple electric circuit without labels; in Fig. 5-1(b) an arbitrary set of names has been added, and in Fig. 5-1(c) reference directions for measurement have been chosen. Figure 5-1(d) gives a corresponding bond graph containing the same information as the electric circuit. From this point on, formulation could proceed by writing some loop and node laws in terms of appropriate currents and voltages and incorporating the element (R, L, and C) characteristics. When the circuit contains active elements, the problem of formulation becomes a bit more complex. If devices such as transistors are present, mild chaos can result unless an equivalent circuit representation is available. Clearly, as the size of the system increases so does the difficulty of generating a useful set of relations in a mutually compatible form. Who has not gotten lost in a set of ten or twelve simultaneous differential equations of

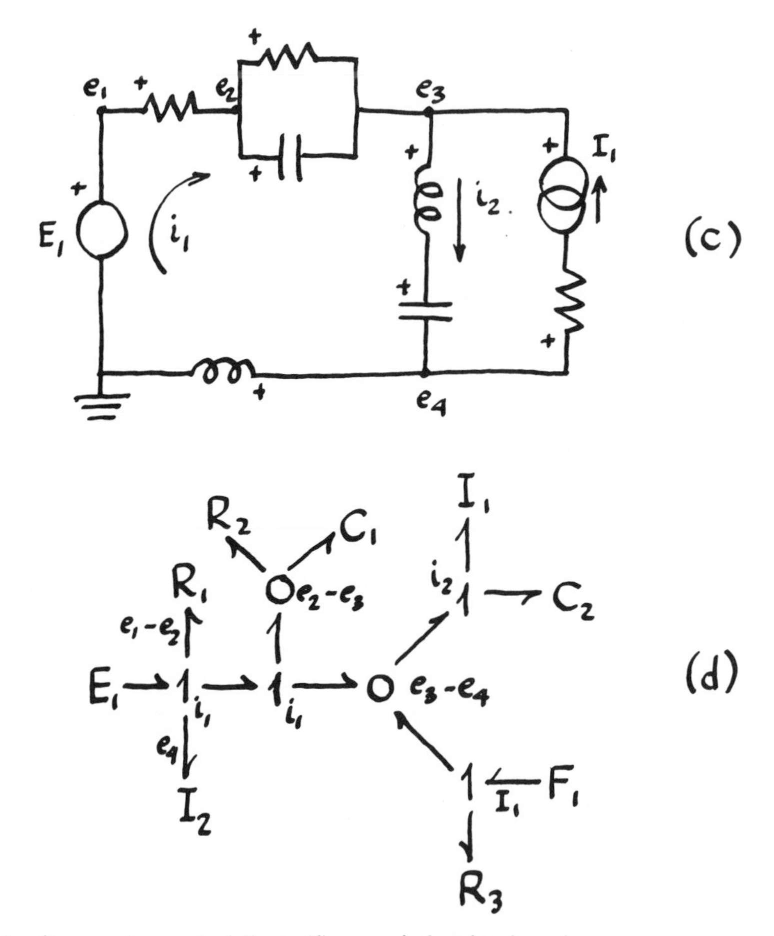

(c) voltages and currents defined, (d) an equivalent bond graph.

various orders and pounded the desk? Only one who hasn't tried such a problem or one who has a systematic method.

Complete graphical description of dynamic systems

Very often it is convenient to represent the entire specification of a dynamic system graphically. The information to be displayed includes the structure, the parameters, the initial state, and the sources. We have already seen that the bond graph is a compact structural description. The use of a simple set of conventions for presenting parametric and variable information enables us to make a complete mathematical description graphically for many dynamic systems. The set of conventions whieh we shall discuss works well for linear and relatively simple nonlinear systems. As the complexity of nonlinear functions or the size of multiport fields (represented by matrices or simultaneous functions) increases, the difficulty of using a completely graphical description is compounded greatly.

The conventions are given in three parts:

(1) parametric information.

For the 1-port elements R, C, and I it is sufficient to place the resistance, capacitance, and inertance parameters, respectively, near the elements, enclosed in parentheses. For example,

$$\underset{(2.5)}{\text{R}}\!\!—, \qquad \underset{(1/k)}{\text{C}}\!\!—, \qquad \text{and} \qquad \underset{(L)}{\text{I}}\!\!—,$$

indicate a resistance value of 2.5 units, a capacitance value (1/k), and an inertance value L, respectively. For nonlinear elements, it is possible to extend the convention to include functions as follows:

$$\underset{\phi_R}{\text{R}}\!\!—, \qquad \underset{\phi_C}{\text{C}}\!\!—, \qquad \text{and} \qquad \underset{\phi_I}{\text{I}}\!\!—,$$

In some cases explicit representation of the functions is best handled by auxiliary defining relations for the ϕ functions.

The 2-port elements TF and GY and the related modulated 2-ports MTF and MGY have a single modulus (scalar or function) associated with them. Therefore we adopt a convention that indicates either the associated modulus or the explicit relations. We illustrate in the case of TF and GY, but the extension to MTF and MGY is obvious, allowing for the need to express function, rather than constants.

To associate a modulus m with a TF, we write $-\underset{m}{\text{TF}}-$. To render the definition explicit we write $\overset{1}{—}\underset{1:m}{\text{TF}}\overset{2}{—}$, which implies that $1 \cdot e_1 = m \cdot e_2$ (and

$m \cdot f_1 = 1 \cdot f_2$). In other words, the use of the colon is spatially associated with the effort relation

In the case of GY, the modulus is expressed in resistive (i.e., effort to flow ratio) terms. If no colon is used, the modulus is considered uncommitted: if a colon is used, it is to be read as the effort to flow ratio. For example, $\overset{1}{-}\underset{r}{GY}\overset{2}{-}$ associates "r" with GY 1 2, but $\overset{1}{-}\underset{r:1}{GY}\overset{2}{-}$ indicates the relations $1 \cdot e_1 = r \cdot f_2$ and $1 \cdot e_2 = r \cdot f_1$.

As an example, consider a system whose structural description is

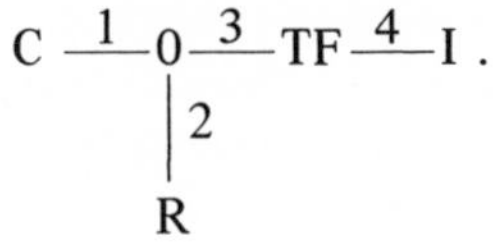

```
C --1-- 0 --3-- TF --4-- I .
        |
        | 2
        |
        R
```

Linear parameters may be indicated by the graph

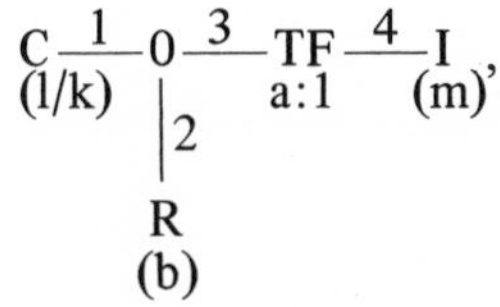

```
  C  --1-- 0 --3-- TF --4-- I  ,
(1/k)      |      a:1      (m)
           | 2
           |
           R
          (b)
```

which implies the set of element relations

C1: $(1/k) \cdot e_1 = q_1$

R2: $e_2 = b \cdot f_2$

I4: $m \cdot f_4 = p_4$

TF34: $a \cdot e_3 = 1 \cdot e_4$

$1 \cdot f_3 = a \cdot f_4$

(2) initial state information.

Typically, information about an initial state is given in terms of a set of variables associated with energy storage elements. Such variables are either e or q on C, and f or p on I, elements. A simple way to indicate initial values on a graph is to use the rule that effort or momentum values (e or p) are written above horizontal bonds or to the left of vertical bonds, and flow or displacement (f or q) values are written below horizontal bonds or to the right of vertical bonds. For the energy-storing elements C and I, there is no ambiguity between e and p or f and q since in each case only one of the pairs is appropriate for determining the initial state of the element. For example,

$\mathrm{C}\overset{10.}{\text{———}}$ indicates that $e(0) = 10.$

$\mathrm{C}\underset{10.}{\text{———}}$ indicates that $q(0) = 10.$

$\mathrm{I}\overset{10.}{\text{———}}$ indicates that $p(0) = 10.$

$\mathrm{I}\underset{10.}{\text{———}}$ indicates that $f(0) = 10.$

On any other bond, a value is associated with either the effort or the flow, unless explicity indicated otherwise (since momenta and displacements on arbitrary bonds are often very difficult to interpret). For example,

$\mathrm{R}\overset{10.}{\text{———}}1$ indicates that $e(0) = 10.$

$1\underset{10.}{\text{———}}\mathrm{TF}$ indicates that $f(0) = 10.$

(3) source specification.

Very simply, one merely writes the source value on its bond in the appropriate place. For example,

$\mathrm{E}\overset{3 \sin 7t}{\text{————}}$ indicates that $e_E(t) = 3 \sin (7t);$

$\mathrm{F}\underset{2u_1(t)}{\text{————}}$ indicates that $f_F(t) = 2u_1(t).$

Thus, a complete description of a forced second-order system with sign-dependent square-law damping is

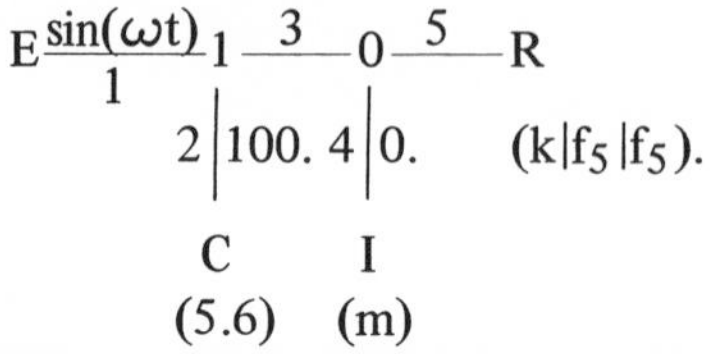

```
 sin(ωt)       3       5
E———————1——————0——————R
    1       |      |
         2 |100. 4 |0.     (k|f5|f5).
            |      |
            C      I
         (5.6)    (m)
```

Note that the minor problem of distinguishing between bond names and initial conditions has been handled through the use of decimal points for the initial conditions. Some associated equations are

E1: $e_1(t) = \sin(\omega t)$

C2: $(5.6)\cdot e_2 = q_2;$ $\quad q_2(0) = 100.$

I4: $(m)\cdot f_4 = p_4;$ $\quad f_4(0) = 0.$

R5: $e_5 = k|f_5|f_5$

In general, treatment of nonlinear functions (such as the resistance relation here given) requires a standard list of functions with an accompanying representation scheme or else the use of a convention such as prefix operator notation.

In succeeding sections we shall have occasion to specify systems in graphical terms, as outlined here. This is particularly true in discussing digital simulation using the ENPORT program (see Section 7.1), where no explicit equations are written in defining systems.

5.1 Naming bonds

In a bond graph, in addition to the multiport element set itself (i.e., the nodes in the graph) there are several variables associated with each bond (i.e., power, energy transfer, effort, momentum, flow, and displacement). A graph would become unreadable if a way were not found to refer to these quantities without having to display all of them explicitly. Fortunately, a very simple reference scheme is available: *name each bond in the graph uniquely.* Any set of unique names will do; however, it is frequently convenient to use a continuous set of integers because of their potential value as indices.

Figure 5-2(a) presents the bond graph of Fig. 5-1(d) named as suggested above. In Fig. 5-2(b) the electric circuit diagram is labeled with a corresponding set of names. Note that both the elements and the variables are named by this manner of labeling.

The method of labeling bonds also becomes important in encoding and transmitting information about system structure (expressed as a bond graph) when one desires to optimize the information transfer under certain circumstances. Reference to an ENPORT example in Section 7.2 will make this point clear (see Fig. 7-1, for instance). Structure coding is discussed in some detail in that section.

Notice in Fig. 5-2(a) that the resistive elements, of which there are three, are labeled R_2, R_5, and R_{13}. The current in each resistor has the same label as the element, as does the voltage difference across it. For example, associated with R_2 are the variables i_2, v_2, and P_2(power in), in addition to some other quantities.

5.2 The augmented bond graph

In order to proceed with any form of analysis or computation we must now make a descent to the signal (e, f, p, q) level. It is appropriate to consider the cause-effect, or independent-dependent, aspects of signal interactions. To make an orderly approach to the treatment of signal relations we exploit the idea of computing *causality* (see Section 3.5).

A procedure for assigning causality to bond graphs

The principal objective in assigning causality to a graph is to find a *complete, consistent causality.* This enables the system relations to be organized in an effective fashion for manipulation (e.g., systematic elimination of variables). A complete causality is one in which every bond in the graph

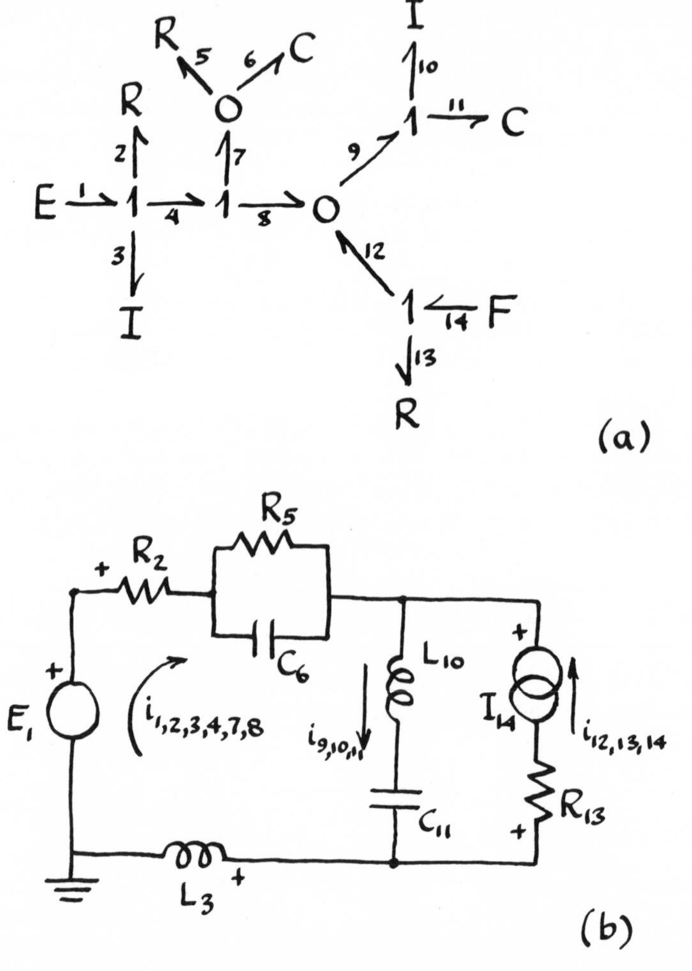

Fig. 5-2 **An example of bond labeling using the graph of Fig. 5-1. (a) naming bonds in a bond graph, (b) equivalent electric circuit diagram with labels.**

is causally directed. A consistent causality is such that each element in the graph has its particular requirements obeyed. Figure 5-3 gives an example of the organizing effects of assigning causality to a graph. The causality was chosen in this case by inspection, because the system is so simple. There are ten equations in ten variables.

Before stating a procedure for assigning causality to a graph, we discuss a hierarchy of causal properties on which the procedure is based. Table 5-1 indicates four levels of significance of causal definitions for the basic multiport elements. The first level, which indicates the highest requirements for

I, 4, F, 1, O, 3, R, 2, C (a)

I, 4, F, 1, O, 3, R, 2, C (b)

acausal relation	element	causal relation
$f_1(t) = F(t)$	. . . F . . .	$f_1(t) = F(t)$
$\phi_2(e_2, q_2) = 0$	. . . C . . .	$e_2(t) = \phi_C^{-1}(q_2)$
$\phi_3(e_3, f_3) = 0$	. . . R . . .	$f_3(t) = \phi_R^{-1}(e_3)$
$\phi_4(f_4, p_4) = 0$	. . . I . . .	$f_4(t) = \phi_I^{-1}(p_4)$
$e_1 = e_2 = e_3 = e_4$	. . . O . . .	$e_1 = e_2, e_3 = e_2, e_4 = e_2$
$f_1 - f_2 - f_3 - f_4 = 0$	. . . O . . .	$f_2 = f_1 - f_3 - f_4$
$q_2 = q_2(0) + \int f_2 dt$	. . . * . . .	$q_2 = q_2(0) + \int f_2 dt$
$p_4 = p_4(0) + \int e_4 dt$	. . . * . . .	$p_4 = p_4(0) + \int e_4 dt$

* by definition. (c)

Fig. 5-3 An example of causal organization of relations. (a) a labeled graph, (b) an augmented graph, (c) acausal and causal relations.

a satisfactory resolution of causality, pertains to the elements 0, 1, GY and TF. If the causal constraints on these elements are not obeyed, the elements lose their meaning. For example, allowing two different effort inputs on a 0-junction destroys the common effort property of the multiport, not to mention the difficulty of interpreting the flow summation relation.

Table 5-1. A causal hierarchy for the basic elements.

Causal hierarchy		Remarks
Level	Element	
1	0,1,GY,TF	Essential that causal constraints be maintained.
2	E,F	Causal form must correspond to physical definition.
3	C,I	Causal form which indicates integration preferred but not essential.
4	R	Causally indifferent if characteristic is bi-unique.

At the second level in the table are the effort and flow sources, E and F. If causality were reversed on one of these elements (e.g., flow determined on an F element) either the graph would have to be treated as physically meaningless or the element would have to be removed as meaningless. As an example, consider the following fragment of a graph:

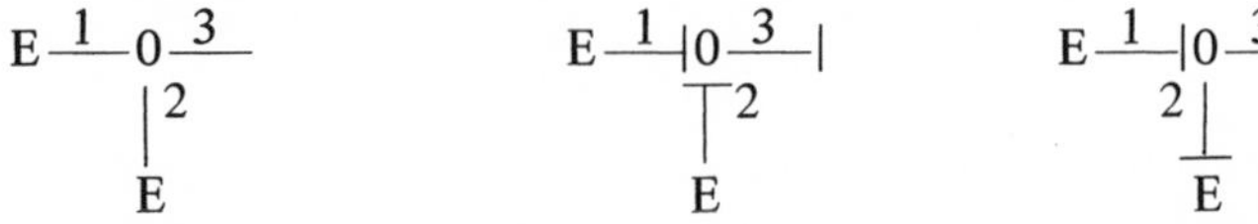

```
E—1—0—3—        E—1—|0—3—|        E—1—|0—3—|
    |2               T2               2|
    |                |                 ⊥
    E                E                 E
```

The first graph shows two effort sources connected by a 0-junction (e.g., two voltage sources in parallel). Two possible causalities are then shown. The first of these violates the causal constraints of the 0-junction and is physically meaningless. The second causal graph shows that E_2 has its effort determined by E_1, which indicates a faulty model or a potentially dangerous physical system, at the least. Only the originator of the graph model can reconcile causal difficulties at levels 1 and 2.

The energy storage elements C and I are at level 3 in the hierarchy. Either effort or flow may be specified as an input in either case. However, if the flow is given as input on C and the effort as input on I, actual manipulation of the element relation in each case will involve *integration* of the input. This is true whether one is analyzing the system or simulating it using an analog or digital method. Reversing the causality convention given will lead to a differentiation operation at some point in subsequent manipulation. The same causal remarks apply to each bond of a C- or I-field; a mixed causality (i.e., some efforts in and some flows in) is also possible, although not desirable.

Finally, the resistive element or resistive multiport (R or R-field), at level 4, will accept any form of causality imposed upon it. As long as the element is bi-unique, no computational difficulties will arise. In some cases, care must be taken in specifying the inverse function for a given R if causality is reversed. For example, suppose an R is governed by the relation $e = k|f|f$, an absolute-square function. This relation corresponds to the flow-in-effort-out causality. If it is necessary to use the effort-in-flow-out form, the corresponding relation is $f = \mathrm{sgn}(e)\,(|e|/k)^{1/2}$.

With respect to linear systems, no great difficulties in inverting C, I, and R causalities are expected, since manipulation of linear operators and arrays is not difficult. However, nonlinear systems may pose very challenging problems in using and manipulating causality as an aid to system analysis.

We now describe a procedure for assigning causality to a bond graph, based on the hierarchy of causal properties given in Table 5-1. In general, there are three types of elements:

(1) causality *extenders*–the elements 0, 1, TF, and GY are used to extend causal information throughout the graph; their constraints must always be met.

(2) *generators* of causal information–the elements E and F always serve as generators of causal information; whenever possible, C and I elements also do because of the preference for integration.

(3) *receivers* of causality–R elements generally have causality imposed upon them; sometimes C and I elements also function as receivers.

The general assignment strategy is to use the generators to introduce some causal information into the graph, then use the extenders to pursue the implications of such information, terminating the extension process at the receivers. It is important to understand the value of a sequential causality assignment procedure, in which a large amount of causal information can be extracted as the assignment proceeds. An algorithm for assigning causality sequentially may be stated as follows:

(1) Assign causality to the first (or next) generator element (e.g., E or F).

(2) Immediately extend the causal information as far as possible throughout the graph, using 0, 1, GY, and TF elements.

(3) When the particular information has been exhausted, ascertain the causal state of the graph. It is either

   (a) incomplete causally, but has no causal conflicts; or it is

   (b) incomplete causally, but has a causal conflict, which must be reconciled before proceeding; or it is

   (c) causally complete.

(4) If the graph is causally complete, the procedure is finished. If the graph is incomplete, one must choose the generator element (still unused) that has the highest causal priority. For this purpose the ordering is E and F, then C and I, then R, then an arbitrary bond in the graph. Figure 5-4 presents the assignment procedure in flow-chart form. The only modification to the basic procedure embodied in the first six blocks is that the generator elements change. Notice that the process continues until causality has been completed, so that the last block has only one answer to the question.

As an example of the use of the procedure, causality is assigned to the following graph below in several simple steps:

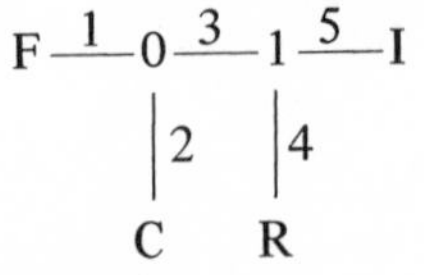

```
F —1— 0 —3— 1 —5— I
      |2    |4
      C     R
```

(a) Assign causality to bond 1, using F.

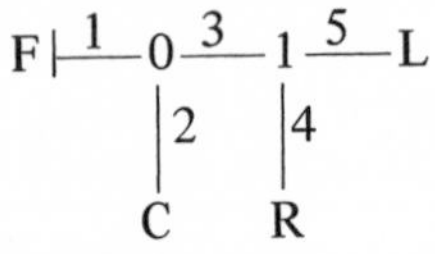

```
F|—1— 0 —3— 1 —5— L
       |2    |4
       C     R
```

No extension is possible.

(b) Assign causality to bond 2, using C.

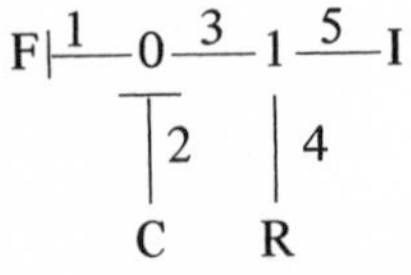

```
F|—1— 0 —3— 1 —5— I
       T2    |4
       C     R
```

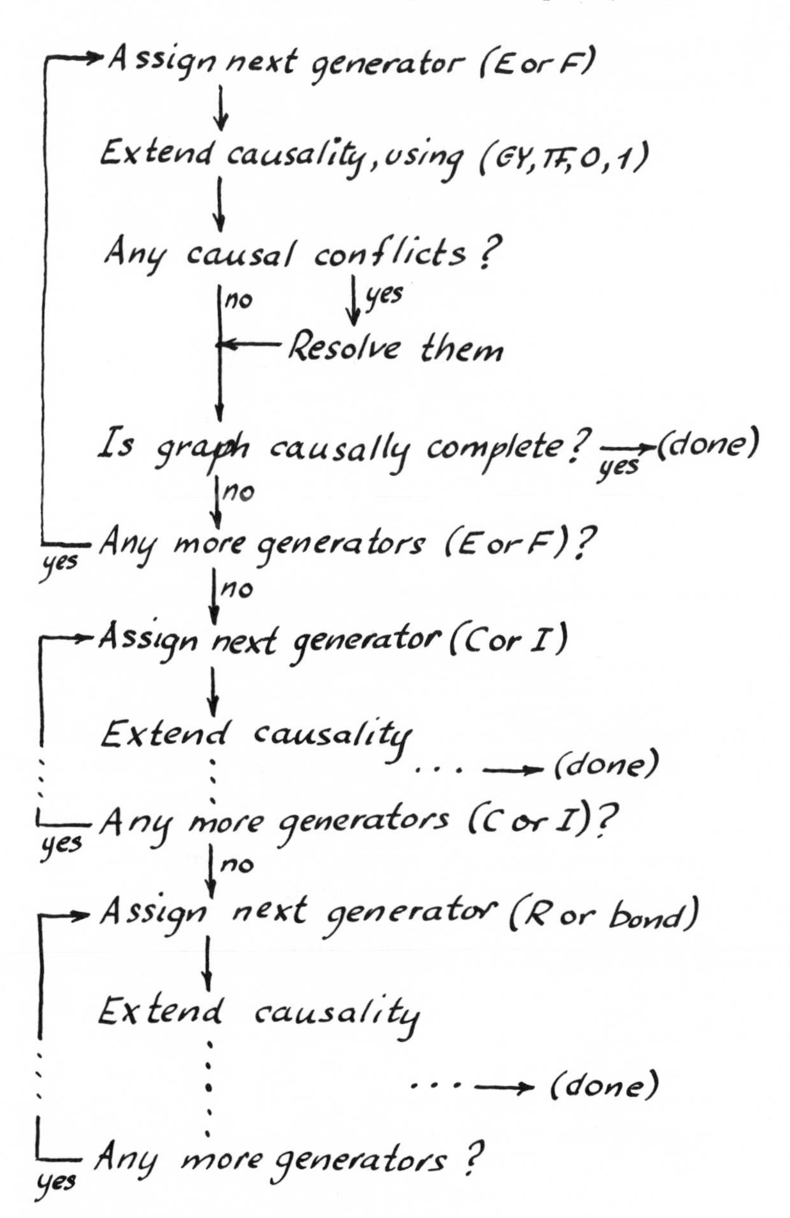

Fig. 5-4 A flow chart of the causality assignment procedure.

Extend the information to bond 3 using the 0-junction. No further extension is possible.

```
F|—1—0—3—|1—5—I
     ⊤      |
     |2     |4
     C      R
```

(c) Assign causality to bond 5, using I.

```
F|—1—0—3—|1—5—|I
     ⊤      |
     |2     |4
     C      R
```

Extend the information to bond 4, using the 1-junction. The graph has been completed causally.

```
F|—1—0—3—|1—5—|I
     ⊤      ⊤
     |2     |4
     C      R
```

In this example it was necessary to use F, C, and I as generator elements. This is commonly the situation and has direct implications for the selection of state variables, to be discussed later in this chapter.

As a second example consider the next graph. In the first few steps F and C are used as generators, and no extension of causal information is possible. Thus an R element must be used as a generator.

```
F—1—0—3—1—5—C
    |     |
    |2    |4
    R     R
```

(a) Assign causality to bond 1, using F.
  No extension is possible.
Assign causality to bond 5, using C.
  No extension is possible.

```
F|—1—0—3—1|—5—C
     |      |
     |2     |4
     R      R
```

(b) Assign causality to bond 2, using the R element (choice is arbitrary, but see the discussion that follows).

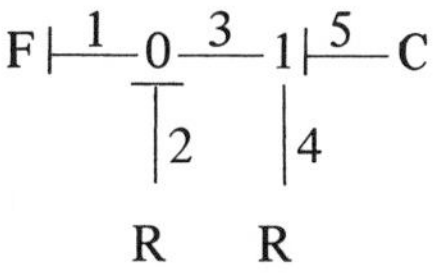

```
F|—1—0—3—1|—5—C
     T      |
     |2     |4
     R      R
```

Extend causal information to bond 3, using the 0-junction.

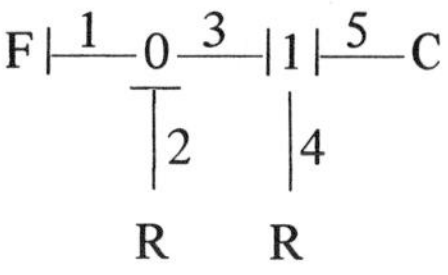

```
F|—1—0—3—|1|—5—C
     T      |
     |2     |4
     R      R
```

Extend causality to bond 4, using the 1-junction.

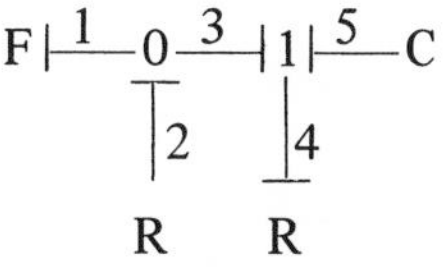

```
F|—1—0—3—|1|—5—C
     T      |
     |2    _|4
     R      R
```

At this point the graph has a complete, consistent causality.

Some remarks on the use of the procedure are in order, although they may have to be re-read when the analyst has gained some experience in the mechanics of assigning causality. The key to the assignment of causality is the use of the 0-junctions and 1-junctions as extenders. There are two senses in which such elements are used, both illustrated in the second example above. The "strong" sense of determinism is:

For a 0-junction, one effort determines the rest;
for a 1-junction, one flow determines the rest.

The "weak" sense of determinism is:

All but one flow is required to determine a 0-junction;
all but one effort is required to determine a 1-junction.

Inspection of part (b) in the example just cited shows that the 0-junction was strongly determined (by effort on bond 2), while the 1-junction was weakly determined (by efforts on bonds 3 and 5).

The notion of strong and weak determinism can be exploited when choosing causality for R elements and arbitrary bonds when they must be used as causality generators. Always choose a causality that determines the neighboring junction in the strong sense (as R in the example determined the 0-junction). The equations that result from such causality will be better organized (i.e., their form will be more explicit) than they would be otherwise.

With some experience in using the assignment procedure, it becomes possible to extract a large amount of information about certain aspects of the system *before* writing equations. If, for example, it is necessary to use an R element as a causal source, and if there are other R elements determined by it, these R's exist as a static R-field. Careful inspection of the second example shows that between bonds 1 and 5 there exists a two-port R-field, which could be written as $\overset{1}{\text{---}}R\overset{5}{\text{---}}$, and subjected to arbitrary port causality.

It is conflicts in causality that yield the most useful insights, however. Since the procedure given requires that every GY, TF, 0, and 1 have consistent causality, all conflicts show up on the 1-port (or field) element, where their effects are quite apparent. For example, Fig. 5-5 shows three types of causal

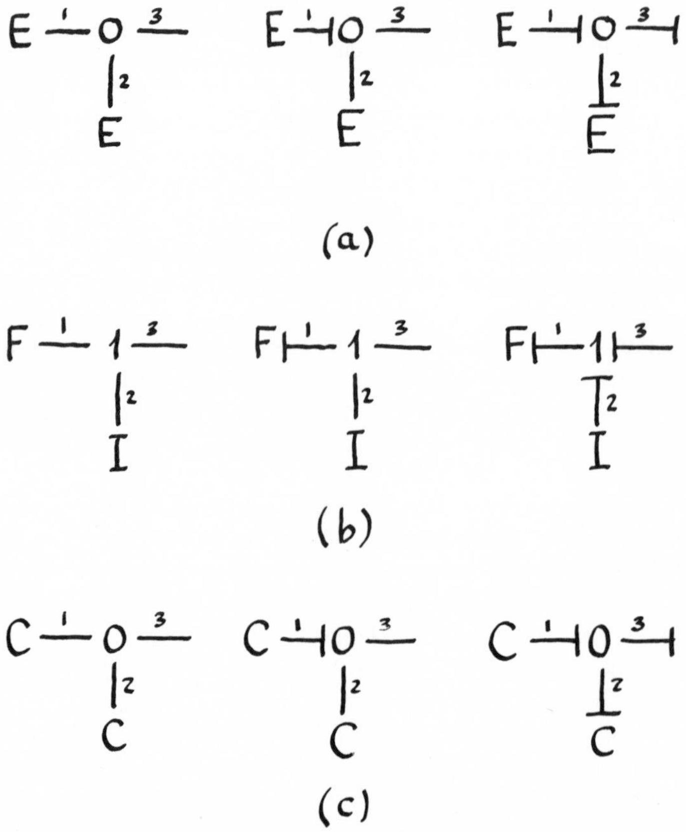

(a)

(b)

(c)

Fig. 5-5 Example of causal conflicts (a) conflict between level-2 elements, (b) level-2-level-3 conflict, (c) conflict between level-3 elements.

conflicts, classified according to interaction among element levels in the causal hierarchy. Case (a) requires reconciliation in the *model;* otherwise there is no mathematical (and certainly no physical) sense to be made of the conflict. Case (b) of the same figure indicates a level-2-level-3 conflict; the net effect is to reduce the level-3 element(s) to a form of parasitic behavior. If we interpret the F as a velocity source and the I as a mechanical inertia, the 1 connection states that the inertia simply "follows" the velocity source according to an arbitrarily prescribed F(t). In addition, the causal graph states that the F source is capable of delivering any power or force required to move the inertia. The engineer must judge for himself whether this is a meaningful phenomenon to include in his model.

Case (c) of Fig. 5-5 is probably the most common type of causal conflict to arise in practice. It is indicated by an interaction (conflict) among several level-3 elements in general. The interpretation is that the elements involved are joined in a manner that does not permit independent setting of effort/flow energy variables in all of the elements. Only a certain number may be set arbitrarily, and the rest will have their states prescribed. That is, the elements exist in a *field*, either an I field or a C field. The particular case shown in Fig. 5-5(c) may be interpreted as two springs in series (sharing of the same force). By setting the force one can set the total energy of the C-field at any value, but the individual energies may not have arbitrary values.

It should be noted that Fig. 5-5 presents only the simplest examples of causal conflict. Frequently the information is imbedded in more obscure fashion in the structure. Figure 5-6 is worthy of study, because it shows how causality can predict the existence of a field without any equations being written. When Fig. 5-6(c) is done, no conflict exists. Yet after Fig. 5-6(d), in which a second inertia has been causally directed, the third inertia has been determined. The roles of the three inertias are causally symmetric, as may be discovered by assigning causality in different sequences. (For example, use I_2 and I_3; then use I_1 and I_3). The graph may be redrawn, as in Fig. 5-7, to show the field more explicitly. The dashed line indicates the boundaries of the 3-port I-field (i.e., the bounding ports).

As another example of the use of causality to predict and avoid analytic difficulties we shall examine a spring and dry-friction 1-port system driven by a velocity source. The system and its bond graph are as follows:

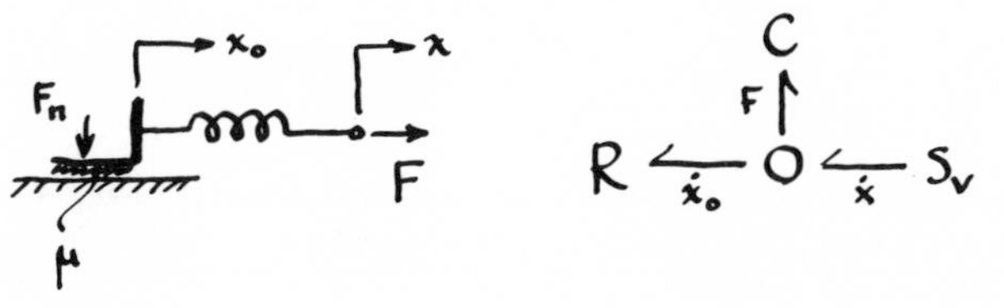

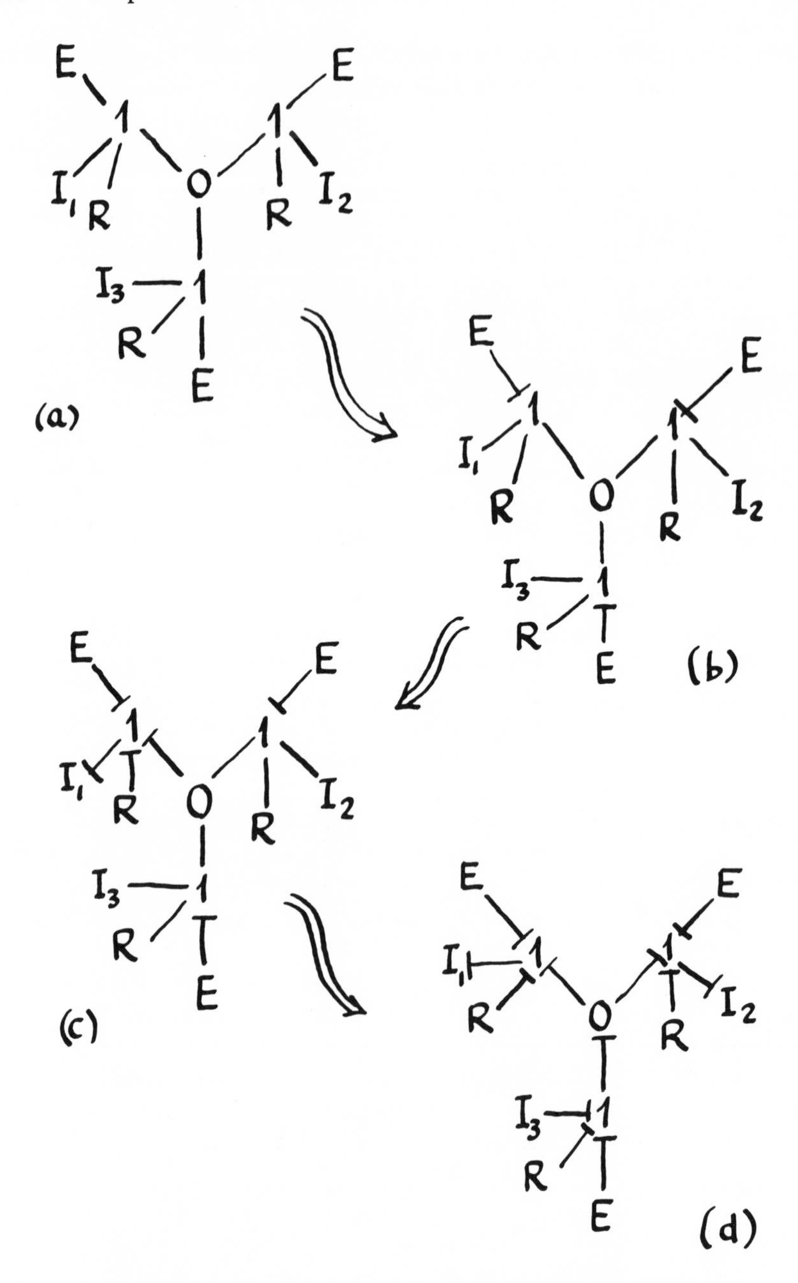

Fig. 5-6 Discovering a static field by using causality. (a) an acausal graph, (b) effort sources completed, (c) I_1 causality assigned and extended, (d) I_2 causality assigned and extended.

If F_f represents the friction force (positive when the spring is in tension) between the slider and the ground, the following relations are valid.

$$F_f = Fo \operatorname{sgn} \dot{x}_o, \text{ if } |x_o| > \epsilon;$$

$$F_f = Fo\, \dot{x}o/\epsilon, \text{ if } |\dot{x}o| \leqslant \epsilon;$$

$$\dot{x} = \dot{x}(t), \text{ given };\ \text{and } Fo = \mu Fn.$$

Attempts to find F as a function of x get involved in considerable organizational difficulties. Use of causality helps to control the process in an orderly way. Standard assignment of causality, based on trying to maintain integration as the preferred operation, leads to the causal graph:

$$\begin{array}{c} \quad\ \ C \\ \quad\ \ \top \\ R \vdash \overset{F_f}{\underset{\dot{x}_o}{—}} 0 \underset{\dot{x}}{—}\!| S_v\ . \end{array}$$

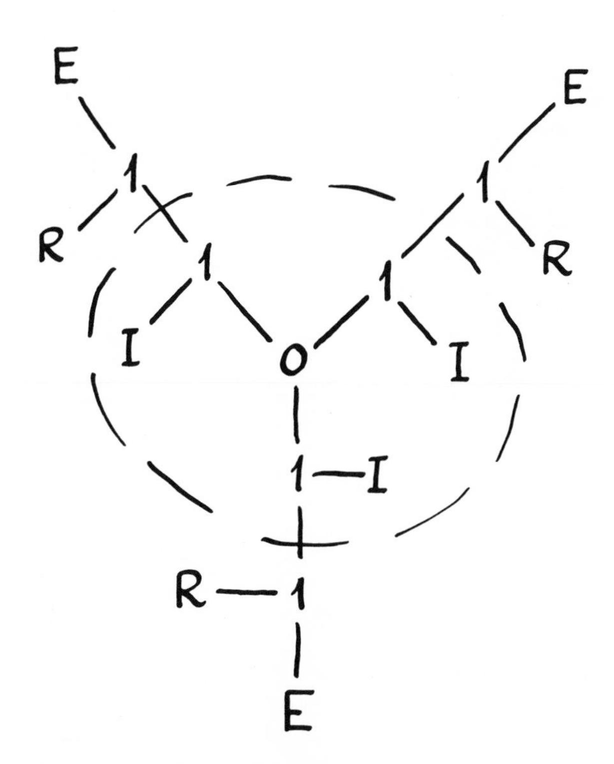

Fig. 5-7 Partitioning the imbedded I-field of Fig. 5-6.

Observe that the R element is to be used in the conductance sense; F_f is the input and $\dot{x}_o$ the output. But this is not an acceptable form of causality for this R element, as we see from the following characteristic in which no unique velocity is determined when $|F_f| = Fo$:

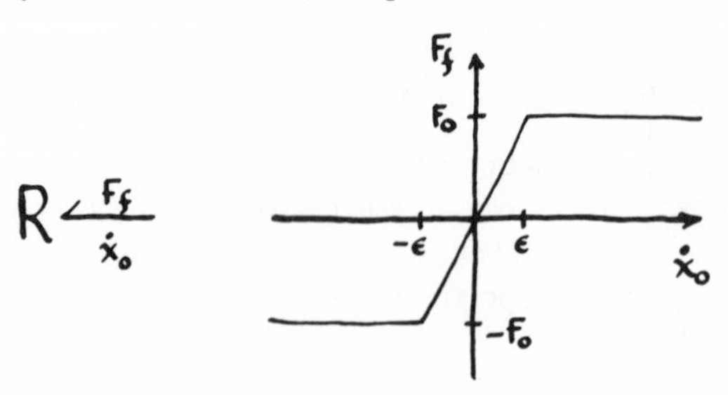

In other words, the element can be used only in the causal sense: "$\dot{x}_o$ in determines F_f out." If the causal graph is modified to indicate this fact, it becomes

```
        C
        ⊤
        |
R ——|0——|Sv,
```

which describes (in a causal sense) the behavior of the system when the spring force equals F_o in magnitude. The spring is moved about at velocity $\dot{x}$ without any change in energy, until the spring force drops below F_o (due to a change in sign of the velocity).

One way to retain the usual causal sense in the system is to introduce a parasitic inertia at the friction end of the spring. Then the bond graph becomes

```
       ẋo   F
R —Ff— 1 —— 0 —— Sv,
       |    |  ẋ
       |    |
       I    C
```

and, with causality assigned,

```
       ẋo
R —Fo—|1|—— 0 ——|Sv .
       |    ⊤  ẋ
       ⊥    |
       I    C
```

Now we observe that the spring functions as an independent element energetically, and the resistance has an acceptable causality. As long as the inertia is kept small (i.e., energy associated with it remains small compared to the other system energies) the prediction of F, x behavior will be close to that of the original model.

As a final observation on this problem we note that, if ϵ in the resistance characteristic goes to zero (Coulomb friction), a second form of causality must be used for the R element. Under these conditions, the characteristic is

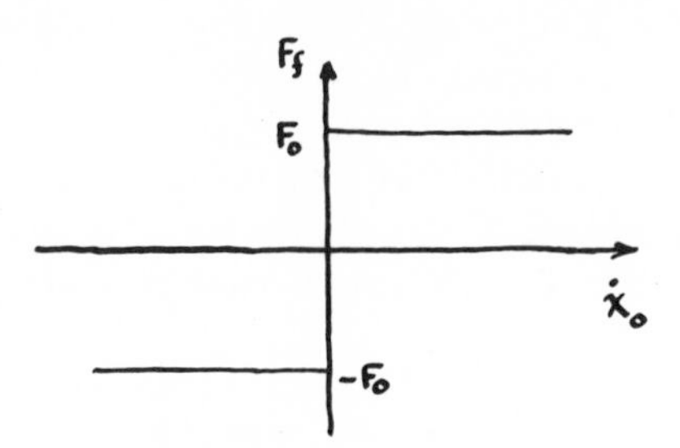

The appropriate causalities and conditions are:

(1) for $|\dot{x}_o| > 0$, $F_f = F_o \operatorname{sgn} \dot{x}_o$, and $R \overset{F_f}{\underset{\dot{x}_o}{\longrightarrow\!\!|}}$;

(2) for $|F_f| < F_o$, $\dot{x}_o = 0$, and $R|\!\overset{F_f}{\underset{\dot{x}_o}{\longrightarrow}}$.

5.3 Selection of variables

In this section we pay careful attention to the selection and naming of variables to be used in the formulation of system equations. In a bond graph with B bonds there are B effort and B flow variables implied, and the same number of displacement and momentum variables. If we consider formulating equations strictly in terms of all the efforts and flows, 2B relations are required to define the 2B effort and flow variables. In order to reduce the number of relations to be written, we shall choose a particular subset of all the bond variables.

In the discussion that follows we first define five types of power variables, and then show how to represent the system in terms of them. Following that, a procedure for putting the equations into a particular desired form is given for two classes of systems: those which are linear with constant parameters, and those for which the C, I, and R elements have nonlinear, bi-unique characteristics.

The first type of power variable is the *energy state* variable, an effort or flow directly associated with an energy. When the energy state variables are all known, the state of the system is fixed. Accordingly, we define *effort on C* and *flow on I* as energy state variables. This usage corresponds with the integration causality, as may be seen by referring to the element definitions in Chapter 3.

The second type of variable is the *source* variable. Quite clearly, source variables are the *effort on E* and *flow on F.*

The third, or *temporary* variables, defined as the output variables on the R elements, serve as an aid in the formulation of equations. They are designated "temporary" because it is usually our intent to eliminate them in condensing the governing relations.

As the fourth type of variable we have the *auxiliary* variable, which is named at opportune places in the junction structure as an intermediate quantity. The auxiliary variables are intended as an aid to formulation and

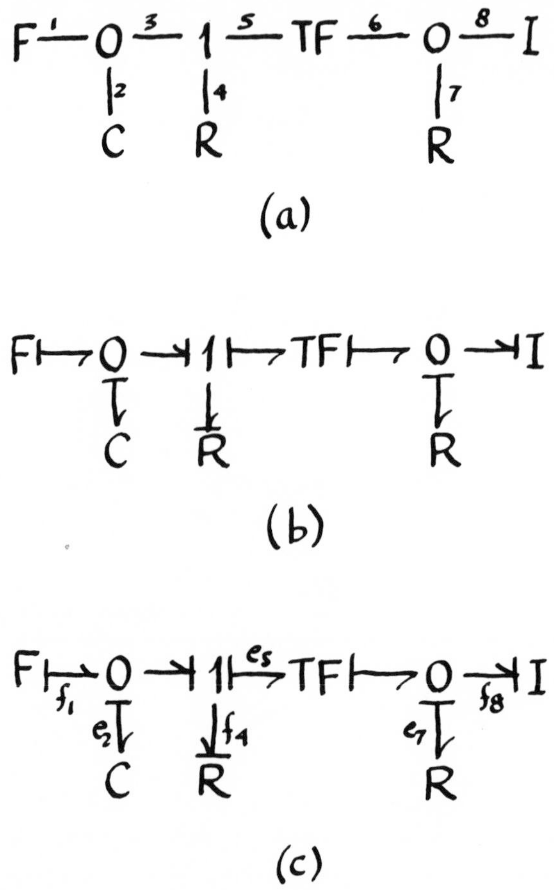

(a)

(b)

(c)

Fig. 5-8 An example of bond graph augmentation. (a) bonds labeled, (b) the causally augmented graph, (c) explicit variables shown.

are eliminated before any of the other types. Experience in using the formulation procedure described in the next section will give each individual a better idea of when he needs to define auxiliary (and also temporary) variables. As one's skill in using an augmented bond graph grows, the number of intermediate variables defined (and hence relations used) decreases.

The fifth category, *observables,* is inserted to conform with standard usage in systems analysis and control. The "observables" are simply those variables which the user wishes to have displayed explicitly, no matter what role they play in formulation or solution. They are sometimes called the system "output" variables.

The five variable types are summarized in Table 5-2. The entire set of explicit bond variables, $\{X, U, T, H\}$, is denoted by $\{V\}$.

Table 5-2. Types of power variables used in system formulation

Type of variable	Set symbol	Remarks	Graph
State	X	Effort associated with C; flow associated with I.	C —e—| I |—f—
Source	U	Effort associated with E; flow associated with F.	E —e—| F|—f—
Temporary	T	Effort or flow associated with R under certain causal conditions.	R —e—| R|—f—
Auxiliary	H	Effort or flow associated with 0 or 1 under certain causal conditions.	
Observable	Y	Chosen by analyst for external purposes.	

As an illustration of the classification of variables according to the types listed in Table 5-2, consider the bond graph example of Fig. 5-8(a). In Fig. 5-8(b) the graph is augmented, and in Fig. 5-8(c) a set of efforts and flows which will prove useful in formulation is shown explicitly. A brief summary of the explicit variable set is given on the next page.

Variable type	Bond variable	Associated element
State, $\{X\}$	e_2	C2
	f_8	I8
Source, $\{U\}$	f_1	F1
Temporary, $\{T\}$	f_4	R4
	e_7	R7
Auxiliary, $\{H\}$	e_5	TF5, 6
Observable, $\{Y\}$	q_3	–

The observable variable, q_3, is appended as an example only.

5.4 Formulation of system equations

Our ultimate objective in using a formulation procedure is to obtain an expression of the system relations in terms of state and source variables. If one follows the plan which we shall describe for graphs with complete, consistent causality, regularities will occur but, needless to say, not all difficulties will disappear. For many practical problems the resulting organization of equations will lead in relatively few steps to the orderly and successful elimination of auxiliary and temporary variables. The result will be a set of first-order integral equations in terms of the state and source variables.

A key part of the formulation procedure is the use of an augmented bond graph with a set of explicit variables, so that any effort or flow variable in the graph can be expressed in terms of the explicit set. This "searching" process requires practice to master but minimizes the writing of extra equations as one gains experience. The searching process will be illustrated in several examples to follow.

Augmented graphs with integration causality

The *formulation procedure* has three steps:

(1) For each energy storage element (C or I), write its constitutive relation in integral form, with the state variable as output. Thus,

$$\text{for C}\longrightarrow\!| : e = \phi_C^{-1}\ [\textstyle\int_o^t f dt + q(o)],$$

$$\text{for I}|\!\longrightarrow : f = \phi_I^{-1}\ [\textstyle\int_o^t e dt + p(o)].$$

The f (or e) under the integral is to be expressed directly as a function of the other variables in the graph that have been named explicitly (i.e., state, temporary, auxiliary, and source variables).

(2) For each temporary variable associated with an R element, write a con-constitutive relation in accordance with the causality. Thus,

$$\text{for R}\longrightarrow\!| : e = \phi_R(f),$$

$$\text{for R}|\!\longrightarrow : f = \phi_R^{-1}(e),$$

where the input f (or e) is expressed in terms of the other explicit graph variables, as mentioned above.

(3) Express each auxiliary variable (associated with a GY, TF, 0, or 1), directly in terms of other explicit variables.

There will then be three sets of equations, in general. The form of relations is

$$\{X\}_i = \phi_{Xi}^{-1}\left(\textstyle\int_o^t F(\{V\})dt + [q_i(o) \text{ or } p_i(o)]\right), \tag{5.1a}$$

$$\{T\}_i = \phi_{Ti}(\{V\}), \tag{5.1b}$$

$$\{H\}_i = \phi_{Hi}(\{V\}), \tag{5.1c}$$

where $\phi(\{V\})$ denotes a function of the explicit variable set.

A reasonable way to try to manipulate the relations is to first eliminate the $\{H\}$ variables, which are governed by a set of static equations, in terms of the $\{X\}$, $\{U\}$, and $\{T\}$ variables. Frequently they do not depend upon themselves in their definition. In that case they may be immediately eliminated by direct substitution in the $\{X\}$ and $\{T\}$ equation sets.

The same approach is repeated with respect to the $\{T\}$ variables, which are also defined by a set of static relations. Again, it is frequently the case that the temporary variables may be directly substituted for in the primary set of integral equations involving $\{X\}$.

As a simple example of use of the formulation procedure, consider the following bond graph, first in existential form, then in augmented form, and then with state, source, and temporary variables indicated:

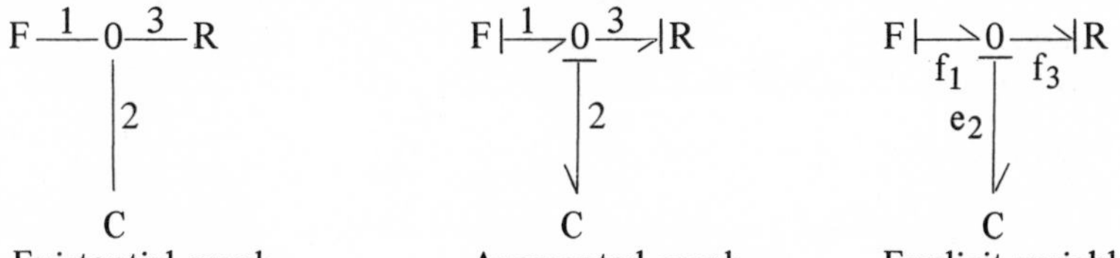

F —1— 0 —3— R; 2; C	F |—1⇀ 0 —3⇀| R; 2; C	F |—⇀ 0 —⇀| R; f_1, f_3, e_2; C
Existential graph	Augmented graph	Explicit variables

The explicit variable set $\{V\}$ is composed of f_1, e_2, and f_3; f_1 is a source variable, e_2 is a state variable, and f_3 is a temporary variable.

The governing relations are

$$e_2 = \phi_C^{-1}(\int_o^t f_2 dt + q_2(o)) \ldots\ldots \text{from C2.}$$

$$e_2 = \phi_C^{-1}(\int_o^t (f_1 - f_3) dt + q_2(o)) \ldots\ldots \text{in terms of } \{V\} \qquad (5.2)$$

$$f_3 = \phi_R^{-1}(e_3) \ldots\ldots \text{from R3.}$$

$$f_3 = \phi_R^{-1}(e_2) \ldots\ldots \text{in terms of } \{V\}. \qquad (5.3)$$

The reader will notice that Eqs. 5.2 and 5.3 are in the form of Eqs. 5.1a and 5.1b, respectively. Each explicit variable (except for source variables), appears exactly once on the left side of the equations expressed in terms of the set $\{V\}$. In this example a simple elimination scheme is to use Eq. 5.3 to eliminate f_3 from the rest of the relations. Then we have

$$e_2(t) = \phi_C^{-1}(\int_o^t [f_1 - \phi_R^{-1}(e_2)]\, dt + q_2(o)). \qquad (5.4)$$

As a more complex example, consider the augmented graph

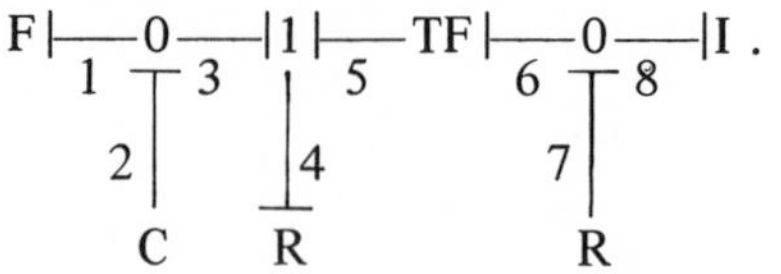

```
F|——0——|1|——TF|——0——|I .
   1 ┬ 3  |  5     6 ┬ 8
     |    |          |
    2|    |4        7|
     C    R          R
```

This is the graph shown in Fig. 5-8 and discussed previously. An explicit variable set is

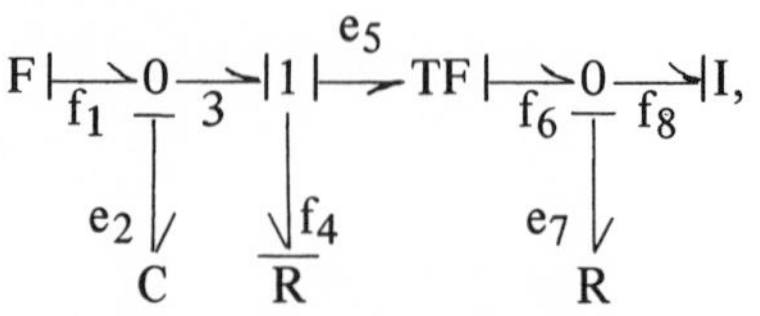

```
                  e5
F|—>0——>|1|——>TF|—>0——>|I,
   f1 ┬ 3           f6 ┬ f8
      |    |           |
   e2 v    v f4     e7 v
      C    R           R
```

where e_2 and f_8 are state variables, f_1 is a source variable, f_4 and e_7 are temporary variables, and e_5 and f_6 are auxiliary variables (introduced for convenience).

The ultimate formulation goal is to have two integral equations in the three $\{X,U\}$ variables f_1, e_2, and f_8. To get these we shall first write six equations.

Step (1). Use C2 and I8 to express e_2 and f_8.

$$e_2 = \phi_{C2}^{-1} [\int_o^t f_2 dt + q_2(o)]$$

Using the searching process to replace f_2 by its $\{V\}$ equivalent,

$$e_2 = \phi_{C2}^{-1}[\int_o^t(f_1 - f_4)dt + q_2(o)]. \quad (5.5a)$$

$$f_8 = \phi_{I8}^{-1}[\int_o^t e_8 dt + p_8(o)].$$

Using "searching" to replace e_8 by its $\{V\}$ equivalent,

$$f_8 = \phi_{I8}^{-1}[\int_o^t(e_7)dt + p_8(o)]. \quad (5.5b)$$

Step (2). Use R4 and R7 to express f_4 and e_7.

$$f_4 = \phi_{R4}^{-1}(e_4)$$

Using "searching" to replace e_4 by its $\{V\}$ equivalent,

$$f_4 = \phi_{R4}^{-1}(e_2 - e_5). \quad (5.5c)$$

$$e_7 = \phi_{R7}(f_7)$$

In terms of $\{V\}$,

$$e_7 = \phi_{R7}(f_6 - f_8). \quad (5.5d)$$

Step (3). Use TF5,6 to express e_5 and f_6.

$$e_5 = m \cdot e_6$$

We have, in terms of $\{V\}$,

$$e_5 = m \cdot e_7. \quad (5.5e)$$

$$f_6 = m \cdot f_5$$

Replacing f_5 by its $\{V\}$ equivalent,

$$f_6 = m \cdot f_4. \quad (5.5f)$$

There are six equations in terms of the six unknowns (e_2, f_8; f_4, e_7; e_5, f_6) and the source variable f_1. In addition, the initial conditions are imbedded in Eqs. 5.5a and 5.5b, in the form $q_2(o)$ and $p_8(o)$, respectively.

Elimination of variables proceeds in orderly fashion from "bottom" to "top," or from auxiliary variables through temporary variables to state relations. Thus we use Eqs. 5.5e and 5.5f to eliminate e_5 and f_6 from Eqs. 5.5c and 5.5d, which yield the coupled pair of equations

$$f_4 = \phi_{R4}^{-1}(e_2 - m \cdot e_7)$$

$$e_7 = \phi_{R7}(m \cdot f_4 - f_8).$$

Assuming that an explicit solution to these equations can be found, of the form $f_4 = \phi_4'(e_2, f_8)$ and $e_7 = \phi_7'(e_2, f_8)$, such results can be inserted into Eqs. 5.5a and 5.5b. Otherwise no further reduction is possible, in general, and we must turn to numerical computation or simulation to extract further information. If an explicit solution exists, the final form for the system equations would be the pair of relations

$$e_2 = \phi_{C2}^{-1}\left(\int_o^t [f_1 - \phi_4'(e_2, f_8)]\,dt + q_2(o)\right),$$

$$f_8 = \phi_{I8}^{-1}\left[\int_o^t \phi_7'(e_2, f_8)dt + p_8(o)\right].$$

Thus, we have been able to achieve our goal of expressing the system relations as a set of nonlinear first-order integral equations in terms of the energy state variables.

The procedure has been stated and carried out in terms of effort and flow variables. The results in terms of e_2 and f_8 may easily be transformed to momentum and displacement variables (q_2 and p_8) as follows: Replace e_2 by $\phi_{C2}^{-1}(q_2)$ and f_8 by $\phi_{I8}^{-1}(p_8)$. Invert the capacitance and inertance relations, respectively. The result is

$$q_2 = \int_o^t \{f_1 - \phi_4'[\phi_{C2}^{-1}(q_2), \phi_{I8}^{-1}(p_8)]\}dt + q_2(o),$$

and

$$p_8 = \int_o^t \{\phi_7'[\phi_{C2}^{-1}(q_2), \phi_{I8}^{-1}(p_8)]\}dt + p_8(o).$$

Considering that we have dealt with a forced second-order system of a rather general nature, the results, in either e_2 and f_8 or q_2 and p_8, are quite compact and tidy. In the next section we shall investigate the formulation procedure as applied to linear, constant parameter systems.

One remark on observable variables should suffice at this point. Suppose the effort on the flow source (e_1) had been designated an observable variable. One merely uses the searching process to find e_1 in terms of $\{V\}$ and then, if possible, reduces the expression to e_1 as a function of $\{X\}$ and $\{U\}$. For this example $e_1 = e_2$, which is in the required form.

Linear system relations

When a system is represented by a graph all of whose elements have constant parameters, and when the graph has been augmented in a complete, consistent way, the following procedure is very convenient for generating system relations as a set of first-order differential equations. In particular, the form to be attained is shown by the following set of first-order matrix differential equations:

$$DX = A \cdot X + B \cdot U \quad (5.6a)$$

$$Y = C \cdot X + D \cdot U, \quad (5.6b)$$

in which D represents the operator d/dt. The vector **X** is the state vector (mixed in efforts and flows), **U** is the source vector, **Y** is the vector of observables or outputs, and **A**, **B**, **C**, and **D** are arrays which contain the system structure and parameter information. The form of Eq. 5.6 is used by many standard systems analysis and modern control books (see, for example, references 1 and 2). It is not our intention here to exploit the use of such state space relations, but to show how they may be obtained systematically.

The formulation procedure is quite similar to the one given in the previous section. Each C and I element is used to generate one equation; this time the derivative, rather than the integration, form is used, but input and output variables remain the same as before.

The *linear formulation procedure* is:

(1) For each C or I, write an equation of the form $C \cdot De = f$, (or $I \cdot Df = e$), where the f (or e) on the right side of the equation is to be expressed directly in terms of the explicit variable set discussed previously.

(2) For each R, write an equation that gives the output, or temporary, variable in terms of the explicit variable set.

(3) For each auxiliary variable, write a relation that defines the variable in terms of the explicit variable set.

The relations may be ordered in matrix form as:

$$F \cdot DX = C_{11}X + C_{12}T + C_{13}H + C_{14}U \quad (5.7a)$$

$$T = C_{21}X + C_{22}T + C_{23}H + C_{24}U \quad (5.7b)$$

$$H = C_{31}X + C_{32}T + C_{33}H + C_{34}U \quad (5.7c)$$

where **X**, **T**, **H**, and **U** are the state, temporary, auxiliary, and source vectors, respectively. **F** is the *field* matrix, which is diagonal if there are only 1-port fields, and the C_{ij}'s are the *connection* matrices.

Elimination of **H** proceeds by solving Eq. 5.7c for **H**; thus,

$$H = (I - C_{33})^{-1} \cdot (C_{31}X + C_{32}T + C_{34}U). \quad (5.8)$$

After this result is introduced into Eqs. 5.7a and 5.7b, a similar procedure may be followed to eliminate **T** from the modified form of Eq. 5.7b. A complete derivation is given in the next section, but the eventual result is a relation of the form:

$$\mathbf{F}\cdot\mathbf{DX} = \mathbf{C}''_{11}\mathbf{X} + \mathbf{C}''_{14}\mathbf{U}, \tag{5.9}$$

where the double primes indicate that the coefficient array has been modified twice (once in eliminating **H** and again in eliminating **T**). Since **F** is a diagonal matrix by virtue of the way the relations were generated, it is inverted by forming the reciprocal of each diagonal element. The resulting array is multiplied into $\mathbf{C}''_{11}$ and $\mathbf{C}''_{14}$ to yield the desired form (that of Eq. 5.6a). Thus,

$$\mathbf{DX} = \mathbf{F}^{-1}\mathbf{C}''_{11}\mathbf{X} + \mathbf{F}^{-1}\mathbf{C}''_{14}\mathbf{U}, \tag{5.10}$$

or $$\mathbf{DX} = \mathbf{A}\cdot\mathbf{X} + \mathbf{B}\cdot\mathbf{U}, \tag{5.6a}$$

where $\mathbf{A} = \mathbf{F}^{-1}\mathbf{C}''_{11}$ and $\mathbf{B} = \mathbf{F}^{-1}\mathbf{C}''_{14}$.

Let us apply this procedure to the graph shown in Fig. 5-8, assuming constant parameters for all constitutive relations and moduli. This is done in Fig. 5-9, step by step. Relations (1) and (2) come from C_2 and I_8, respectively, and they form the first two rows in the matrix format. Rows 3 and 4 come from the **T** vector relations, generated by R_4 and R_7. And **H**, the auxiliary vector, accounts for rows 5 and 6, which are related to TF in this case. An experienced bond graph analyst would not need to define e_5 and f_6 explicitly. In the linear case some of the components of **H** and **T** function as memory aids, since causal inversion of the typical linear relation merely involves forming a reciprocal quantity or shifting sides in an equation. We complete the reduction of the relations given in Fig. 5-9 by first using direct substitution to eliminate **H** (e_5 and f_6). Then we have

$C_2\cdot De_2 = 0$	0	$-f_4$	0	$+f_1$	(5.11a)
$I_8\cdot Df_8 = 0$	0	0	$+e_7$		(5.11b)
$f_4 = \frac{1}{R_4}e_2$	0	0	$\frac{-m}{R_4}e_7$		(5.11c)
$e_7 = 0$	$-R_7f_8$	$+R_7mf_4$	0		(5.11d)

Solution for f_4 and e_7 must proceed simultaneously by use of Eqs. 5.11c, d. This is not unexpected; assigned causality indicated this interdependence. Some further remarks about this point will be made in Section 5.5.

The solution of Eqs. 5.11c and 5.11d gives

$$f_4 = \frac{1}{R_4 + m^2R_7}(e_2 + mR_7f_8) \tag{5.12a}$$

and

$$\text{Fl} \overset{}{\underset{f_1}{\longrightarrow}} 0 \longrightarrow 1 \overset{e_5}{\longrightarrow} \underset{\ddot{m}}{\text{TF}} \underset{f_6}{\longrightarrow} 0 \underset{f_8}{\longrightarrow} \text{I}$$

(bond graph: $0 \xrightarrow{e_2} C$; $1 \xrightarrow{f_4} R$; $0 \xrightarrow{e_7} R$)

$\underline{X} = (e_2, f_8)$

$\underline{U} = (f_1)$

$\underline{T} = (f_4, e_7)$

$\underline{H} = (e_5, f_6)$

$$(1) \quad C_2 \cdot De_2 = f_1 - f_4$$

$$(2) \quad I_8 \cdot Df_8 = e_7$$

$$(3) \quad f_4 = R_4^{-1} \cdot (e_2 - e_5)$$

$$(4) \quad e_7 = R_7 \cdot (f_6 - f_8)$$

$$(5) \quad e_5 = m \cdot e_7$$

$$(6) \quad f_6 = m \cdot f_4$$

In array form—

$$\begin{bmatrix} C_2 & 0 \\ 0 & I_8 \end{bmatrix} D \begin{bmatrix} e_2 \\ f_8 \end{bmatrix} = \begin{bmatrix} 0 & 0 & -1 & 0 & 0 & 0 \\ 0 & 0 & 0 & 1 & 0 & 0 \end{bmatrix} \begin{bmatrix} e_2 \\ f_8 \\ f_4 \\ e_7 \\ e_5 \\ f_6 \end{bmatrix} + \begin{bmatrix} 1 \\ 0 \end{bmatrix} \begin{bmatrix} f_1 \end{bmatrix}$$

$$\begin{bmatrix} f_4 \\ e_7 \\ e_5 \\ f_6 \end{bmatrix} = \begin{bmatrix} R_4^{-1} & 0 & 0 & 0 & -R_4^{-1} & 0 \\ 0 & -R_7 & 0 & 0 & 0 & R_7 \\ 0 & 0 & 0 & m & 0 & 0 \\ 0 & 0 & m & 0 & 0 & 0 \end{bmatrix} \begin{bmatrix} e_2 \\ f_8 \\ f_4 \\ e_7 \\ e_5 \\ f_6 \end{bmatrix} + \begin{bmatrix} 0 \\ 0 \\ 0 \\ 0 \end{bmatrix}$$

Fig. 5-9 An example of the linear formulation procedure.

$$e_7 = \left(\frac{1}{R_4 + m^2 R_7}\right) \; (mR_7 e_2 - R_4 R_7 f_8), \tag{5.12b}$$

which may now be inserted directly into Eqs. 5.11a, b. In standard form the resulting relations are:

$$De_2 = \frac{1}{R_{eq} C_2} e_2 - \frac{mR_7}{R_{eq} C_2} f_8 + \frac{1}{C_2} f_1, \tag{5.13a}$$

$$Df_8 = \frac{mR_7}{I_8 R_{eq}} e_2 - \frac{R_4 R_7}{I_8 R_{eq}} f_8, \tag{5.13b}$$

where $R_{eq} \equiv R_4 + m^2 R_7$. The matrices A and B (see Eq. 5.6a) may be identified as

$$A = \begin{bmatrix} -\dfrac{1}{R_{eq} C_2} & \dfrac{mR_7}{R_{eq} C_2} \\ \dfrac{mR_7}{I_8 R_{eq}} & \dfrac{R_4 R_7}{R_{eq} I_8} \end{bmatrix} \text{ and } B = \begin{bmatrix} \dfrac{1}{C_2} \\ 0 \end{bmatrix}$$

The observables vector **Y** is constructed in a manner similar to the procedure just described. In this case the first step is to express the quantity desired in terms of the explicit variables, and also time operators if required. Then each **H** and **T** variable that appears can be eliminated from the definition of Y_i by using the relations already found in the basic elimination procedure. The result is an equation relating Y_i to the **X** and **U** vectors. As an example, consider the observable q_3 for the graph of Fig. 5-8. First we seek the flow variable f_3. From this q_3 may be found by integration. Referring to the augmented graph in that figure, we see that $f_3 = f_4$, where f_4 is a temporary variable. But f_4 has already been defined by Eq. 5.12a in terms of **X** and **U**. We now present the relevant relations for finding q_3:

$$f_3 = \frac{1}{R_{eq}} e_2 + \frac{mR_7 f_8}{R_{eq}}, \tag{5.14a}$$

$$q_3 - q_3(o) = \int_o^t f_3 dt. \tag{5.15b}$$

These lead to the standard form expression

$$(q_3 - q_3(o)) = \left(\frac{1}{R_{eq} D}\right) e_2 + \left(\frac{mR_7}{R_{eq} D}\right) f_8 \tag{5.15}$$

To summarize, we emphasize that the formulation procedure given—naming explicit variables, generating an initial set of relations, and subsequently eliminating the auxiliary and temporary variables systematically—produces a set of linear first-order differential equations for a graph that has a complete, consistent causality.

Elimination of variables in the formulation of linear system equations

As described in the previous section, the first form for linear system relations is:

$$\mathbf{F \cdot DX - C_{11}X + C_{12}T + C_{13}H + C_{14}U} \quad (5.7a)$$

$$\mathbf{T = C_{21}X + C_{22}T + C_{23}H + C_{24}U} \quad (5.7b)$$

$$\mathbf{H = C_{31}X + C_{32}T + C_{33}H + C_{34}U} \quad (5.7c)$$

It is our purpose to reach the form given by Eq. 5.6a. This transformation may be accomplished by the following steps:

(a) Solve for **H** in terms of **H**, **T**, and **U**.

$$\mathbf{H = (I - C_{33})^{-1} (C_{31}X + C_{32}T + C_{34}U)},$$

or

$$\mathbf{H = C'_{31}X + C'_{32}T + C'_{34}U}$$

(b) Solve for **T** in terms of **X** and **U**, having first substituted for **H** from Eq. 5.16 into Eqs. 5.7a, b.

$$\mathbf{T = (C_{21} + C_{23}C'_{31})X + (C_{22} + C_{23}C'_{32})T + (C_{24} + C_{23}C'_{34})U};$$

$$\mathbf{T = [I - (C_{22} + C_{23}C'_{32})]^{-1} [(C_{21} + C_{23}C'_{31})X + (C_{24} + C_{23}C'_{34})U};$$

or

$$\mathbf{T = C'_{21}X + C'_{24}U}. \quad (5.17)$$

(c) Substitute from Eq. 5.17 into Eq. 5.7a to eliminate **T**.

$$\mathbf{F \cdot DX = (C_{11} + C_{12}C'_{21} + C_{13}C'_{31} + C_{13}C'_{32}C'_{21})X}$$
$$\mathbf{+ (C_{14} + C_{12}C'_{24} + C_{13}C'_{34} + C_{13}C'_{32}C'_{24})U};$$

$$\mathbf{F \cdot DX = C''_{11}X + C''_{14}U}. \quad (5.18)$$

(d) As the last step, invert F and premultiply Eq. 5.18.

$$DX = (F^{-1}C''_{11})X + (F^{-1}C''_{14})U,$$

which yields the correspondences

$$A = F^{-1}C''_{11} \text{ and } B = F^{-1}C''_{14}.$$

5.5 Further remarks on formulation

The previous sections have started from an augmented graph with complete integration causality. In this section we wish to consider information that can be exploited in the process of assigning causality and naming explicit variables. One important condition arises when it is not possible to obtain an integration causality in part of the graph. One case is due to a C or I field imbedded in the system. A second important situation is due to R fields. In this case it is not possible to complete the causality without assigning causality to at least one R element. There is an even more subtle effect due to structural redundancy. In such a case it is necessary to add a causal stroke to an arbitrary bond in the junction structure in order to complete the causality. Each of these cases will be discussed in terms of an example. It is our purpose to extract a maximum of information about the equations to be obtained prior to writing them down.

If, as causality is being assigned, one names a variable as it is used causally, then certain predictions with regard to formulation become possible. Consider the example shown in Fig. 5-10, which is a fragment of the graph of Fig. 5-6. We introduce variable names and causality at the same time, and observe the following:

(1) after step (b) nothing is known about f_8 and f_{10};
(2) after step (d) f_{10} is statically determined by f_2 and f_8 taken together.

Therefore, in the formulation procedure two effects are to be expected; $-f_2$, f_8, and f_{10} will be related in a static fashion; and the simple diagonal form of the field matrix **F** will be modified as the effects of the element I_{10} are distributed throughout the system relations. The reduction of equations for the graph is carried out completely in Fig. 5-11. The explicitly defined variables are the three flows on the I elements, the three effort sources, and one auxiliary variable. Note that the expression 4 for the auxiliary variable e_9 requires the use of the derivative of f_{10}. First the auxiliary variable e_9 is eliminated and the derivative terms are all shifted to the left side, into the **F** array (see Eq. 5.7 a, steps 5, 6, and 7). Then the static state variable relation 7 is differentiated, and the result used to elim-

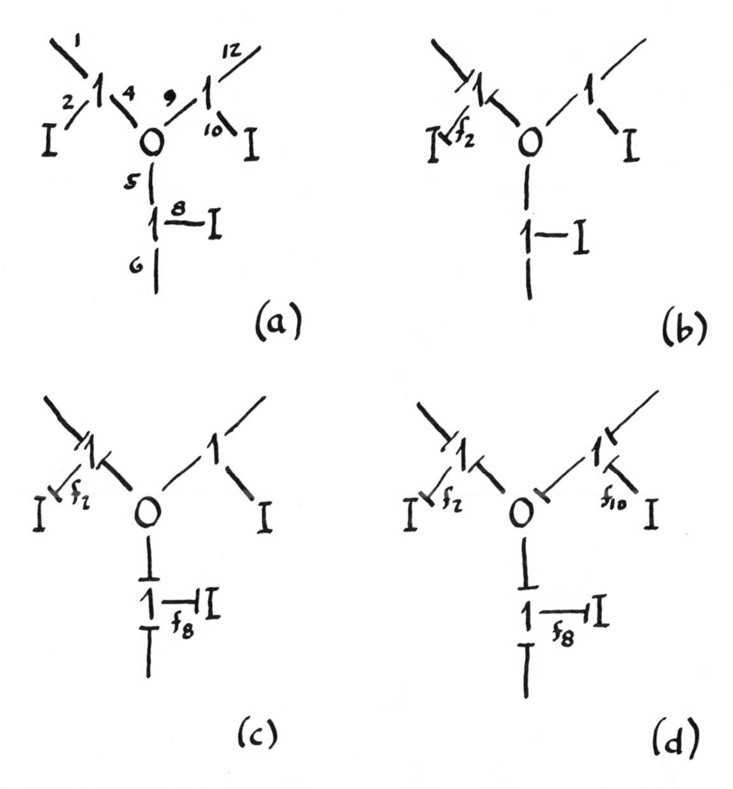

Fig. 5-10 **An illustration of the interaction between assigning causality and naming variables. (a) bonds labeled, (b) f_2 defined and extended, (c) f_8 defined and partially extended, (d) f_8 fully extended.**

inate Df_{10} from F. The final forms, 8 and 9, show how the effects of I_{10} are distributed over the remaining state variables. Inversion of **F** now requires slightly more effort than simply taking the reciprocal of each diagonal element. The largest subarray to be inverted directly, however, is smaller than the initial number of state variables in the largest field. The causal assignment procedure allows us to keep the **F** array diagonalized in subarrays, with each field localized around the diagonal. This fact is still useful, because the inverse of a diagonalized array has the same form with the diagonal arrays inverted. Thus,

$$\text{for } \mathbf{F} = \begin{bmatrix} \mathbf{F}_{11} & \mathbf{0} & \mathbf{0} \\ \mathbf{0} & \mathbf{F}_{22} & \mathbf{0} \\ \mathbf{0} & \mathbf{0} & \mathbf{F}_{23} \end{bmatrix}, \quad \mathbf{F}^{-1} = \begin{bmatrix} \mathbf{F}_{11}^{-1} & \mathbf{0} & \mathbf{0} \\ \mathbf{0} & \mathbf{F}_{22}^{-1} & \mathbf{0} \\ \mathbf{0} & \mathbf{0} & \mathbf{F}_{33}^{-1} \end{bmatrix},$$

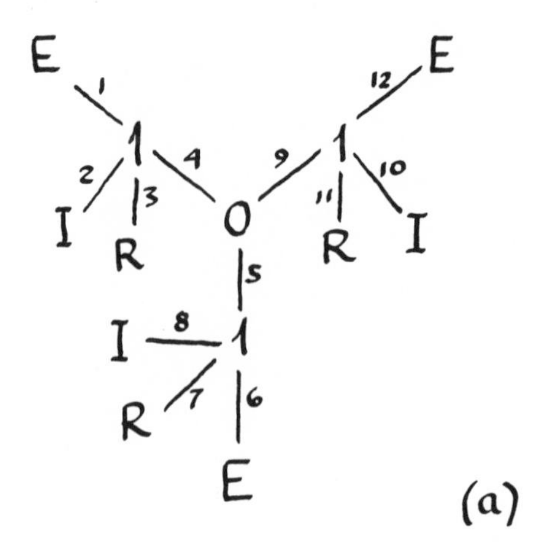

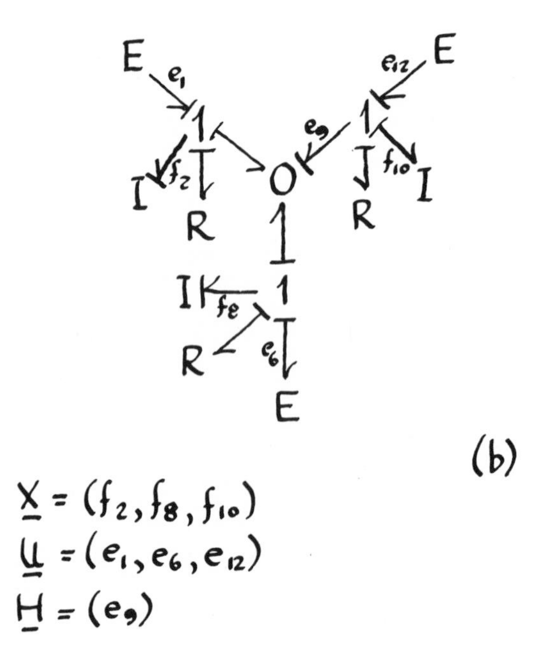

Fig. 5-11 Reduction of equations for a graph containing an I-field. (a) bonds labeled, (b) augmented graph,

$$
\begin{matrix} (1) \\ (2) \\ (3) \end{matrix}
\begin{bmatrix} I_2 \cdot Df_2 & 0 & 0 \\ 0 & I_8 \cdot Df_8 & 0 \\ 0 & 0 & 0 \end{bmatrix}
\begin{matrix} = \\ = \\ = \end{matrix}
\begin{bmatrix} -R_3 f_2 + 0 + 0 - e_9 \\ +0 - R_7 f_8 + 0 - e_9 \\ + f_2 + f_8 + f_{10} + 0 \end{bmatrix}
+
\begin{bmatrix} +e_1 \\ +e_6 \\ +0 \end{bmatrix}
$$

$$
(4) \qquad e_9 = R_{11} f_2 + R_{11} f_8 - I_{10} Df_{10} \quad + e_{12}
$$

Eliminate e_9, using (4) in (1) and (2).

$$
\begin{matrix} (5) \\ (6) \\ (7) \end{matrix}
\begin{bmatrix} I_2 \cdot Df_2 + 0 - I_{10} \cdot Df_{10} \\ 0 + I_8 Df_8 - I_{10} Df_{10} \\ 0 + 0 + 0 \end{bmatrix}
\begin{matrix} = \\ = \\ = \end{matrix}
\begin{bmatrix} -(R_3 + R_{11}) f_2 - R_{11} f_8 + 0 \\ - R_{11} f_2 - (R_7 + R_{11}) f_8 + 0 \\ f_2 + f_8 + f_{10} \end{bmatrix}
+
\begin{bmatrix} e_1 - e_{12} \\ e_6 - e_{12} \\ 0 \end{bmatrix}
$$

Eliminate f_{10}, using $0 = Df_2 + Df_8 + Df_{10}$.

$$
\begin{matrix} (8) \\ (9) \end{matrix}
\begin{bmatrix} (I_2 + I_{10}) Df_2 + I_{10} Df_8 \\ I_{10} Df_2 + (I_8 + I_{10}) Df_8 \end{bmatrix}
=
\begin{bmatrix} -(R_3 + R_{11}) f_2 - R_{11} f_8 \\ - R_{11} f_2 - (R_7 + R_{11}) f_8 \end{bmatrix}
+
\begin{bmatrix} e_1 - e_{12} \\ e_6 - e_{12} \end{bmatrix}
$$

(c)

(c) reduction of equations.

where $\mathbf{F}_{ii}$ are arrays. Even in a high-order state space (in which **F** is large) it is rare for a local field (e.g., $\mathbf{F}_{ii}$) to reach a high order. The same line of argument applies to the number of independent state variables for static, nonlinear fields, as indicated by causality. In this situation the number of simultaneous nonlinear algebraic equations to be satisfied (or solved) can be directly related to its corresponding field in each case. For example, if the I elements in the graph of Fig. 5-10 were nonlinear, there still would be two independent flows and a set of nonlinear relations governing the substitution and elimination of the third flow variable. Since the solution of simultaneous nonlinear algebraic equations is a very difficult topic to dis-

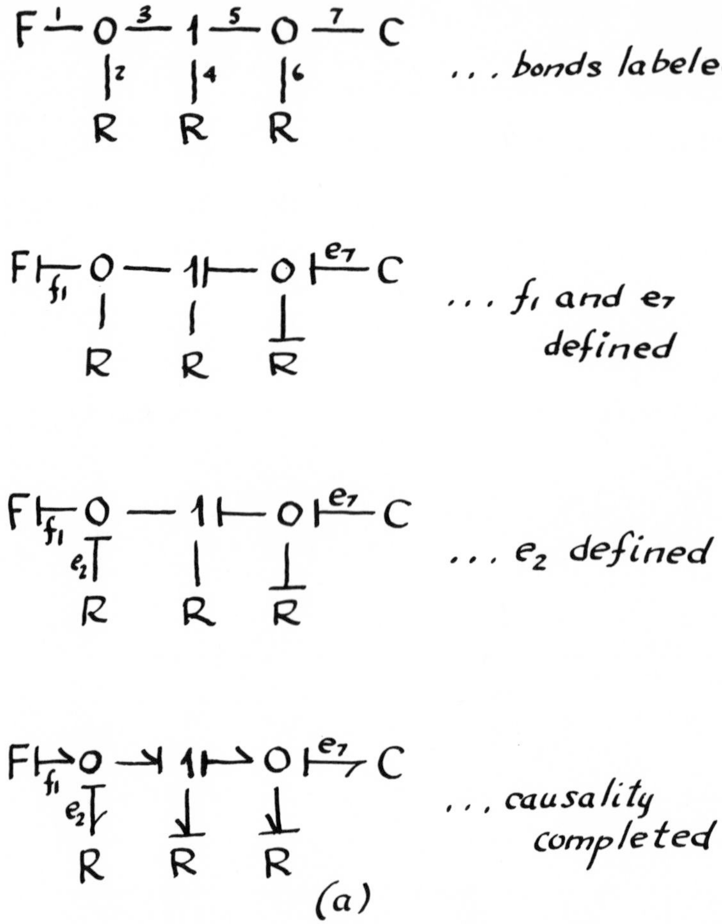

. . . bonds labeled

. . . f_1 and e_7 defined

. . . e_2 defined

. . . causality completed

(a)

Fig. 5-12 Reduction of equations for a graph containing an R-field. (a) augmented graph,

cuss with any generality, we shall not pursue such nonlinear systems further here.

As a second significant circumstance, consider the case in which all E, F, C, and I elements have had causality assigned but the graph is still not causally complete. Such a situation is illustrated in Fig. 5-12. Prior to the third step of Fig. 5-12(a), any R elements that were causally directed need not have been assigned explicit variables, because the input (and hence the output) variables were expressible directly in terms of the previously defined set. In the second step of Fig. 5-12(a) the state of R_6 has been defined by the state variable e_7; no temporary variable need be used for R_6. Neither R_2 nor R_4 has been causally defined as yet. Therefore, one of them must be used now. The third step shows the choice of e_2 and the implications

A first set of relations is

(1) $C_7 \cdot De_7 = -R_6^{-1} \cdot e_7 + R_4^{-1} \cdot (e_2 - e_7)$ ... using C_7.

(2) $e_2 = R_2 \cdot (f_1 - R_4^{-1} \cdot (e_2 - e_7))$ ... using R_2.

From (2) we find that

(3) $$e_2 = \frac{R_2}{R_2 + R_4} e_7 + \frac{R_2 R_4}{R_2 + R_4} f_7 .$$

Finally, eliminating e_2 from (1),

(4) $$C_7 \cdot De_7 = -\left(\frac{1}{R_6} + \frac{1}{R_2 + R_4}\right) e_7 + \left(\frac{R_2}{R_2 + R_4}\right) f_1 .$$

(b)

(b) reduction of equations.

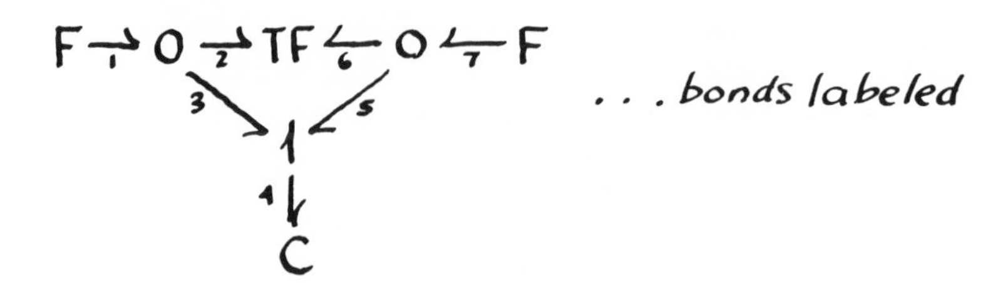

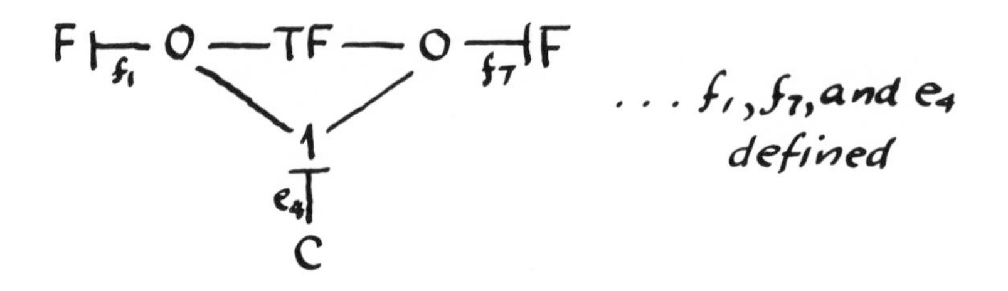

. . . f_3 defined

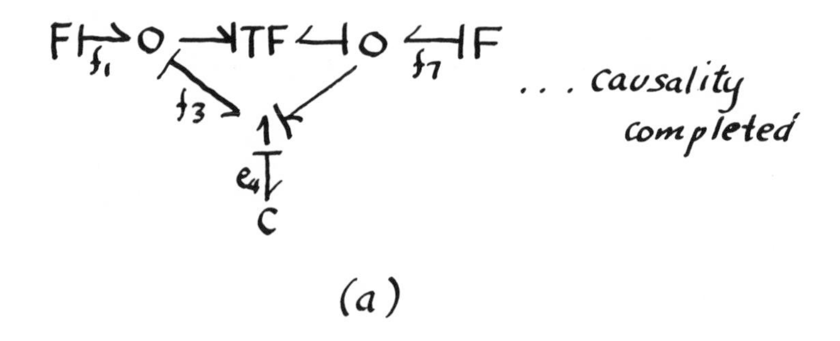

Fig. 5-13 Reduction of equations for a graph having a redundant structure. (a) augmented graph,

of that choice. Since we have not defined any extra variables beyond those indicated by causality, the system relations should be quite compact. It only remains to eliminate temporary variable e_2 (which depends upon itself, as shown in step 2 of Fig. 5-12(b)), to get to the form shown in step 4. In fact, the final relation should be divided through by C_7 to reach the desired form. The reader who wonders about the apparently arbitrary choice of e_2 is advised to try defining f_4 (or f_2 or e_4) after the second step in Fig. 5-12(a), and then use the standard formulation procedure. Relevant here is the discussion of strong and weak causal determination of 0- and 1-junctions. Once again we observe that the preceding discussion is applicable to nonlinear R-fields, but reduction becomes more difficult.

As a final case we study the example shown in Fig. 5-13 for a graph with a redundant structure. After the second step all E, F, C, and I sources of causality have been used (F_1, F_7, and C_4), but causality is not complete. Therefore we assume the causality for bond 3 as shown in the next step, and extend its implications, as indicated in the step following. From this point on relations are handled according to the usual procedure, resulting in

A first set of relations is

(1) $C_4 \cdot De_4 = f_3$

(2) $f_3 = f_1 - (-m(f_7 - f_3))$

These reduce to

(3) $C_4 \cdot De_4 = \frac{1}{1+m} f_1 + \frac{m}{1+m} f_7$

(b)

(b) reduction of equations.

Eq. 3 of Fig. 5-13(b). Again, the interested reader is advised to experiment with other auxiliary variables and causal choices on bonds 2, 3, 5, and 6. All formulations will eventually result in Eq. 3, of course.

It has been our purpose in this chapter to show how the systematic assignment and use of causality on a bond graph aids in the formulation and reduction of linear, and certain types of nonlinear, equations. The fact that one can start with an (acausal) physical model of a system in terms of a bond graph and convert that graph directly to a signal-directed (causal) computing diagram is unique to the bond graph representation. More conventional methods of obtaining computational or signal-directed representations are discussed in the next chapter.

References

1. R.J. Schwarz and B. Friedland, *Linear Systems,* McGraw-Hill Book Co., New York, 1965.
2. Julius T. Tou, *Modern Control Theory,* McGraw-Hill Book Co., New York, 1964.

6. BOND GRAPHS AND BLOCK DIAGRAMS, FLOW GRAPHS AND IMPEDANCE METHODS

Thus far we have discussed the representation of physical and engineering systems in terms of bond graphs, and considered procedures for generating equations from augmented bond graphs. In the first two sections of this chapter some relations between bond graphs and block diagrams, and between bond graphs and signal flow graphs, will be presented. The relations will be considered at the graphical level; no equations need appear in the discussion.

In Section 6.3 some development of impedance methods as applied to bond graphs for linear systems will be given, followed by a brief discussion of transfer functions. This section is not intended to be exhaustive; rather, it is suggestive of the approaches which can be taken.

The final section of the chapter presents techniques for the manipulation of linear 2-port transmission matrices, which occur quite commonly in the analysis of certain types of engineering systems.

6.1 Block diagrams

A principal motivation for generating a block diagram for a physical system comes from a desire to conduct an analog simulation of the transient response. It is frequently convenient to maintain the functional uniqueness of each of the physical parameters. This permits direct manipulation of the block diagram to effect corresponding changes in physical components or values.

On occasion the block diagram is used to present a system description in graphical terms which are mathematically explicit (Fig. 6-1). For this purpose the bond graph is to be preferred when the system is predominantly passive (i.e., composed of energetically coupled physical elements, rather than isolated signal-coupled "functional boxes"). The principal reason is that the bond graph inherently maintains the proper pairing of signals to give actual powers, whereas the same signal pairs are apt to be separated and somewhat dispersed in manipulating a block diagram.

In order to generate a block diagram that corresponds to a given bond graph we must do two things: augment the bond graph, and substitute signals and signal relations for the bonds and multiports, respectively. It is then customary to "tidy up" the resulting block diagram and label certain signals. In the following discussion it will be assumed that all bond graphs have been augmented.

Bond-signal equivalents

Substitution of signal pairs for bonds is a very simple matter. The causal bond indicates the sense of directedness of the effort signal and the flow signal simultaneously. It is most convenient in making the substitution to preserve the "effort signal above/left, flow signal below/right" convention that has been used in labeling variables previously. Thus, for bonds 1 and 2 between systems A and B, the following simple transformations may be made:

A —1—| B

becomes

A ⇄ B (upper arrow e_1 from A to B, lower arrow f_1 from B to A)

A (bond 2, causal stroke at A) B becomes A, B (arrow e_2 up toward A, arrow f_2 down toward B)

There is no provision for transferring sign information from the bond to the the signal pairs; this information will show up later, associated with signal relations.

Multiport-signal relation equivalents

Although there are a variety of ways in which augmented bond graph elements can be replaced by signal relations, Fig. 6-2 presents a set of standard

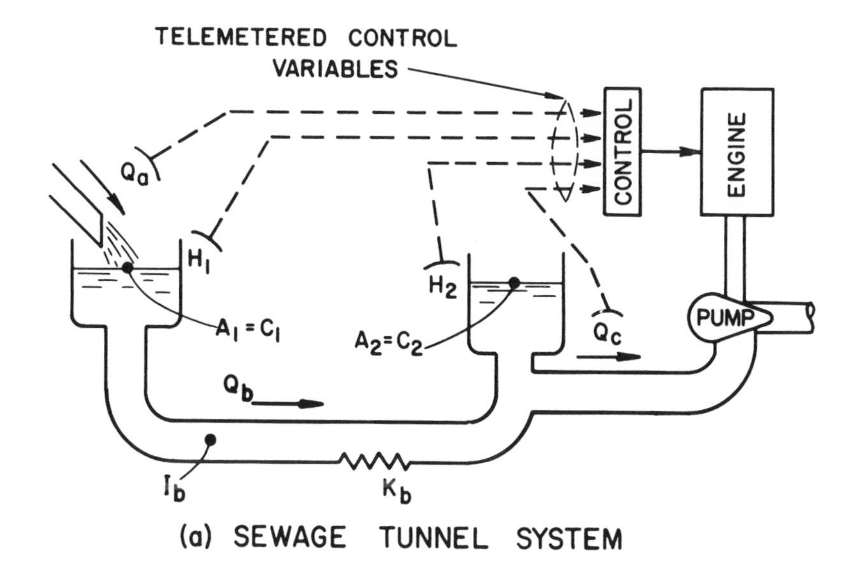

(a) SEWAGE TUNNEL SYSTEM

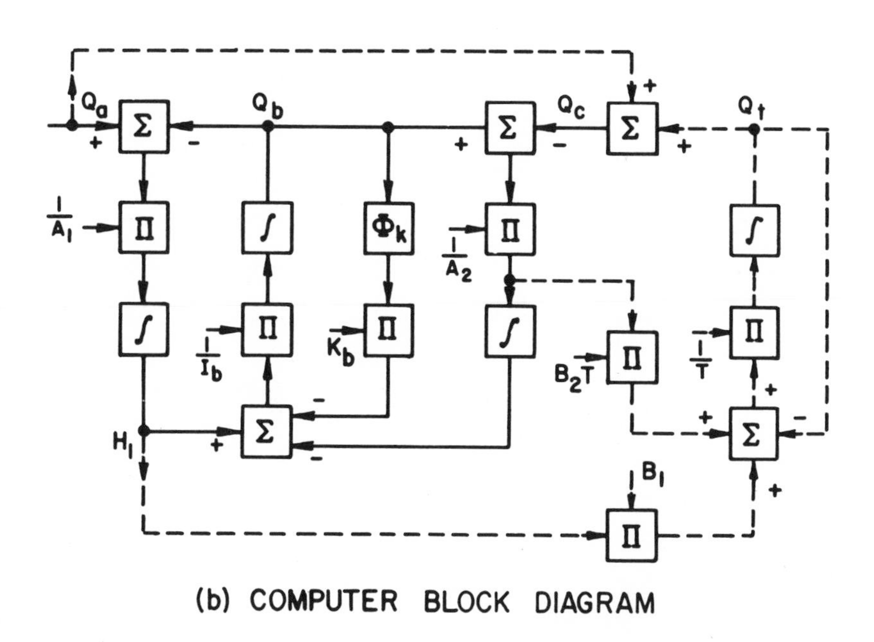

(b) COMPUTER BLOCK DIAGRAM

Fig. 6-1 Description of a physical system using a block diagram (taken from Ezekiel and Paynter, reference 6, reprinted by permission).

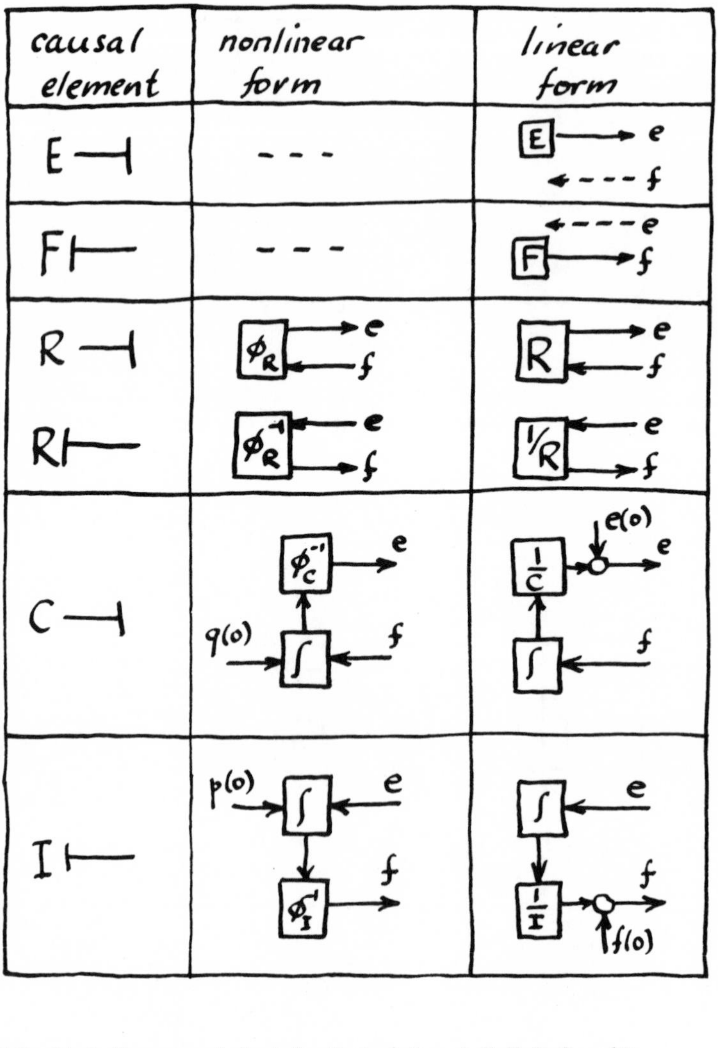

causal element	nonlinear form	linear form
E⊣	- - -	E, e, f
F⊢	- - -	e, F, f
R⊣	ϕ_R, e, f	R, e, f
R⊢	ϕ_R^{-1}, e, f	1/R, e, f
C⊣	ϕ_C^{-1}, e, q(0), ∫, f	$\frac{1}{C}$, e(0), e, ∫, f
I⊢	p(0), ∫, e, ϕ_I^{-1}, f	∫, e, $\frac{1}{I}$, f, f(0)

Fig. 6-2 Block diagram equivalents for the basic 1-ports E, F, R, C, and I.

equivalences we shall use. A detailed development for the capacitance element is

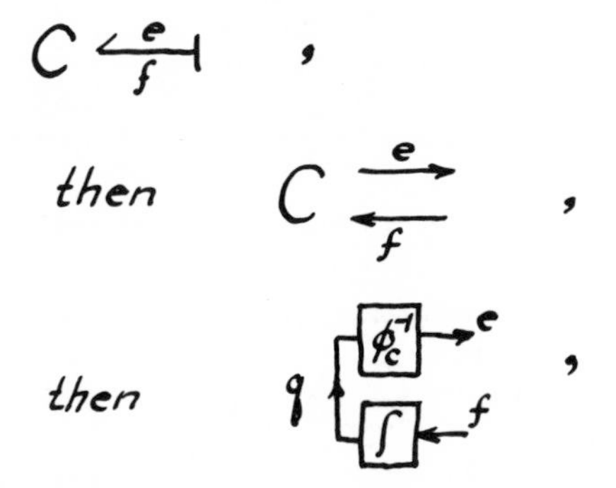

where ϕ_c is the compliance relation: $q = \phi_c(e)$.
The integration relation has been used; associated with the element is the initial value q(0) (e.g., spring displacement, capacitor charge, volume of liquid in a tank).

When the element is linear, another form is sometimes more convenient to use, which arises from interchanging the order of the operations; thus,

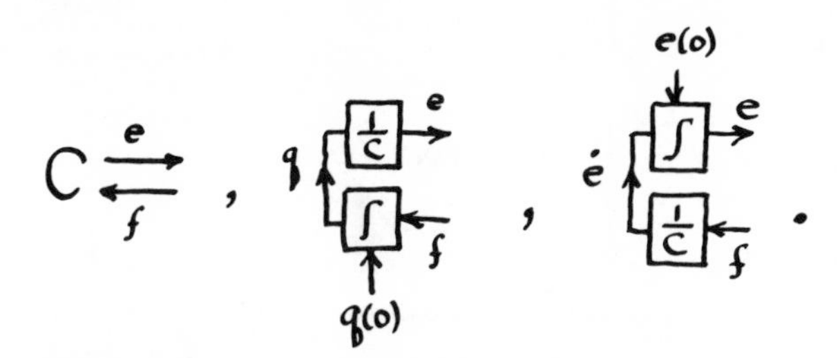

The last form is sometimes written, for brevity, as

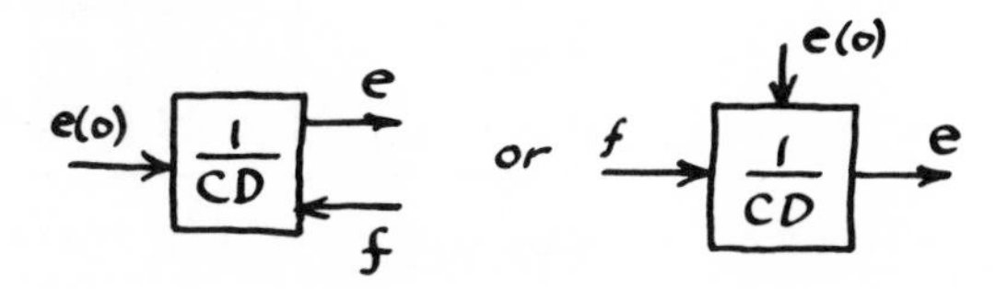

All of the 1-ports of Fig. 6-2 have been developed in a similar fashion. The reader need only become familiar with the substitution values of the elements to be well on his way to direct conversion of bond graphs to block diagrams.

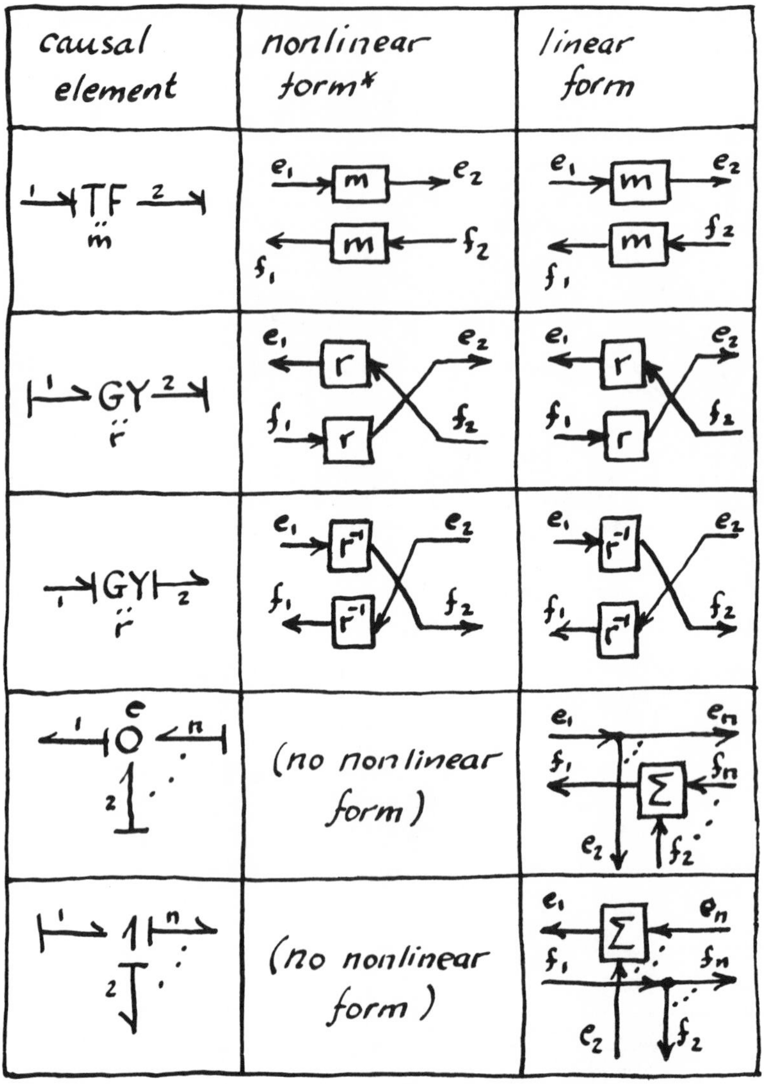

causal element	nonlinear form*	linear form
TF, m (ports 1, 2)	e_1, m, e_2; f_1, m, f_2	e_1, m, e_2; f_1, m, f_2
GY, r (ports 1, 2)	e_1, r, e_2; f_1, r, f_2	e_1, r, e_2; f_1, r, f_2
GY, r (ports 1, 2)	e_1, r^{-1}, e_2; f_1, r^{-1}, f_2	e_1, r^{-1}, e_2; f_1, r^{-1}, f_2
0, e (ports 1, 2, …, n)	(no nonlinear form)	e_1, e_n, f_1, Σ, f_n, e_2, f_2
1 (ports 1, 2, …, n)	(no nonlinear form)	e_1, Σ, e_n, f_1, f_n, e_2, f_2

* Moduli m and r can depend upon the state.

Fig. 6-3 Block diagram equivalents for the basic multiports GY, TF, 0, and 1.

Equivalences for the ideal 2-ports TF and GY are summarized in the first three rows of Fig. 6-3. The signal relations are straightforward. Note, however, that if the power directions were *opposed*, rather than through the element, one of the modulus signs would be the *negative* of the other. If the problem derives from a physical prototype, the choice of sign will be determined simply from the choice of physical variables.

As an example of development of the graph equivalents, consider the element $\vdash\!\xrightarrow{1}\underset{r}{GY}\xrightarrow{2}\!|$, which implies

$$\begin{array}{c} e_1 \leftarrow \\ f_1 \rightarrow \end{array} \underset{r}{GY} \begin{array}{c} \rightarrow e_2 \\ \leftarrow f_2 \end{array} ,$$

which in turn implies

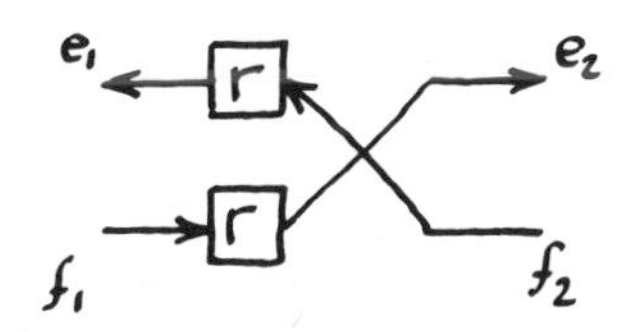

Whether the modulus r is constant or not, the block diagram form for the element is the same. Of course, use of a modulus r that is not practically realizable with analog or digital computing equipment is not likely to be helpful when the block diagram is put to actual use.

The final pair of equivalences, and perhaps the most interesting, is that for the ideal multiports 0 and 1, shown in the last two rows of Fig. 6-3. These equivalent are sometimes called the "spot-and-dot" convention, in which the spot is a summing relation and the dot a common signal relation. If one recalls the original definitions for the 0-junction (efforts are common; flows sum to zero), plus the influence of causality (selection of one effort as input and the corresponding flow as output), the block diagram relations will be apparent. A similar statement may be made for the 1-junction.

It sometimes happens that one has a set of data or equations for an n-port field. As discussed in previous sections, such a field may be treated in compatible fashion with the rest of the system. As an example of the treatment of such an element Fig. 6-4 gives two block diagram equivalents for a 2-port inertance field (e.g., a pair of coils with mutual inductance). In both cases the integration causality has been used. We generate the momenta (p_i) from the input efforts and operate on the p_i with appropriate static relations to get the output flows. The extension to n-ports for $n > 2$ should be apparent. Furthermore, the role played by the matrix representation for

Two-port I-field ...

Integration causality ...

Signal pairs ...

Nonlinear form ...

Linear form ...

Matrix form for linear 2-port ...

$$\begin{bmatrix} f_1 \\ f_2 \end{bmatrix} = \begin{bmatrix} F_{11} & F_{12} \\ F_{21} & F_{22} \end{bmatrix} \begin{bmatrix} p_1 \\ p_2 \end{bmatrix}$$

Fig. 6-4 Block diagram equivalents for a 2-port I-field.

a linear field (e.g., stiffness matrix for a C-field in mechanics should be obvious.

Bond graph to block diagram conversion

In converting a bond graph to a block diagram, there are three steps to follow:

(1) augment the bond graph;
(2) draw pairs of directed effort-flow signal pairs to replace the bonds;
(3) substitute the equivalent signal relations for the bond graph elements, as indicated in Figs. 6-2, 6-3, and 6-4.

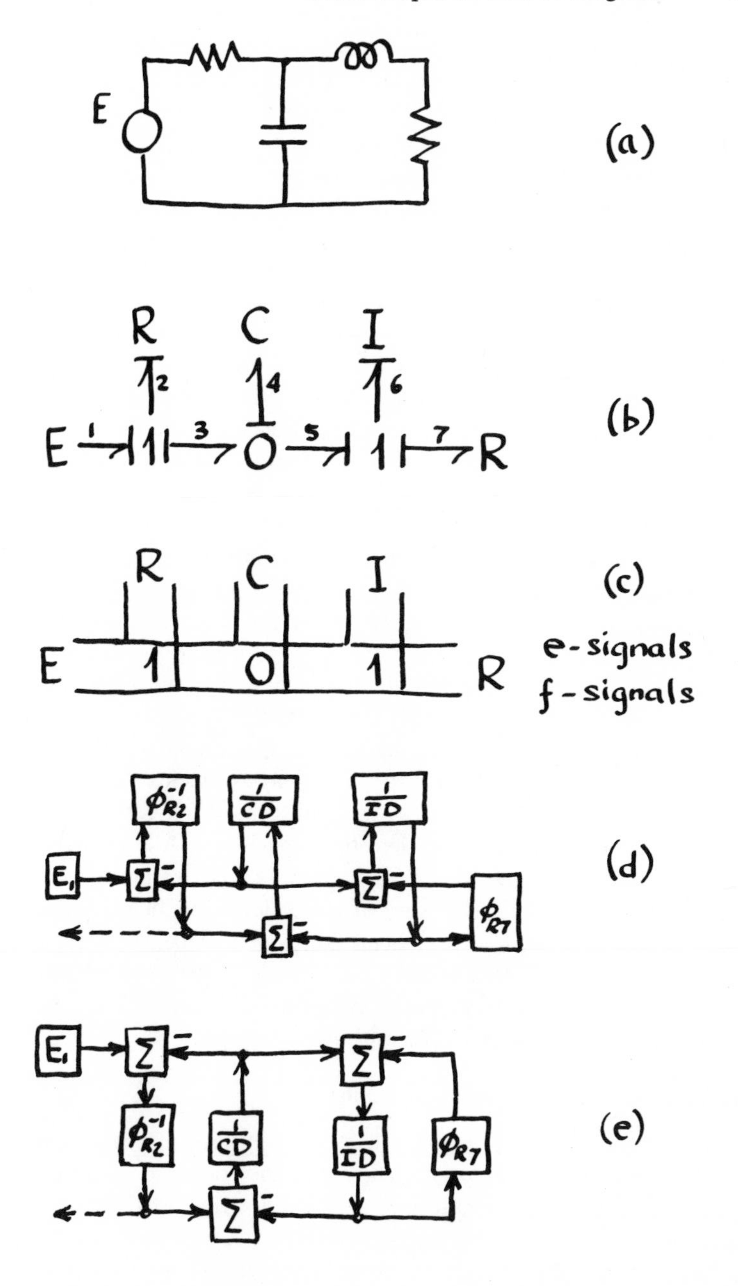

Fig. 6-5 Conversion of a bond graph to a block diagram–example 1. (a) electric circuit diagram, (b) augmented bond graph, (c) laying out signal lines, (d) substitution for bond graph elements, (e) rearrangement of block diagram.

The principal art of the conversion is in laying out the signal pair lines between which the relations are inserted. A few examples should give an indication of how the process goes. In Fig. 6-5 a simple electric circuit is converted to an augmented bond graph; then the bond graph is converted to a block diagram. No equations need be written.

A more complicated system, that of the pressure-controlled valve modeled in Fig. 4-19, is converted to a block diagram in Fig. 6-6. The diagram remains in a state suitable for connection to other subsystems or for experimental testing of the model under selected source-load conditions. For example, referring to Fig. 4-19, if it is reasonable to neglect the back force from the valve, the signal input labeled S_F can be omitted in connecting the pressure-controlled valve to the fluid valve in the line. Only if the initial model includes all the interactive coupling effects can one test assumptions that certain "back" effects are negligible. This is particularly important in hard-driven systems and when intuition runs low.

In this example, as in the one of Fig. 6-5, the first step is to replace each bond by the appropriate signal pairs, trying to anticipate "main lines" for the effort and flow signals. In Fig. 6-6(b), the 1-junction with four 1-port elements (C_2, R_l, R_c, and I) was replaced by four equivalent 1-junctions, with a single 1-port on each. The purpose was to make the direct conversion simpler. However, when the effort and flow lines are separated, as in step c, there is no need to use such a technique.

The general point of view in trying to form block diagrams that look like those in Figs. 6-5(e) and 6-6(c) is that the 1-port elements "go between" the effort line and the flow line. A junction occurs as a common dot on one signal line and a summer on the other signal line. A brief inspection of loops in the diagram shows that each loop has a negative product, as it should for local stability. This kind of inspection technique is useful in ensuring that the sign relations have been transferred properly. A final point to note in Fig. 6-6(c) is that each of the original 1-port physical entities has been preserved in isolation; it can be manipulated directly. The 2-port modulus m appears in two distinct places, however.

Bilateral block diagrams and bond graphs

On occasion it is of interest to construct (or try to construct) a bond graph equivalent from a block diagram. The art of the conversion procedure is in the association of signal pairs to give physical powers. At times this may require the insertion of additional simple relations, such as summations, that had been contracted into different form in the original generation of the block diagram. In general, unless the block diagram exists in bilateral signal form, the task of producing an equivalent bond graph with as few active bonds as possible is difficult.

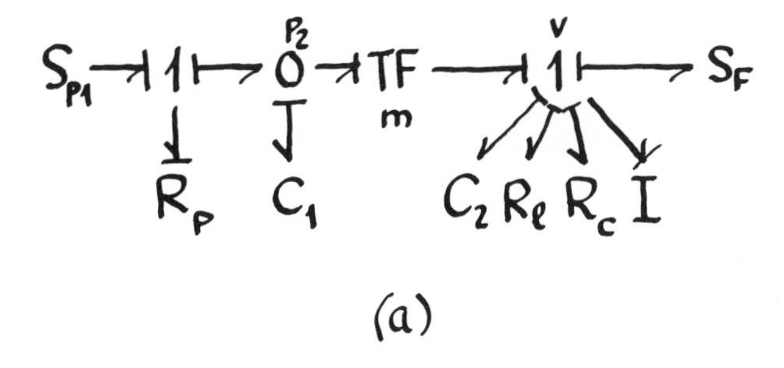

(a)

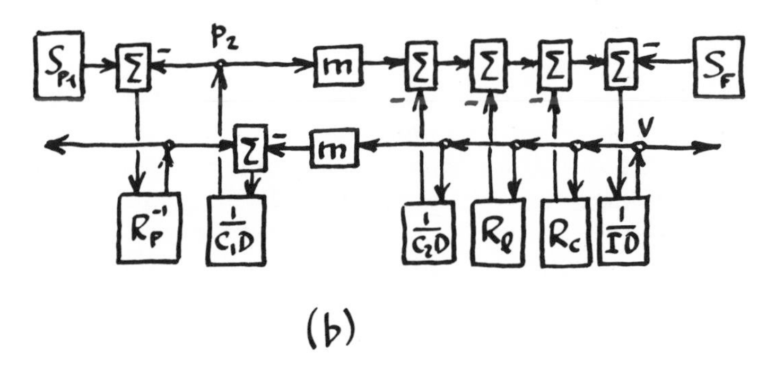

(b)

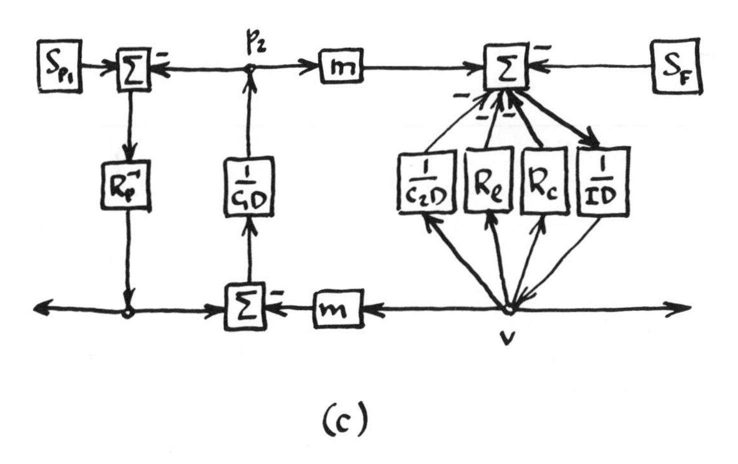

(c)

Fig. 6-6 Conversion of a bond graph to a block diagram–example 2. (a) augmented bond graph (rearranged slightly from Fig. 4-19), (b) block diagram for (a), (c) rearranged block diagram for (b).

An example of a predominantly bilateral block diagram is presented in Fig. 6-7(a). This is the same diagram as shown in Fig. 6-1(b). It has been rearranged slightly to make it conform more closely to the format of diagrams generated by use of the bond graph conversion procedure described previously. In particular, several extra summation relations have been added, to call attention to the "spot-sum" pairs that suggest 0- and 1-junctions. The top signal line, which has the Q signals, we shall call the *flow line,* and the bottom one we shall designate as the *effort line.* Each dashed line in Fig. 6-7(a) represents a control signal (i.e., a pure signal flow) and is conveniently represented by an active bond. The final bond graph may be related to the original physical representation of Fig. 6-1(a) for confirmation. The starred element (I^*, R_I^*, and R^*) correspond to passive realization of the required control functions; they do not necessarily (nor are they likely to) have passive elements as physical counterparts. The fact that they can be found in this case suggests the stabilizing nature of the controls.

Some indication of the type of insight required in converting a block diagram of typical format into a bond graph is given by the example of Fig. 6-8. In Fig. 6-8(a) a common linear second-order differential equation is represented by a block diagram; the variables used suggest a forced mass-spring-damper system. By focusing on, and separating, force and velocity signals, the arrangement of Fig. 6-8(b) may be obtained. From that point on conversion is quite direct. The result is given in Fig. 6-8(c). In this case the 0-junction is somewhat unnecessary, and could be omitted.

One point not considered here in detail is that, with respect to signs, the bond graph should have its bonds directed (i.e., power oriented) to reflect 1-port definitions and summation relations. For the passive 1-ports (C, I, R) this typically means power directed into the element; for the sources (S_F, S_E), power directed away from the element.

6.2 Signal flow graphs

Signal flow graphs, in which the signals are associated with nodes and the edges or branches represent relations, have proven to be extremely useful in linear system study. Although they have been in use for only about fifteen years (see references 1, 2, and 3), having been invented by Mason in 1953, their success seems in part a tribute to the power of graphical methods of manipulation. Since signal flow graphs are causal graphs we shall assume that any bond graph to be transformed into a flow graph has been augmented causally.

The conversion procedure, similar to the one described in the previous section for block diagrams, typically consists of three steps: replace each bond by its signal equivalents; replace each bond graph element by its equivalent relation(s); and simplify the resulting signal flow graph.

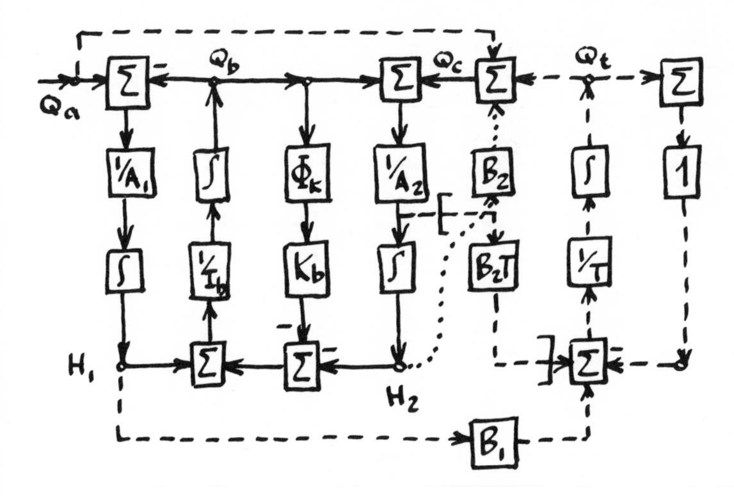

Note. Path B_2T from [to] replaced by path B_2, shown as ....> .

(a)

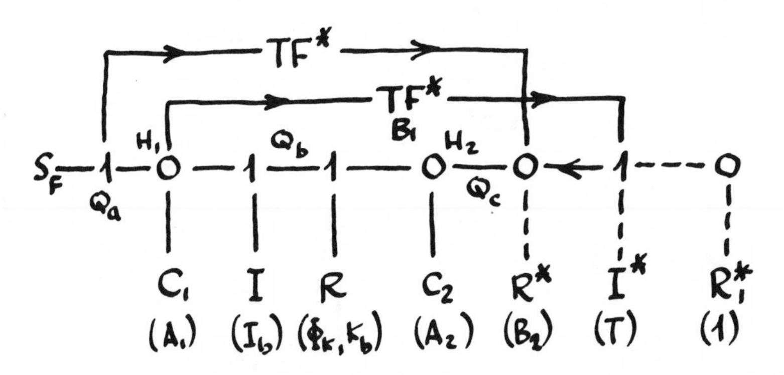

* elements associated with control functions.

(b)

Fig. 6-7 Bond graph equivalent to a block diagram—example 1. (a) block diagram (see also Fig. 6-1), (b) bond graph equivalent to (a).

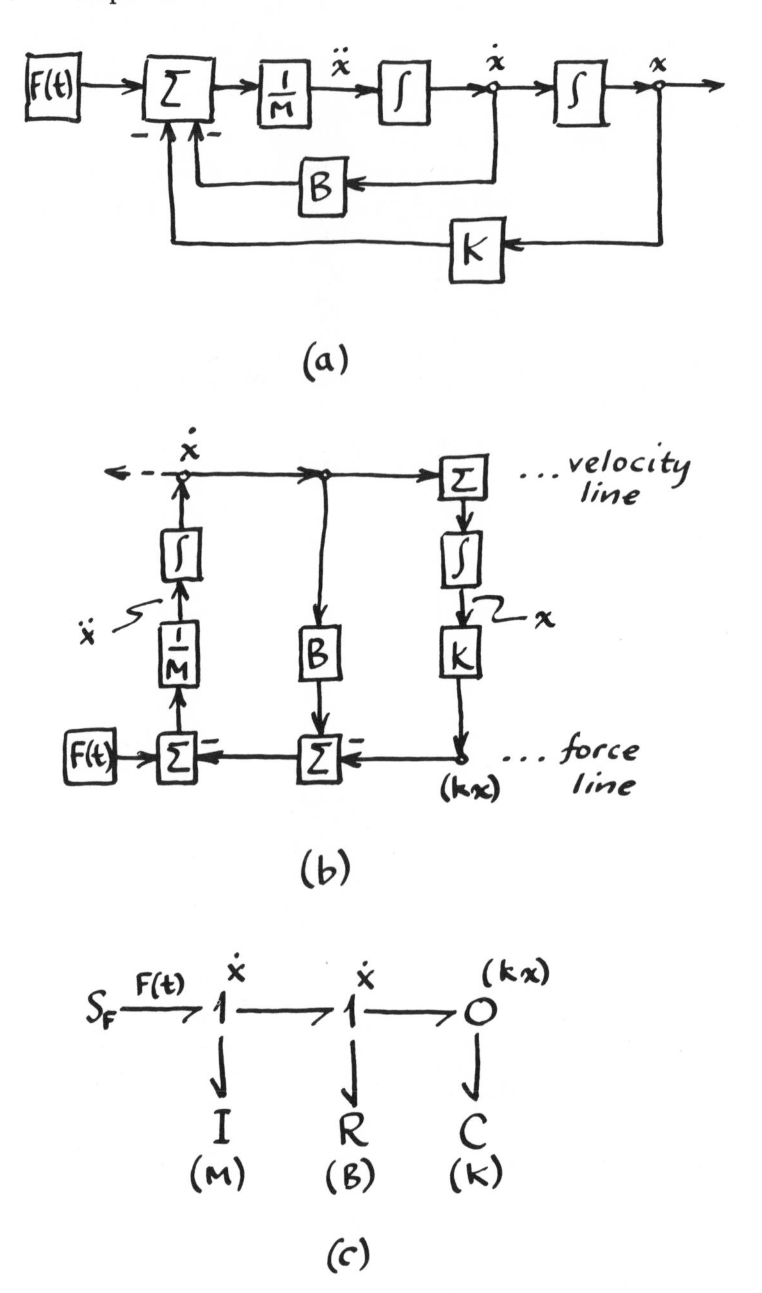

Fig. 6-8 **Bond graph equivalent to a common block diagram–example 2. (a) block diagram for $M\ddot{X} + B\dot{X} + KX = F(t)$, (b) block diagram of (a) rearranged to emphasize force and velocity signals, (c) bond graph equivalent to (b).**

Bond-signal equivalents

Associated with each bond is a pair of signals, which may be replaced by a pair of nodes corresponding to effort and flow, respectively. As before, one tries to maintain the "effort above or left, flow below or right" sense of order, which makes substituting relations simpler. For example, the following bonds have the equivalents shown.

This step does not produce any structural information; however, it defines the node set of the signal flow graph.

Bond graph element equivalents

Consider the 1-port linear capacitance element. In augmented integration form the flow is input and the effort is output. The pair of relations–integration, and scaling by the inverse capacitance value–are first represented together and then separated into two distinct operations. The intermediate variable is the displacement.

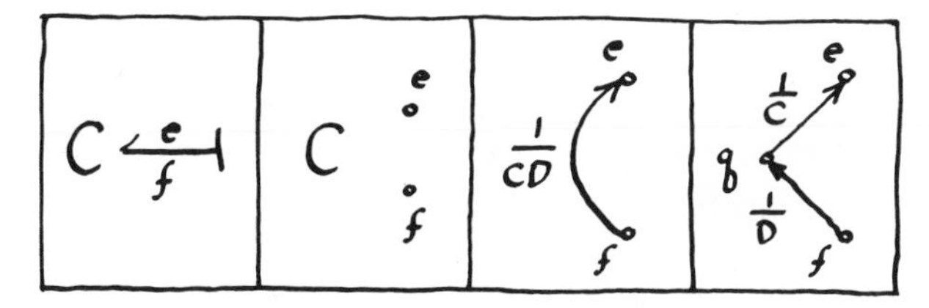

It is also easy to see from this graph the effect of reversing the input and output variables. In that case, taking e in and f out, it is necessary to reverse the relations on the branches.

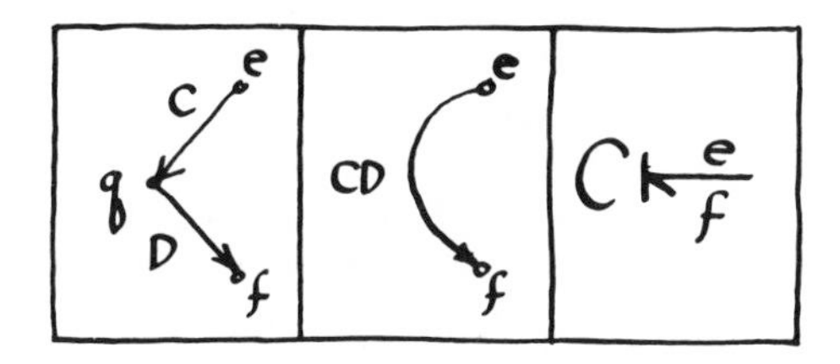

Figure 6-9(a) summarizes the equivalents for the basic linear 1-ports, while in Fig. 6-9(b) the 2-port elements GY and TF are represented by four nodes each, plus two relations. If the powers on a 2-port were opposed (i.e., both in or both out) then one of the relations in the corresponding signal flow graph would have a negative sign.

It is not until we come to Fig. 6-9(c) that an interesting aspect of signal flow graphs becomes evident. A look at the 0-junction shows that the common effort is represented by a single node (labeled e_1), which has two dependent nodes (e_2 and e_3). The +1 relations on the branches are omitted for simplicity. The summation relation of the flows is *implicit* in the f_1 node; this is a major limitation on the usefulness of signal flow graphs in treating certain classes of nonlinear systems. The particular relation described, the signs of which are derived from the power directions of the bond graph, is $f_1 = -f_2 + f_3$. A similar discussion of the 1-junction flow graph can be given.

Conversion of bond graphs to signal flow graphs

As with block diagrams, conversion can proceed very directly from the equivalents of Fig. 6-9. The principal art is in laying out the bond graph along a "main line," if possible, before substitution. A simple example is shown in Fig. 6-10; it is the same problem as that treated in Fig. 6-8, a forced mass-spring-dashpot system. Generation of a signal flow graph, as in the third part of Fig. 6-10, is straightforward, albeit a little tedious. However, remarkable simplification of the flow graph usually occurs next, when redundant nodes are joined and loops and paths are contracted. The last part of Fig. 6-10 shows a very tidy graph for the system. Notice that each loop has a negative product, as it should for this problem.

In Fig. 6-11 a more complicated bond graph with activity present is converted to a flow graph. It is a model of the integrator circuit shown. The first step is to replace the bonds by node pairs; this is done in the second part of Fig. 6-11, where the bonds are left in outline form to help in identifying correspondences. In the same part the relations are "strung in" between the signal nodes. Note that all +1 operators have again been omitted for visual clarity. Observe that the active TF requires only one relation. In the next part most of the common nodes have been joined, and the currents that do not influence the circuit behavior have been left out. At this stage, information about the current drawn from the amplifier is lost. Finally, a simplified version of the integrator circuit is presented as a signal flow flow graph. The key variables are e_i, e_o, e, and a variable x representing a partial sum of voltage $(e_i - e)$. This graph may be converted very easily to

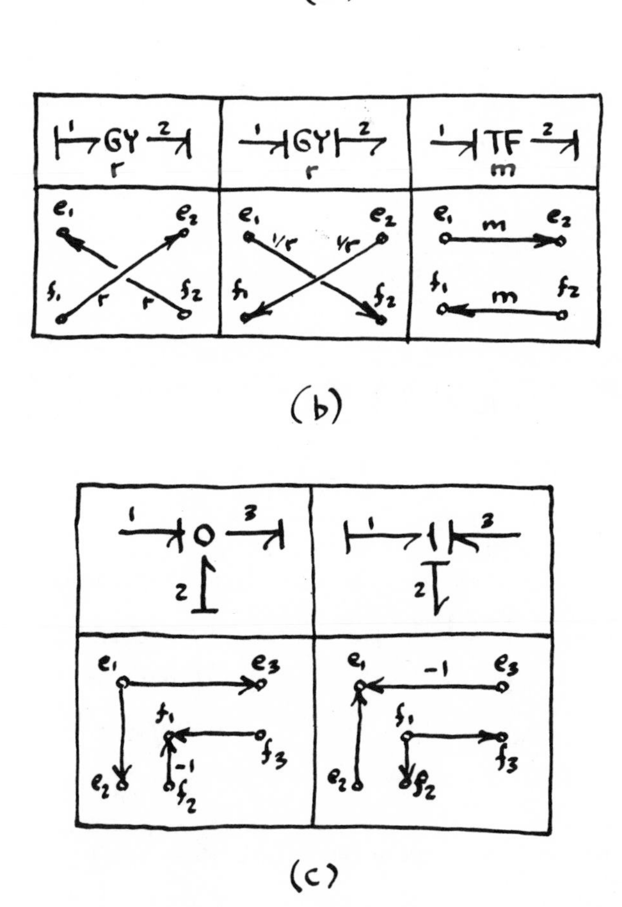

Fig. 6-9 Signal flow graph equivalents for some bond graph elements. (a) C, I, R, E, and F equivalents, (b) GY and TF equivalents, (c) 0-junction and 1-junction equivalents.

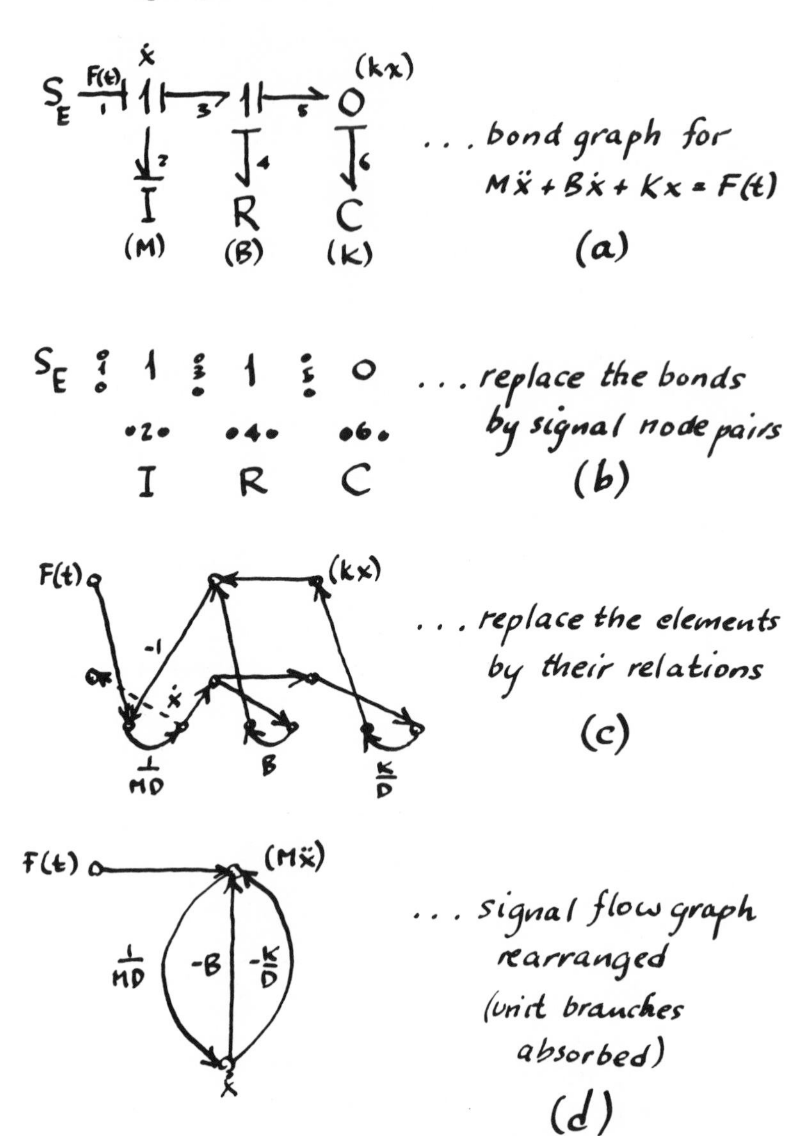

Fig. 6-10 Conversion of a bond graph to a signal flow graph—example 1.

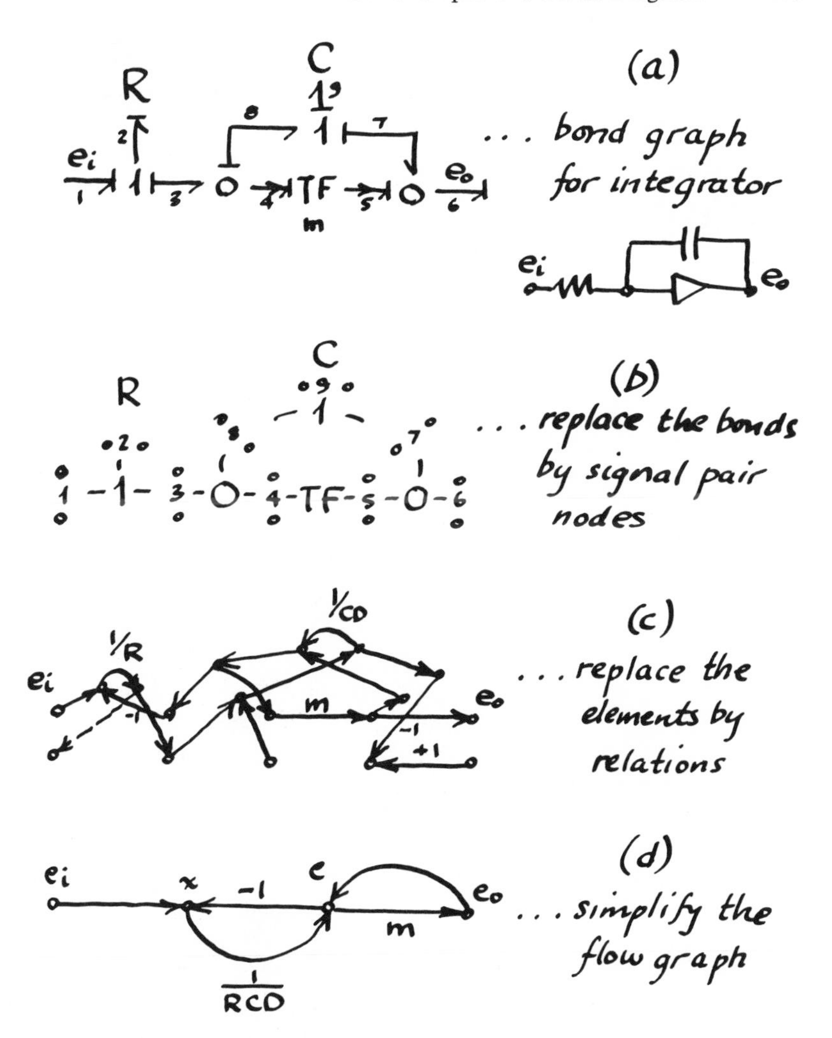

Fig. 6-11 Conversion of a bond graph to a signal flow graph–example 2.

equations and solved for e_o/e_i, as is done below. Alternatively, signal flow graph procedures may be employed directly, to aid in the reduction.

The equations are

$$e_o = me \tag{6.1}$$

$$e = e_o + \frac{1}{RCD}x \tag{6.2}$$

$$x = e_i - e \tag{6.3}$$

and their combination and partial solution gives

$$\frac{e_o}{m} = e_o + \frac{1}{RCD}e_i - \frac{1}{RCD}\frac{e_o}{m} \tag{6.4}$$

If $m \gg 1$, Eq. 6.4 yields the following (approximate) relation

$$e_o = -\frac{1}{RCD}e_i, \tag{6.5}$$

which is the integration relation for which the circuit was designed.

Bilateral flow graphs

Although "bilateral" signal flow graphs are sometimes found in which the nodes are paired to show powers, no extensive discussion will be given here of the conversion of such graphs to bond graphs. Any "method" for such a conversion contains a large proportion of art, tempered by a slight idea of what to look for in the signal flow graph format.

Figure 6-12 presents an example of a "bilateral" flow graph. That is, the efforts and the flows have been arranged in lines, paired to indicate powers. In Fig. 6-12(a) the upper line contains five effort nodes, and the lower line six flow signals. All +1 operators are implicit in the graph; such edges are unlabeled. In Fig. 6-12(b) a bond graph corresponding to the flow graph is shown. The key part of the conversion is associating an effort node and a flow node, such that one of them has one input (common signal) and the other node one output and possibly several inputs (summation relation). When such a pair has been identified, the nodes can be replaced by a 0- or 1-junction. For the reader interested in pursuing the example further, Fig. 6-12(c) gives an electric circuit corresponding to the graphs of Figs. 6-12(a) and (b).

6.3 Impedance methods

The impedance concept arises in the attempt to extend the (simple) form of Ohm's law, $v = R \cdot i$, to include a broader class of systems. In this section

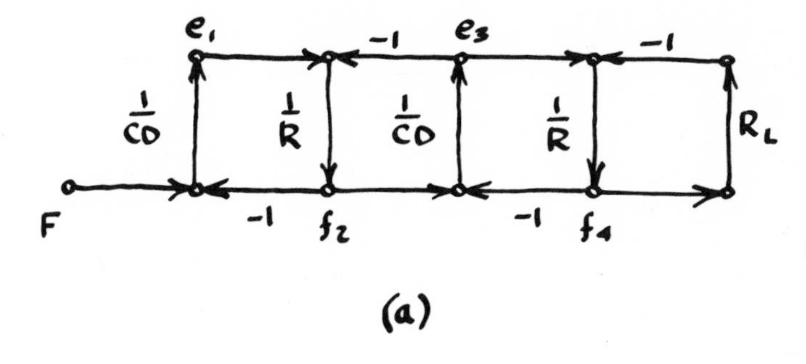

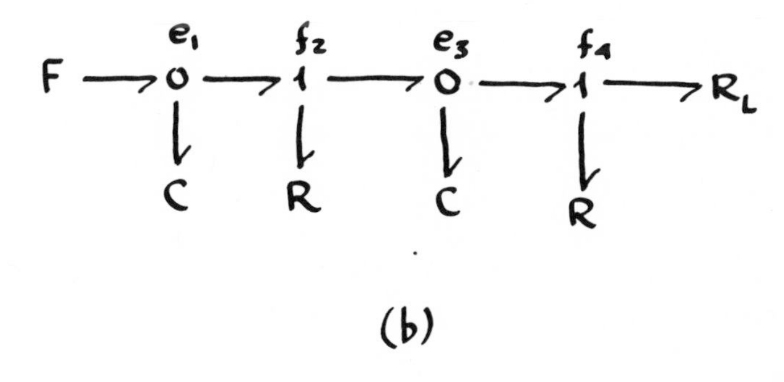

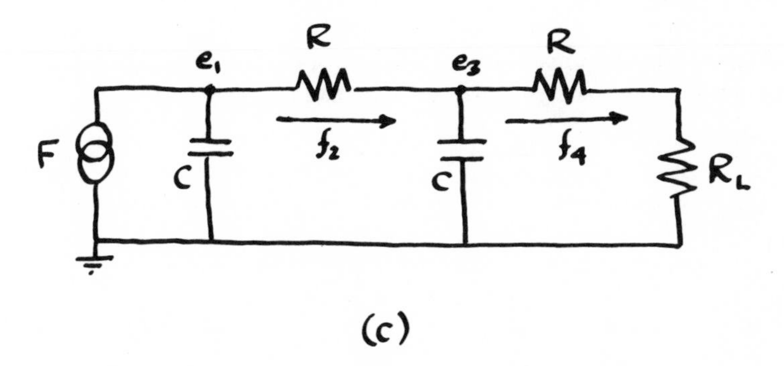

Fig. 6-12 Conversion of a signal flow graph to a bond graph. (a) a "bilateral" signal flow graph, (b) a bond graph equivalent to (a), (c) an electric circuit equivalent to (b).

we shall be concerned with linear systems that have constant parameters for all elements. Any 1-port then has an (input) impedance defined in either of the two reciprocal forms

$$e = Z(D) \cdot f \qquad \text{or} \qquad f = Y(D) \cdot e,$$

where D is the operator d/dt, Z the *impedance,* and Y the *admittance.* Since bond graphs are symmetrical in treatment of e and f, they are also symmetrical with respect to Z and Y; both forms will occur frequently and both are useful to us. It is common practice to impose test input signals of the form $e^{j\omega t}$ on linear systems. This type of input leads to the characterization of impedances by the complex quantities $Z(j\omega)$ and $Y(j\omega)$. For a given frequency ω the impedance is a complex number; it is often expressed as a magnitude and phase angle.

In this section we shall consider the conversion of bond graphs to impedance graphs, in which all dynamic elements have been transformed to equivalent impedance form. Then methods useful for finding 1-port and 2-port impedance operators will be discussed, followed by some comments on the use of A and B matrices for evaluating such operators. The word 'impedance' will be used here in two senses: the specific ratio of an effort to a flow at a single port, and a more general ratio of any pair of port variables.

Impedance values of standard elements

In Fig. 6-13(a) a tabulation of impedances and related operators for the 1-port elements C, I, and R is given. Provided the power is always directed *into* the element, the signs of relations are valid as given. Considering that impedances are typically thought of as generalized resistances, "power in" is a natural convention and will be assumed throughout this chapter.

In Fig. 6-13(b) the impedance effects of the ideal 2-ports GY and TF are summarized. The first result may be demonstrated as follows:

$$\vdash \xrightarrow{a} \underset{r}{GY} \xrightarrow{b} \dashv S$$

$$e_a = r f_b, \tag{6.6}$$

$$f_b = Y_s e_b, \tag{6.7}$$

$$e_b = r f_a, \tag{6.8}$$

$$Z_a \equiv e_a/f_a = \frac{r \cdot (Y_S(r \cdot f_a))}{f_a} = r^2 Y_S. \tag{6.9}$$

element	$Z(D)$	$Y(D)$	$Z(j\omega)$	$Y(j\omega)$
C ⟵	$\frac{1}{CD}$	CD	$\frac{1}{j\omega C}$	$j\omega C$
I ⟵	ID	$\frac{1}{ID}$	$j\omega I$	$\frac{1}{j\omega I}$
R ⟵	R	$\frac{1}{R}$	R	$\frac{1}{R}$

(a)

element	impedance	admittance
$\xrightarrow{1}$ GY $\xrightarrow{2}$ S (r)	$Z_1 = r^2 Y_s$	$Y_1 = \frac{1}{r^2} Z_s$
$\xrightarrow{1}$ TF $\xrightarrow{2}$ S (1:m)	$Z_1 = m^2 Z_s$	$Y_1 = \frac{1}{m^2} Y_s$

(b)

Fig. 6-13 Impedance operators for some bond graph elements. (a) operators for C, I, and R, (b) impedance effects of GY and TF.

Thus the gyrator inverts the impedance/admittance operator, and scales by the square of the modulus. The other results of Fig. 6-13 may be demonstrated in a similar fashion.

1-port impedances

In using a bond graph to aid in finding a 1-port impedance operator for a system, a procedure similar to the systematic analysis method given in Chapter 5 may be employed. The method is based on the idea that each 1-port element (C, I, R), when replaced by its impedance operator, becomes indifferent to the causality assigned it. This fact may be exploited by defining intermediate variables carefully while assigning causality to the *impedance graph* (i.e., a bond graph whose 1-ports are impedances and sources).

Basically, the procedure is to define as few 1-port variables as possible causally, to extend the causality implied by each variable as previously discussed, and to formulate a set of linear algebraic equations in terms of this set of variables. Powers should be directed into all 1-port impedances and through (i.e., in and out of) all two-ports (GY and TF). All other power choices are arbitrary.

Figs. 6-14, 6-15, and 6-16 present three examples, each being demonstrated in some detail. The reader may notice that Z and Y operators are freely mixed. Also, the naming of variables as shown keeps the number of simultaneous equations to a minimum, simplifying the task of combining them. The causality chosen for the over-all impedance graph determines whether an equivalent Z or Y is sought. (There are degenerate systems for which Z may exist but Y not, and conversely. These are not common physically and will not be discussed here.)

2-port transfer functions

The methods employed in the preceding section, based on the impedance graph, generalize directly to the 2-port case. There are *four* port variables for a 2-port, shown, in their various input-output forms, in Fig. 6-17(a). We shall return to these forms and discuss their treatment using matrices in Section 6.4. The methods discussed below will prove useful in studying systems such as that shown in Fig. 6-17(b), which depicts a bond graph representation of the circuit of Fig. 1-1.

The only difference between 2-port and 1-port methods is that *two* causalities must be imposed on a 2-port to indicate the desired ratio. The input variable not associated with the required ratio may be taken as zero, since we are dealing with linear systems. Consider the problem presented in

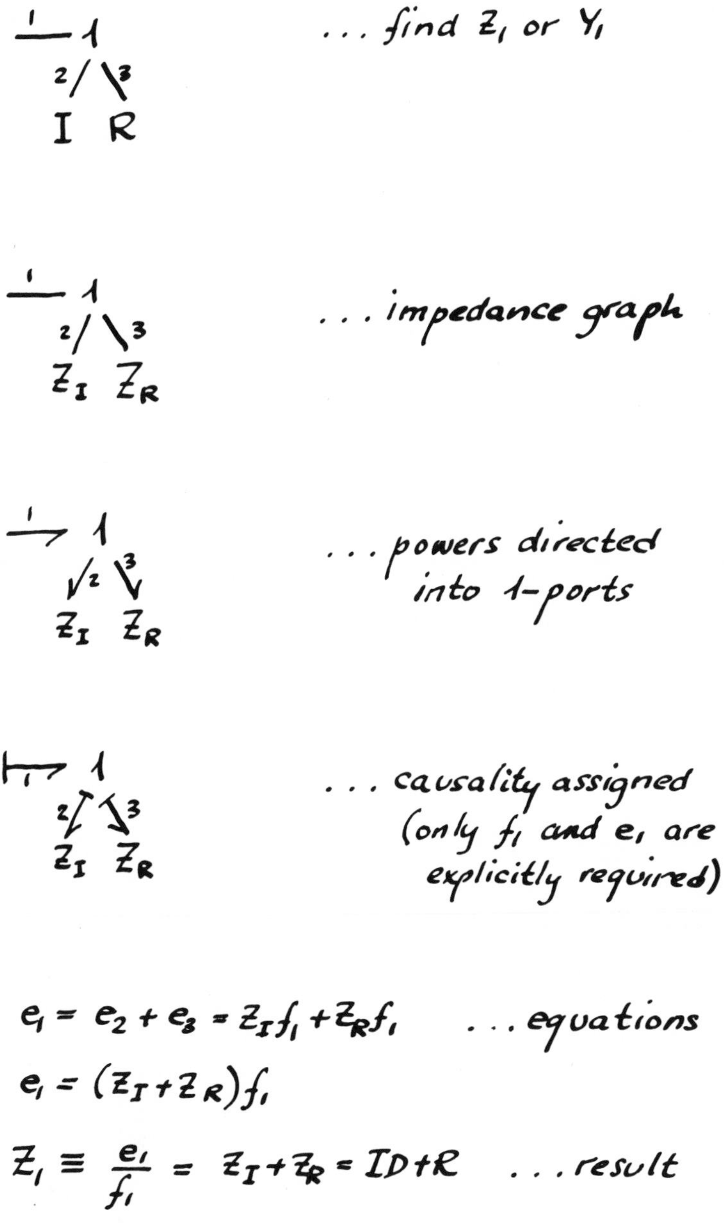

$\overset{1}{—}\, 1$; $2 / \backslash 3$; I R ... find Z_1 or Y_1

$\overset{1}{—}\, 1$; $2 / \backslash 3$; Z_I Z_R ... impedance graph

$\overset{1}{\rightharpoonup}\, 1$; $\swarrow 2 \searrow 3$; Z_I Z_R ... powers directed into 1-ports

$\vdash_1 \rightharpoonup 1$; $2 \swarrow \searrow 3$; Z_I Z_R ... causality assigned (only f_1 and e_1 are explicitly required)

$e_1 = e_2 + e_3 = Z_I f_1 + Z_R f_1$ ... equations

$e_1 = (Z_I + Z_R) f_1$

$Z_1 \equiv \frac{e_1}{f_1} = Z_I + Z_R = ID + R$ ... result

Fig. 6-14 Finding an equivalent 1-port impedance operator—example 1.

```
e0
—— 0 —— GY —— 0 —— Z3        ... find Z0 or Y0
f0  |     r     |
    Z1          Z2
```

```
—⇀ 0 —⇀ GY —⇀ 0 —⇀ Z3         ... powers
   ↓     r     ↓                  directed
   Z1          Z2
```

```
e0
——⇀| 0 —⇀|GY|—⇀ 0 —⇀ Z3       ... e0 defined
f0   ↓      r     ↓               as input
     Z1           Z2
```

```
e0
——⇀| 0 —⇀|GY|—⇀ 0 —⇀| Z3      ... e2 defined
f0   ↓      r   e2 ↓              (causality
     Z1            Z2              completed)
```

$$e_2 = Z_2\left(\frac{1}{r}e_0 - Y_3 e_2\right)$$

... equations

$$f_0 = Y_1 e_0 + \frac{1}{r} e_2$$

$$Y_0 \equiv \frac{f_0}{e_0} = Y_1 + \frac{1}{r^2(Y_2+Y_3)}$$

... result

Fig. 6-15 Finding an equivalent 1-port impedance operator—example 2.

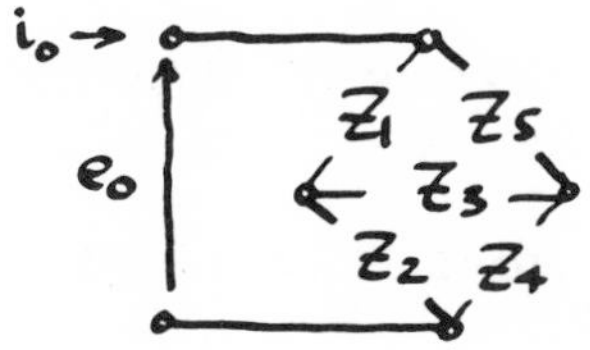

. . . Wheatstone bridge circuit (find Z_0 or Y_0)

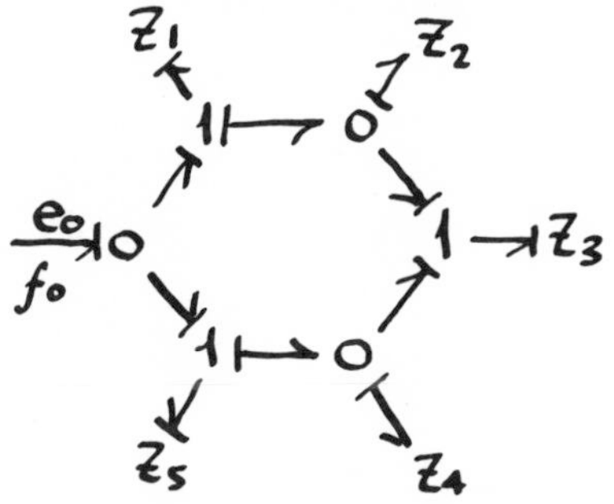

. . . bond graph with e_0, e_2, and e_4 defined (f_0 is output)

$$f_0 = f_1 + f_5 = Y_1(e_0 - e_2) + Y_5(e_0 - e_4) \quad \text{. . . equations}$$

$$e_2 = Z_2(f_1 - f_3) = Z_2[Y_1(e_0 - e_2) - Y_3(e_2 + e_4)]$$

$$e_4 = Z_4(f_5 - f_3) = Z_4[Y_5(e_0 - e_4) - Y_3(e_2 + e_4)]$$

For the case where $Y_1 = Y_2 = Y_4 = Y_5 = Y$, and $Y_3 = Y^*$,

$$Y_0 \equiv \frac{f_0}{e_0} = \frac{Y(Y + 2Y^*)}{(Y + Y^*)} \quad \text{. . . result}$$

Fig. 6-16 Equivalent input impedance for a Wheatstone bridge structure.

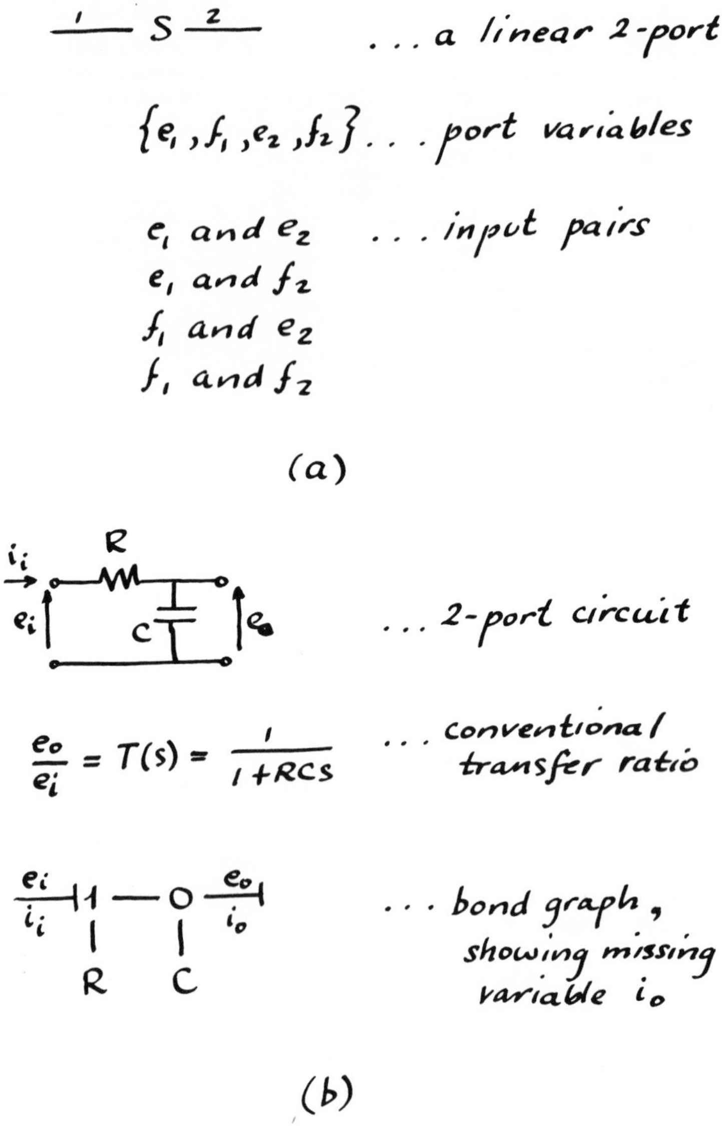

$\overset{1}{—}S\overset{2}{—}$ . . . a linear 2-port

$\{e_1, f_1, e_2, f_2\}$ . . . port variables

e_1 and e_2 . . . input pairs
e_1 and f_2
f_1 and e_2
f_1 and f_2

(a)

. . . 2-port circuit

$$\frac{e_o}{e_i} = T(s) = \frac{1}{1+RCs}$$ . . . conventional transfer ratio

. . . bond graph, showing missing variable i_o

(b)

Fig. 6-17 Port variables for linear 2-ports. (a) causal port variable pairs, (b) loading considerations.

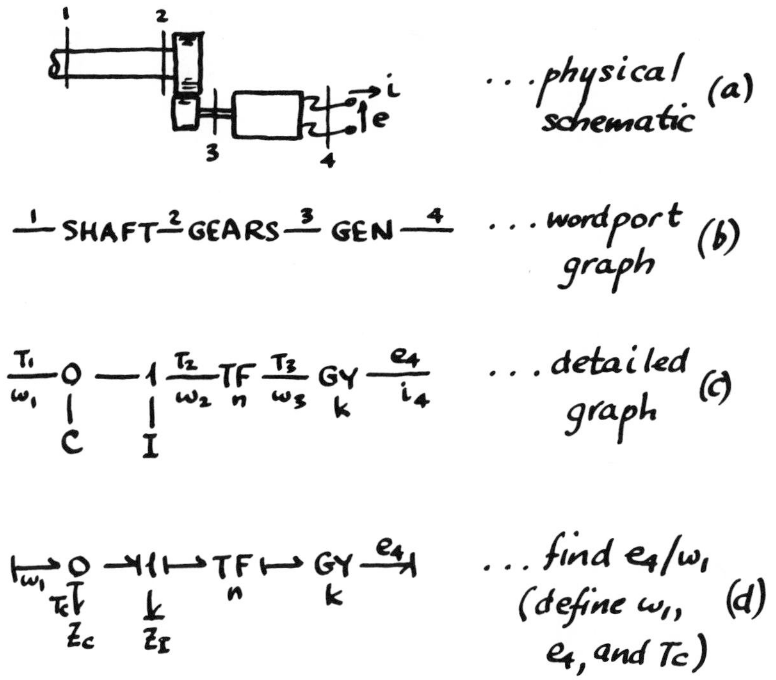
1
2
3
4
i
e
... physical schematic (a)
1 SHAFT 2 GEARS 3 GEN 4
... wordport graph (b)
T1 ω1 0 1 T2 ω2 TF n T3 ω3 GY k e4 i4
C
I
... detailed graph (c)
ω1 0 1 TF n GY k e4
Tc Zc
ZI
... find e4/ω1 (define ω1, e4, and Tc) (d)

$$(1)\quad e_4 = k[n(Y_I(T_c - 0))] = knY_I T_c$$

(set $i_4 = 0$) (e)

$$(2)\quad T_c = Z_c[\omega_1 - Y_I(T_c - 0)] = Z_c(\omega_1 - Y_I T_c)$$

Eliminating T_c,

$$(3)\quad \frac{e_4}{\omega_1} = \frac{kn}{1 + Z_I Y_c} = \frac{kn}{1 + ICD^2}$$

Fig. 6-18 Finding a 2-port transfer ratio.

Fig. 6-18, in which we seek a transfer ratio between the angular velocity of the shaft and the output voltage. Figure 6-18(b) displays an engineering multiport model in which the components are delineated by their port variables; each component is then represented by a mathematical model. In Figs. 6-18(c) and (d) an augmented impedance graph is developed. The defined (or explicit) variables are ω_1, e_4, and T_c. The first two are required as part of the problem statement; T_c will prove useful in writing the relations. The equations are developed in Fig. 6-18(e); one is written for e_4 (the output), and another for T_c (an intermediate variable). Notice the zero, shown explicitly, which occurs because i_4 was taken as zero. In fact, one can activate the graph to indicate the consequences of setting various sources to zero; some saving of effort in formulating equations will result. The final equation gives the desired ratio in terms of the four system parameters k, n, I, and C.

If more than one transfer ratio is to be found, an efficient technique is to develop the several ratios by formulating the equations once, keeping all inputs active (i.e., nonzero). Then each particular ratio may be found by setting all but one input to zero.

Direct manipulation of the state space format

Suppose the standard state space formulation for a linear system is available so that we have $D\mathbf{X} = \mathbf{AX} + \mathbf{BU}$. If the desired transfer ratio is x_i/u_j, the following procedure obtains the operator in several simple steps:

(1) Set all elements of $\mathbf{U}$ except u_j to zero; the forcing array becomes a column vector, $\mathbf{B}_j u_j$.

(2) Evaluate the (operator) determinant of $(\mathbf{I}D - \mathbf{A})$;

$$\Delta(D) \equiv |\mathbf{I}D - \mathbf{A}|.$$

(3) Evaluate the (operator) determinant of the array $(\mathbf{I}D - \mathbf{A})^{(i)}$, in which column i of $(\mathbf{I}D - \mathbf{A})$ is replaced by $\mathbf{B}_j$; call it N(D);

$$N(D) \equiv |(\mathbf{I}D - \mathbf{A})^{(i)}|.$$

(4) The desired ratio is given by (see, for example, reference 4)

$$\frac{x_i}{u_j} = \frac{N(D)}{\Delta(D)} .$$

An example of the use of this procedure is given in Fig. 6-19, in which a voltage transfer ratio is computed. Figs. 6-19(a) and (b) show the circuit and bond graphs, respectively. The desired ratio is e_2/E. The bond graph model requires a (zero) flow source at the open circuit port. The equations need not be reduced to A and B form; if fields are present, it is more con-

R_1 e_1 R_2 e_2 E + C_1 C_2

. . . an electric circuit (find e_2/E) (a)

R_1 C_1 R_2 C_2 E 1 0 1 0 F e_1 e_2

. . . augmented bond graph (set $F = 0$) (b)

$$\begin{bmatrix} C_1 & 0 \\ 0 & C_2 \end{bmatrix} D \begin{bmatrix} e_1 \\ e_2 \end{bmatrix} = \begin{bmatrix} -\left(\frac{1}{R_1}+\frac{1}{R_2}\right) & \frac{1}{R_2} \\ \frac{1}{R_2} & -\frac{1}{R_2} \end{bmatrix} \begin{bmatrix} e_1 \\ e_2 \end{bmatrix} + \begin{bmatrix} \frac{1}{R_1} \\ 0 \end{bmatrix} [E] \qquad (c)$$

$$\Delta(D) = s^2 C_1 C_2 + s\left[C_1/R_2 + C_2\left(1/R_1 + 1/R_2\right)\right] + 1/R_1R_2$$

$$N(D) = \begin{vmatrix} sC_1 + \left(1/R_1 + 1/R_2\right) & 1/R_1 \\ -1/R_2 & 0 \end{vmatrix} = 1/R_1R_2 \qquad (d)$$

$$\frac{e_2}{E} = \frac{N(D)}{\Delta(D)} = \frac{1}{s^2 C_1 C_2 R_1 R_2 + s\left(C_1 R_1 + C_2(R_1 + R_2)\right) + 1} \qquad (e)$$

Fig. 6-19 Evaluation of a transfer ratio using state equations.

venient to stop at the point shown in Fig. 6-19(c). In Fig. 6-19(d), $\Delta(D)$ and and N(D) are found; the ratio $N(D)/\Delta(D)$ yields the appropriate transfer ratio, as indicated in Fig. 6-19(e).

One additional modification is required when the transfer ratio includes a variable that is not a state variable. In that case it is appropriate to replace one of the state variables by the required variable and then to proceed as already outlined. Typically, the matrix form will be

$$\mathbf{E} \cdot D\mathbf{X}^* = \mathbf{A}^* \cdot \mathbf{X}^* + \mathbf{B}^* \cdot u_j,$$

where $\mathbf{E}$ is not necessarily diagonal, $\mathbf{X}^*$ includes the desired variable, $\mathbf{A}^*$ and $\mathbf{B}^*$ are modified versions of the original $\mathbf{A}$ and $\mathbf{B}$, and u_j is the input variable in the ratio.

6.4 Transmission and impedance matrix methods

Matrix representations of linear 2-ports, used in conjunction with bond graphs, prove particularly valuable for the easy manipulation of transfer operators. This section first presents some 2-port matrix forms and shows how they may be generated from bond graphs. Then the use of the different forms in relation to bond graph structures is illustrated by some examples. The treatment is not exhaustive but is intended to suggest the approach based on matrix-graph manipulation.

Some matrix forms for linear two-ports

Figure 6-20 summarizes the four causal possibilities for selecting inputs and outputs, names each form, and shows its matrix representation. In addition, an acausal form called the *transmission matrix* is shown, based upon a spatial correspondence (in the graph sense) of ports and variables. The powers are chosen *in* on bond 1 and *out* on bond 2 in every case. These matrices are the building blocks which we use to develop over-all characterizations of linear 2-ports.

Given any particular matrix form of a linear 2-port, it is possible to transform the representation to any of the other four forms (except for certain degenerate cases when an operator may become infinite). The simple correspondences are given in Fig. 6-21, where the basic form is taken to be the transmission matrix M.

name	element	definition*
M transmission	—1— S —2—	$\begin{bmatrix} e_1 \\ f_1 \end{bmatrix} = \begin{bmatrix} n_{11} & z_{12} \\ y_{21} & n_{22} \end{bmatrix} \begin{bmatrix} e_2 \\ f_2 \end{bmatrix}$
Z impedance	$\vdash$—1— S —2—$\dashv$	$\begin{bmatrix} e_1 \\ e_2 \end{bmatrix} = \begin{bmatrix} z_{11} & z_{12} \\ z_{21} & z_{22} \end{bmatrix} \begin{bmatrix} f_1 \\ f_2 \end{bmatrix}$
H immittance	$\vdash$—1— S $\vdash$—2—	$\begin{bmatrix} e_1 \\ f_2 \end{bmatrix} = \begin{bmatrix} z_{11} & n_{12} \\ n_{21} & y_{22} \end{bmatrix} \begin{bmatrix} f_1 \\ e_2 \end{bmatrix}$
G adpedance	—1—$\dashv$ S —2—$\dashv$	$\begin{bmatrix} f_1 \\ e_2 \end{bmatrix} = \begin{bmatrix} y_{11} & n_{12} \\ n_{21} & z_{22} \end{bmatrix} \begin{bmatrix} e_1 \\ f_2 \end{bmatrix}$
Y admittance	—1—$\dashv$ S $\vdash$—2—	$\begin{bmatrix} f_1 \\ f_2 \end{bmatrix} = \begin{bmatrix} y_{11} & y_{12} \\ y_{21} & y_{22} \end{bmatrix} \begin{bmatrix} e_1 \\ e_2 \end{bmatrix}$

* $[n]$ is dimensionless,
$[z]$ is $[e/f]$, and
$[y]$ is $[f/e]$.

Fig. 6-20 Two-port impedance forms.

Suppose we develop a 2-port matrix characterization of the following dual systems:

$\xrightarrow{1} 1 \xrightarrow{2}$, with a bond from 1 down to Z	*acausal graph*	$\xrightarrow{1} 0 \xrightarrow{2}$, with a bond from 0 down to Z
$\xrightarrow{1}\mid 1 \mid\xrightarrow{2}$, with a bond from 1 down to Y	*admittance, impedance form*	$\mid\xrightarrow{1} 0 \xrightarrow{2}\mid$, with a bond from 0 down to Z
$f_1 = Ye_1 - Ye_2$ $f_2 = Ye_1 - Ye_2$	*equations in causal form*	$e_1 = Zf_1 - Zf_2$ $e_2 = Zf_1 - Zf_2$
$\begin{bmatrix} e_1 \\ f_1 \end{bmatrix} = \begin{bmatrix} 1 & Z \\ 0 & 1 \end{bmatrix} \begin{bmatrix} e_2 \\ f_2 \end{bmatrix}$	*acausal matrix equations*	$\begin{bmatrix} e_1 \\ f_1 \end{bmatrix} = \begin{bmatrix} 1 & 0 \\ Y & 1 \end{bmatrix} \begin{bmatrix} e_2 \\ f_2 \end{bmatrix}$

From this transmission matrix form and the correspondences given in Fig. 6-21, it is easy to obtain any other desired form.

Let us consider, as one more example, the ideal 2-ports GY and TF, in a dual development:

$\xrightarrow{1} GY \xrightarrow{2}$	*acausal graph*	$\xrightarrow{1} TF \xrightarrow{2}$
$\mid\xrightarrow{1} GY \xrightarrow{2}\mid$	*causal form*	$\mid\xrightarrow{1} TF \mid\xrightarrow{2}$
$e_1 = r \cdot f_2$ $e_2 = r \cdot f_1$	*causal equations*	$e_1 = m \cdot e_2$ $f_2 = m \cdot f_1$
$\begin{bmatrix} e_1 \\ f_1 \end{bmatrix} = \begin{bmatrix} 0 & r \\ 1/r & 0 \end{bmatrix} \begin{bmatrix} e_2 \\ f_2 \end{bmatrix}$	*acausal equations*	$\begin{bmatrix} e_1 \\ f_1 \end{bmatrix} = \begin{bmatrix} m & 0 \\ 0 & 1/m \end{bmatrix} \begin{bmatrix} e_2 \\ f_2 \end{bmatrix}$

name	bond graph	matrix form
M	$\overset{1}{\rightharpoondown} M \overset{2}{\rightharpoondown}$	$\begin{bmatrix} e_1 \\ f_1 \end{bmatrix} = \begin{bmatrix} A & B \\ C & D \end{bmatrix} \begin{bmatrix} e_2 \\ f_2 \end{bmatrix}$
Z	$\vdash\!\overset{1}{\rightharpoondown} Z \overset{2}{\rightharpoondown}\!\dashv$	$\frac{1}{C}\begin{bmatrix} A & -\Delta^* \\ 1 & -D \end{bmatrix}$
H	$\vdash\!\overset{1}{\rightharpoondown} H \vdash\!\overset{2}{\rightharpoondown}$	$\frac{1}{D}\begin{bmatrix} B & \Delta \\ 1 & -C \end{bmatrix}$
G	$\overset{1}{\rightharpoondown}\!\dashv G \overset{2}{\rightharpoondown}\!\dashv$	$\frac{1}{A}\begin{bmatrix} C & \Delta \\ 1 & -B \end{bmatrix}$
Y	$\overset{1}{\rightharpoondown}\!\dashv Y \vdash\!\overset{2}{\rightharpoondown}$	$\frac{1}{B}\begin{bmatrix} D & -\Delta \\ 1 & -A \end{bmatrix}$

$* \; \Delta = |M| = A \cdot D - B \cdot C$

Fig. 6-21 Matrix equivalents for linear 2-ports.

Clearly, the methods given in Section 6.3 on the use of the augmented impedance graph may be employed to generate a matrix characterization of any linear 2-port in some convenient causal form. This matrix may be put into acausal (M) form. The 2-port will then be available for subsequent manipulation according to the methods discussed next.

Cascade coupling

When several 2-ports are connected end to end, resulting in an over-all 2-port system, they are said to be connected in cascade. The most convenient way to evaluate an over-all system characteristic matrix is by use of the transmission matrices of the individual components. The result is indicated as the first entry in Fig. 6-22, where the net transmission matrix is simply the product of the individual transmission matrices.

Two common examples, developed below in analogous fashion, are the *pi* and *tee* networks:

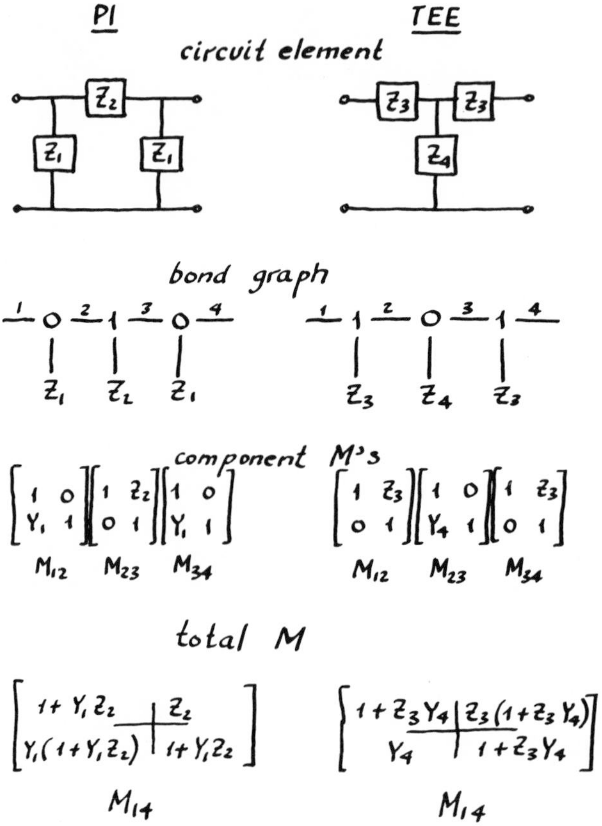

PI | TEE

circuit element

bond graph

component M's

PI: $\begin{bmatrix} 1 & 0 \\ Y_1 & 1 \end{bmatrix}\begin{bmatrix} 1 & Z_2 \\ 0 & 1 \end{bmatrix}\begin{bmatrix} 1 & 0 \\ Y_1 & 1 \end{bmatrix}$ (M_{12}, M_{23}, M_{34})

TEE: $\begin{bmatrix} 1 & Z_3 \\ 0 & 1 \end{bmatrix}\begin{bmatrix} 1 & 0 \\ Y_4 & 1 \end{bmatrix}\begin{bmatrix} 1 & Z_3 \\ 0 & 1 \end{bmatrix}$ (M_{12}, M_{23}, M_{34})

total M

PI: $M_{14} = \begin{bmatrix} 1+Y_1Z_2 & Z_2 \\ Y_1(1+Y_1Z_2) & 1+Y_1Z_2 \end{bmatrix}$

TEE: $M_{14} = \begin{bmatrix} 1+Z_3Y_4 & Z_3(1+Z_3Y_4) \\ Y_4 & 1+Z_3Y_4 \end{bmatrix}$

We can conclude from these expressions that if the two models are to represent the same physical system, their impedances must be related by

$$Z_3 = \frac{Z_2}{1 + Y_1Z_2} \quad \text{and} \quad Y_4 = Y_1(1 + Y_1Z_2).$$

name	structure*	over-all impedance
M	$\xrightarrow[1]{} A \rightarrow B \xrightarrow[2]{}$	$M_{12} = M_A \cdot M_B$
Z	$\xrightarrow{1} 1 \begin{smallmatrix} \nearrow A \searrow \\ \searrow B \nearrow \end{smallmatrix} 1 \xrightarrow{2}$	$Z_{12} = Z_A + Z_B$
H	$\xrightarrow{1} 1 \begin{smallmatrix} \nearrow A \searrow \\ \searrow B \nearrow \end{smallmatrix} 0 \xrightarrow{2}$	$H_{12} = H_A + H_B$
G	$\xrightarrow[1]{} 0 \begin{smallmatrix} \nearrow A \searrow \\ \searrow B \nearrow \end{smallmatrix} 1 \xrightarrow{2}$	$G_{12} = G_A + G_B$
Y	$\xrightarrow{1} 0 \begin{smallmatrix} \nearrow A \searrow \\ \searrow B \nearrow \end{smallmatrix} 0 \xrightarrow{2}$	$Y_{12} = Y_A + Y_B$

* A and B are linear 2-ports.

Fig. 6-22 Some useful 2-port equivalence relations.

As a second example we model an element of a lossless shaft by the following bond graph:

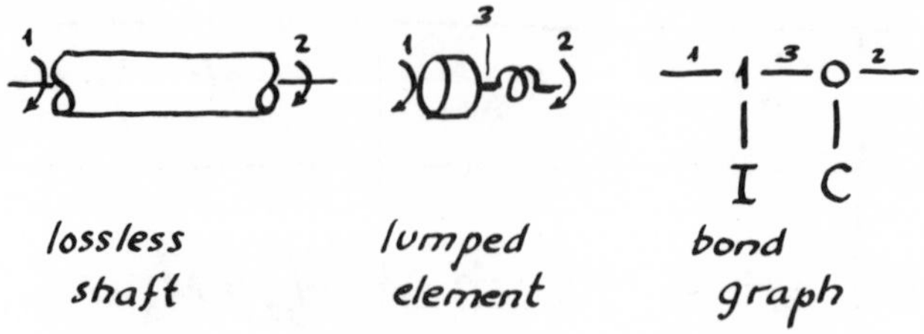

lossless shaft — lumped element — bond graph

From this we observe that

$$M_{12} = M_{13} \cdot M_{32} = \begin{bmatrix} 1 & I_D \\ 0 & 1 \end{bmatrix} \begin{bmatrix} 1 & 0 \\ C_D & 1 \end{bmatrix} = \begin{bmatrix} 1 + ICD^2 & I_D \\ CD & 1 \end{bmatrix}$$

Suppose we wish to find the input impedance of the shaft at port 1 when port 2 is terminated in viscous damping. We seek

$$Z_1 = e_1/f_1 \quad \text{when} \quad e_2 = Rf_2.$$

The transmission relations may be used directly by replacing e_2 by Rf_2, solving the second relation for f_2, and then evaluating e_1.

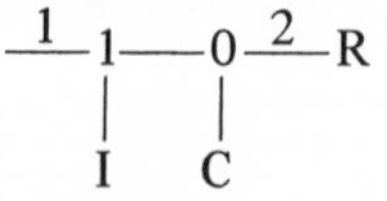

M_{12} known;

$e_2 = Rf_2$

$$f_1 = CDe_2 + 1 \cdot f_2 = CD \cdot Rf_2 + 1 \cdot f_2$$

$$f_2 = \frac{1}{1 + RCD} f_1 \tag{6.10}$$

$$e_1 = (1 + ICD^2)e_2 + IDf_2$$

$$e_1 = (1 + ICD^2)Rf_2 + IDf_2$$

$$e_1 = \frac{R(1 + ICD^2) + ID}{1 + RCD} f_1 \tag{6.11}$$

$$Z_1 = \frac{e_1}{f_1} = ID + \frac{R}{1 + RCD} \tag{6.12}$$

As a final example of cascade 2-port evaluation, let us find the input impedance for the circuit of Fig. 4-7, which contains an active element. For convenience, we reproduce the circuit and its bond graph here:

electric circuit

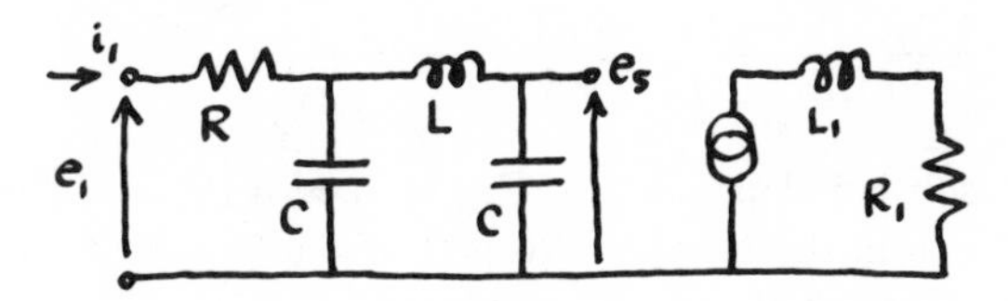

bond graph

```
 1     2     3     4     5      6     7
--> 1 --> 0 --> 1 --> 0 --> GY --> 1 --> R1
    |     |     |     |     h      |
    R     C     I     C            I
               (L)                (L1)
```

(1) $\mathbf{M}_{17} = \mathbf{M}_{;2} \cdot \mathbf{M}_{23} \cdot \mathbf{M}_{34} \cdot \mathbf{M}_{45} \cdot \mathbf{M}_{56} \cdot \mathbf{M}_{67}$,

$$\mathbf{M}_{17} = \begin{bmatrix} 1 & R \\ 0 & 1 \end{bmatrix} \begin{bmatrix} 1 & 0 \\ CD & 1 \end{bmatrix} \begin{bmatrix} 1 & LD \\ 0 & 1 \end{bmatrix} \begin{bmatrix} 1 & 0 \\ CD & 1 \end{bmatrix} \begin{bmatrix} 0 & h \\ 0^* & 0 \end{bmatrix} \begin{bmatrix} 1 & L_1D \\ 0 & 1 \end{bmatrix} .$$

*Zero is the result of activity on bond 5.

(2) Given $\begin{bmatrix} e_1 \\ f_1 \end{bmatrix} = \mathbf{M}_{17} \begin{bmatrix} e_7 \\ f_7 \end{bmatrix}$ and $e_7 = R_1 f_7$,

we can solve for e_1/f_1:

$$\begin{bmatrix} e_1 \\ f_1 \end{bmatrix} = \left[\begin{array}{c|c} 0 & h(1 + 2RCD + LCD^2 + RLC^2D^3) \\ \hline 0 & hCD(2 + LCD^2) \end{array}\right] \begin{bmatrix} e_2 \\ f_2 \end{bmatrix},$$

$$f_2 = \frac{1}{hCD(2 + LCD)^2} f_1$$

and

$$e_1 = h(1 + 2RCD + LCD^2 + RLC^2D^3)f_2 ,$$

$$e_1 = \frac{(1 + 2RCD + LCD^2 + RLC^2D^3)}{CD(2 + LCD^2)} f_1 ,$$

or

$$Z_1 = \frac{e_1}{f_1} = \frac{1 + 2RCD + LCD^2 + RLC^2D^3}{CD(2 + LCD^2)} .$$

Observe that the result is independent of R_1, L_1, and h (the coupling factor), as it should be from the physics. No part of the circuit "downstream" of bond 5 has any effect on the input impedance.

More general forms of coupling

The preceding section showed how to condense any cascade of linear 2-ports into an equivalent transmission matrix form, so that the over-all sequence can be considered as a single graph element. Here we investigate ways of manipulating more complex structures that may be realized using the 0- and 1-junction elements.

The basic strategy is revealed by Fig. 6-22, in which the structural imbedding of the 2-port elements is the determining factor in the selection of the matrix format for each element. As an example we shall demonstrate the validity of the last result in the table; namely, admittance matrices add for two 2-ports connected in zero-zero (or shunt-shunt) fashion.

Given the system

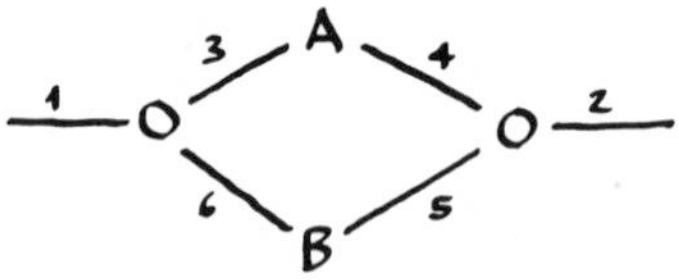

we wish to find Y_{12}, assuming the characteristics of A and B are known. Y_{12} is defined by

$$\begin{bmatrix} f_1 \\ f_2 \end{bmatrix} = Y_{12} \begin{bmatrix} e_1 \\ e_2 \end{bmatrix} .$$

First the graph is augmented:

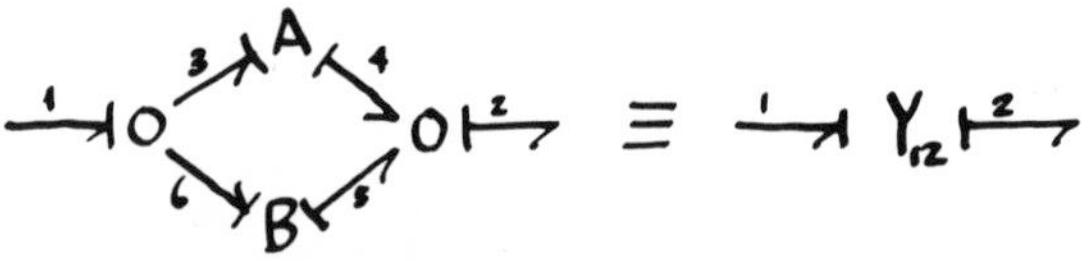

Notice that each 2-port has its powers defined in an "in-out" sense (i.e., A, B, and Y_{12}). Thus all the results in the various figures are directly applicable. The development will be carried out in parallel from each end of the system.

$f_1 = f_3 + f_6$	(1)	$f_2 = f_4 + f_5$
$f_3 = y_{A11}e_3 + y_{A12}e_4{}^{\dagger}$	(2)	$f_4 = y_{A21}e_3 + y_{A22}e_4{}^{\dagger}$
$f_6 = y_{B11}e_6 + y_{B12}e_5{}^{*}$		$f_5 = y_{B21}e_6 + y_{B22}e_5{}^{*}$
$e_3 = e_1,\ e_4 = e_2;$	(3)	$e_3 = e_1,\ e_6 = e_1;$
$e_6 = e_1,\ e_5 = e_2$		$e_4 = e_2,\ e_5 = e_2$
$f_1 = (y_{A11} + y_{B11})e_1 + (y_{A12} + y_{B12})e_2$	(4)	$f_2 = (y_{A21} + y_{B21})e_1 + (y_{A22} + y_{B22})e_2$

*characteristic of B $\qquad$ †characteristic of A

$$\begin{bmatrix} f_6 \\ f_5 \end{bmatrix} = \begin{bmatrix} y_{B11} & y_{B12} \\ y_{B21} & y_{B22} \end{bmatrix} \begin{bmatrix} e_6 \\ e_5 \end{bmatrix} \qquad \begin{bmatrix} f_3 \\ f_4 \end{bmatrix} = \begin{bmatrix} y_{A11} & y_{A12} \\ y_{A21} & y_{A22} \end{bmatrix} \begin{bmatrix} e_3 \\ e_4 \end{bmatrix}$$

The relations (4) expressed in matrix form, are

$$(5) \quad \begin{bmatrix} f_1 \\ f_2 \end{bmatrix} = \begin{bmatrix} (y_{A11} + y_{B11}) & (y_{A12} + y_{B12}) \\ (y_{A21} + y_{B21}) & (y_{A22} + y_{B22}) \end{bmatrix} \begin{bmatrix} e_1 \\ e_2 \end{bmatrix}$$

or

$$(6) \quad \begin{bmatrix} f_1 \\ f_2 \end{bmatrix} = [Y_A + Y_B] \begin{bmatrix} e_1 \\ e_2 \end{bmatrix} = [Y_{12}] \begin{bmatrix} e_1 \\ e_2 \end{bmatrix}$$

The results given in Fig. 6-22, combined with the equivalences given in Fig. 6-21, are a remarkably useful set of data for finding transfer functions and impedances. As a final example, let us derive the input impedance of a Wheatstone bridge circuit, studied in Fig. 6-16 by use of augmented impedance graph methods, by 2-port matrix methods.

(1) The directed graph is

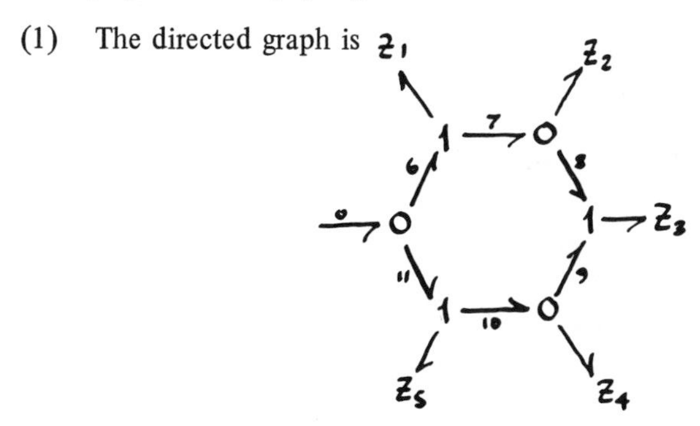

(2) Evaluate the graph in the following way:

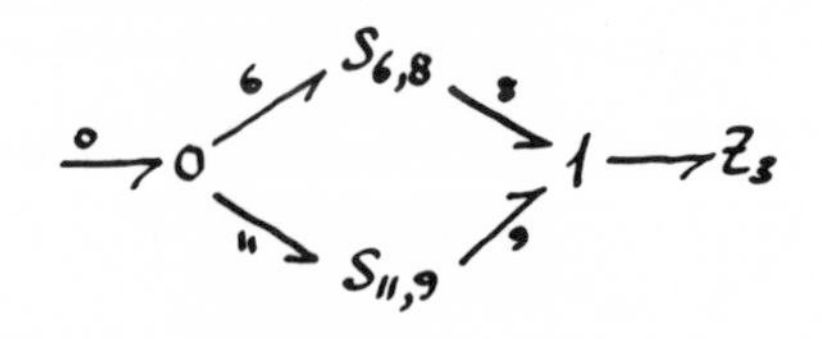

(3) The structural form of 2 suggests that (see Fig. 6-22)

$$\mathbf{G}_{0,3} = \mathbf{G}_{6,8} + \mathbf{G}_{11,9} \quad \text{and} \quad e_3 = Z_3 f_3 .$$

(4) Evaluation of $\mathbf{G}_{6,8}$ may be done in two steps (see Fig. 6-21). $\mathbf{G}_{11,9}$ may be found in analogous fashion.

$$\mathbf{M}_{6,8} = \mathbf{M}_{6,7} \cdot \mathbf{M}_{7,8} = \begin{bmatrix} A & B \\ C & D \end{bmatrix} \quad \text{and} \quad \mathbf{G}_{6,8} = \frac{1}{A}\begin{bmatrix} C & \Delta \\ 1 & -B \end{bmatrix}.$$

Some intermediate results are

$$\mathbf{M}_{6,8} = \begin{bmatrix} 1 & Z_1 \\ 0 & 1 \end{bmatrix} \begin{bmatrix} 1 & 0 \\ Y_2 & 1 \end{bmatrix} = \begin{bmatrix} 1 + Y_1Y_2 & Z_1 \\ Y_2 & 1 \end{bmatrix},$$

$$\mathbf{G}_{6,8} = \frac{1}{1 + Z_1Y_2}\begin{bmatrix} Y_2 & 1 \\ 1 & -Z_1 \end{bmatrix},$$

$$\mathbf{M}_{11,9} = \begin{bmatrix} 1 & Z_5 \\ 0 & 1 \end{bmatrix} \begin{bmatrix} 1 & 0 \\ Y_4 & 1 \end{bmatrix} = \begin{bmatrix} 1 + Y_4Z_5 & Z_5 \\ Y_4 & 1 \end{bmatrix},$$

$$\mathbf{G}_{11,9} = \frac{1}{1 + Y_4Z_5}\begin{bmatrix} Y_4 & 1 \\ 1 & -Z_5 \end{bmatrix}, \text{ and}$$

$$\mathbf{G}_{0,3} = \left[\begin{array}{c|c} Y_2/(1 + Z_1Y_2) + Y_4/(1 + Y_4Z_5) & 1/(1 + Z_1Y_2) + 1/(1 + Y_4Z_5) \\ \hline 1/(1 + Z_1Y_2) + 1/1(+ Y_4Z_5) & -Z/(1 + Z_1Y_2) - Z_5(1 + Y_4Z_5) \end{array}\right]$$

Since $\begin{bmatrix} f_0 \\ e_3 \end{bmatrix} = [G_{0,3}] \begin{bmatrix} e_0 \\ f_3 \end{bmatrix}$ and $e_3 = Z_3 f_3$, we find that (letting the elements of $\mathbf{G}_{0,3}$ be $[g_{ij}]$)

$$f_3 = \frac{g_{21}}{Z_3 - g_{22}} e_0 ,$$

and

$$\frac{f_0}{e_0} = Y_0 = \frac{g_{12}g_{21} - g_{11}g_{22} + g_{11}Z_3}{Z_3 - g_{22}} .$$

For the case where $Y_1 = Y_2 = Y_4 = Y_5 = Y$ and $Z_3 = Z^*$ (or $Y_3 = Y^*$) (as in Fig. 6-16),

$$Y_0 = Y \frac{(2Y^* + Y)}{Y^* + Y)} .$$

As a concluding note on transfer ratio methods, we emphasize the utility of Figs. 6-21 and 6-22 combined with a strategy of decomposing systems into 2-port chains. With experience, one learns to form transmission matrices by inspection; two-by-two matrix manipulaton takes care of the rest of the solution.

References

1. S. J. Mason, "Feedback Theory: Some Properties of Signal Flow Graphs," *Proc. IRE,* v. 41, 1953, pp. 1144-1156.
2. S. J. Mason, "Feedback Theory: Further Properties of Signal Flow Graphs," *Proc. IRE,* v. 44, 1956, pp. 920-926.
3. C. S. Lorens, *Flowgraphs for the Modeling and Analysis of Linear Systems,* McGraw-Hill Book Co., New York, 1964.
4. F. B. Hildebrand, *Advanced Calculus for Engineers,* Prentice-Hall, Inc., Englewood Cliffs, N. J., 1955, pp. 21ff.
5. R. C. Dorf, *Modern Control Systems,* Addison-Wesley Publ. Co., Reading, Mass., 1967, pp. 31-32.
6 F. D. Ezekiel and H. M. Paynter, Computer Representations of Engineering Systems Involving Fluid Transients, *Trans. ASME,* Nov. 1957, pp. 1840-1850.

7. COMPUTER SIMULATION TECHNIQUES

In this chapter some of the implications of bond graph techniques for simulation of system behavior are discussed. Three types of computing systems are considered: digital, analog, and hybrid. A description of the ENPORT digital computer program, which has been operated successfully for some time, is given in Section 7.1. This is followed by a discussion, in Section 7.2, of analog computing considerations based upon block diagrams derived from bond graphs. Finally, some remarks about hybrid computing and brief mention of a small hybrid computer operated at M.I.T. are made in Section 7.3.

7.1 Digital simulation

Digital simulation methods for studying the behavior of static and dynamic physical systems have become increasingly popular in recent years. The development of programs[1] such as BLODI, STRUDL, CIRCAL, DSL/90, and DYANA has been spurred on by the increasing size and speed of modern digital computers, as well as their use in a time-shared, or interactive, mode. Problem-oriented languages, designed for particular problem areas, make it relatively convenient for an engineer who is not a programming expert to use available computing power in his studies. This trend promises to to continue as the cost of computing decreases.

The use of bond graphs for representing and analyzing physical system dynamics has given rise to a simulation program called ENPORT, which is a digital computer implementation of many of the procedures described in earlier chapters.

The ENPORT program

ENPORT is the name given to a set of digital computer procedures designed to allow direct simulation of dynamic physical systems represented by bond graphs. The primary objective is to create a program such that, once a structural model is developed and the characteristics fixed, no further human intervention is necessary to produce time and frequency response information. The general concept (and the name) of ENPORT originated with H. M. Paynter. Development and implementation of algorithms and procedures have been the responsibility of R. C. Rosenberg. As is common with complex and evolving programs, versions of ENPORT with differing characteristics have been created and are under development. The particular version to be discussed in this section is ENPORT-1:

ENPORT-1 operates in the interactive environment of Project MAC's Compatible Time-Sharing System (CTSS) at M.I.T.[2] Access to the program is through a (remote) teletype terminal. All examples in this section were generated on such a console. The program is continually being modified; the version discussed here is the system of record on June 30, 1967. The basic computer in the CTSS is an IBM 7094 with a memory size of 32K. Times of operation mentioned in connection with the examples must be judged relative to this computer and the CTSS.

ENPORT-1 simulates the transient response of linear, constant, lumped-parameter systems containing active and passive elements. Bonds may be activated, thus introducing the ability to represent control and forcing functions as well as certain physical phenomena. The particular element set is (C, I, R, E, F, GY, TF, 0, 1, and *activation*). The sources E and F must be constant; source modeling is made possible by use of activation, as illustrated by the second example of this section. Most types of energy fields (C-fields and I-fields) are not permitted in ENPORT-1. When they are detected (either in the node set or by causal conflict) a suitable message is printed and the simulation process stops.

Example of the use of ENPORT-1

In several examples that follow we present some of the capabilities of ENPORT-1 by the use of annotated transactions between a user and the program. The examples are intended to give the reader a feeling for the basic ways of using the program. The size of the problems has deliberately been kept very small to simplify the transactions. In fact, ENPORT-1 can handle graphs with 26 nodes, 26 bonds, and 8 state variables. This size can be increased to fill computer memory as the need arises. And further modifications can of course be made to allow use of secondary memory at the price of slower system response. The sequence of examples proceeds from a typical study of a passive system to the representation of a triangle-wave source and then to the study of a nonlinear system.

Figure 7-1 illustrates the specification of a series electrical circuit in ENPORT-1. The major components in the description are the *structure,* the *parameters,* and the *initial state.* First, a bond graph model of the circuit is made and the bonds are labeled uniquely. After ENPORT-1 has been called "into action" by the resume request (R ENPORT), the structure is described by the use of a line code. The code is simply a serial array of node-bond groups, with the node given first in each group. The program then checks for coding or graph errors (such as free bonds, or non-unique names). If none are found, it tries to assign causality. Upon satisfactory completion of causality, the state variables are listed. The general power and energy variables (e, f, p, and q) are used by ENPORT-1, whatever the particular physics of the problem. Therefore the user must keep track of the actual units.

Next the parameters and values of the (constant) sources are given, followed by a statement of the initial conditions for the state variables. Finally, an estimate of DT, the time sampling interval, is made by the user. If the interval is too large to permit satisfactory computation, it is automatically scaled down. Based on this interval and the number of state variables, the time range for which the results will be computed and stored is given (TMAX). At this point a complete specification of system information has been given. The first request for output will cause ENPORT-1 to calculate the transient response.

Figure 7-2 follows immediately upon the transaction in Fig. 7-1 and illustrates the use of output requests for plotting at the teletype (HPLOT) and printing tables of data (TABLE). The request

```
HPLOT
0 . ,20 . , .5
S(1)  S(2)
```

states that the user wishes a teletype plot from the time 0. to time 20. in steps of .5. The variables to be plotted are state variable 1 (voltage on the capacitor) and state variable 2 (current in the inductor). The request

```
TABLE
80., 83., 1.
S(1) S(2)
```

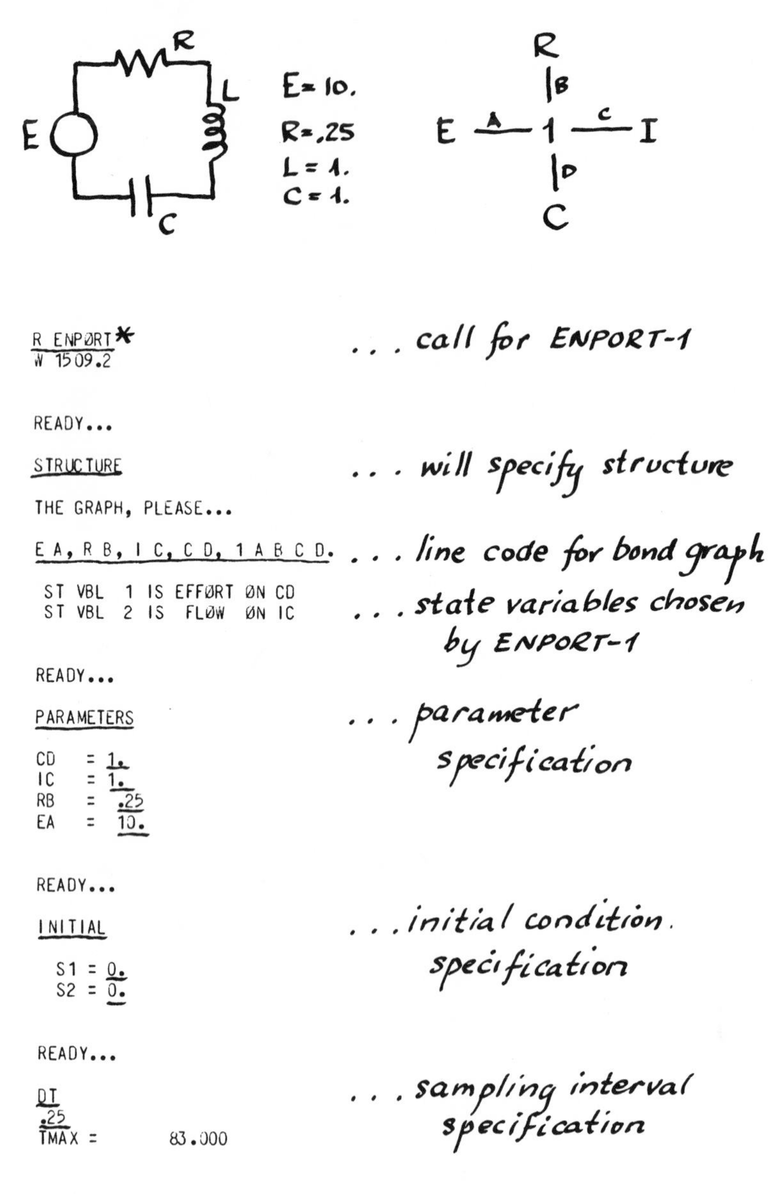

Fig. 7.1 An example of system specification in ENPORT-1.

```
READY...

HPLØT
0.,20.,.5
S(1) S(2)

     1...S(1)
     2...S(2)

 .16637E 02
   .
   .       111
   .          1
   .      1    1          1111
   .                     1    1        1111111
   .    2       1       1         11   11          11111
   .   212       1    1             11
   .                111
   .   21  2             22
   .                    2  2                2
   . .1....2......2....2.......22.222......222
   . 2             2       22    22        222222
   .         2                  222
   .          2  2
   .            22
   .
   .
   .
   .
   .
   .
 -.16637E 02

TIME FRØM   0.    TØ  20.000  IN  INTERVALS ØF    .500 .

READY...

TAN"BLE
80.,83.,1.
S(1) S(2)

    TIME        S(1)            S(2)

  80.000     .10000E 02     -.33721E-03
  81.000     .99999E 01     -.38955E-03
  82.000     .99997E 01     -.11227E-03
  83.000     .99997E 01      .19613E-03
```

...user requests plot

...user requests table

Fig. 7-2 Examples of output for the system of Fig. 7-1.

causes the same pair of variables to be displayed in tabular form from time 80. to time 83. in steps of 1. From the data we observe that the steady state has been reached, correct to a precision of three decimal figures. If more data were desired, the state variable values at time 83. could be entered as new initial conditions, and the results would be extended by another 83. time units (TMAX=83.).

The variables available for output include the effort, flow, displacement (charge), momentum (flux), instantaneous power, and cumulative energy transfer for every bond in the graph. In addition, the instantaneous energies associated with C and I elements are available. These quantities are computed from the state variables upon user request, and stored temporarily.

In Fig. 7-3 an example of on-line modification of parameters is given, to suggest the ease with which design studies may be carried out. The previous circuit is modified by having the resistance value increased to 2.(PAR). The same variables are plotted, showing a marked increase in damping of the transients. In order to investigate the initial response more closely, the sampling interval is decreased from (DT =) .25 to (DT =) .1. Notice that the stored results are curtailed in time range by the same ratio (TMAX = 33.2). The peak in flow (current) is seen to occur between 0.9 and 1.1 under these conditions. The reader may be interested to know that the time required to conduct this brief investigation shown in Figs. 7-1, 7-2, and and 7-3 was about 20 seconds of IBM 7094 time in CTSS, and 12 minutes of "real," or user, time. Most of the 20 seconds of computer time was spent in swapping in and out of core. In batch mode it would have cost about 8 seconds of time.

In Fig. 7-4 several of the graph error detection features of ENPORT-1 are shown. Fig. 7-4(a) gives a graph with three types of errors: an unrecognizable node (Q), violation of a graph property of a defined node (C is only permitted to have one bond), and inclusion of a free bond (probably due to omitting another node from the graph). These errors are straightforward and easily rectified. In Fig. 7-4(b) an example is given of a graph containing an implicit field, which is discovered by the program when causality is assigned. In ENPORT-1, the problem is turned back to the user, who must find a satisfactory field equivalent before continuing. In this case one possibility is shown in Fig. 7-4(c), where the three initial I values have been converted into two new I values and a transformer modulus.

In the next example we illustrate the use of bond activation in constructing an approximate triangle wave flow source. The basic approach is to consider a Fourier series representation of the wave form, and then use a set of independent oscillators to realize the terms of the series. Each I-C oscillator is tuned to an appropriate frequency by adjusting the values of I and C. The flows can be summed by a 0-junction. Independence of each oscillator

```
READY...

PAR                                      ...modify parameter
RB                                          (all others
2.                                              unchanged)
Q

READY...

HPLØT                                    ...plot response
0.,10.,.25
S(1) S(2)

      1...S(1)
      2...S(2)

  .9995OE 01
     .
     .              11111111111111111111111
     .          1111
     .        11
     .       1
     .     11
     .    1
     .  222222
     .    1   222
     . 2 1      2222
     . .11...........2222222222222222222222222

  0.0

TIME FRØM   0.    TØ  10.000 IN INTERVALS ØF    .250 .

READY...

DT                                       ...select smaller
.1                                            time increment
TMAX =        33.200

READY...

TABLE                                    ...seek peak S_2 from
.7,1.3,.1                                     table
S(1) S(2)

    TIME      S(1)           S(2)

    .600    .12190E 01     .32929E 01
    .700    .15580E 01     .34761E 01
    .800    .19121E 01     .35946E 01
    .900    .22752E 01     .36591E 01 <-
   1.000    .26424E 01     .36788E 01 <-
   1.100    .30097E 01     .36616E 01 <-
   1.200    .33737E 01     .36143E 01
   1.300    .37318E 01     .35429E 01
```

Fig. 7-3 Modification to the system of Fig. 7-1.

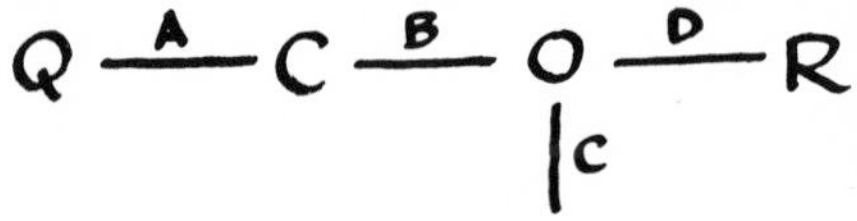

```
READY...

STRUCTURE

THE GRAPH, PLEASE...

Q A, C A B, O B C D, R D.

LINE 1 ØF THE GRAPH HAS AN ILLEGAL NØDE '00000Q'.

BØND C      IS A FREE BØND.

NØDE CAB    HAS  2 BØNDS.

THE ABØVE NØDES HAVE INCØRRECT BØND CØUNTS.

THIS GRAPH WILL BE DELETED.
```

(a)

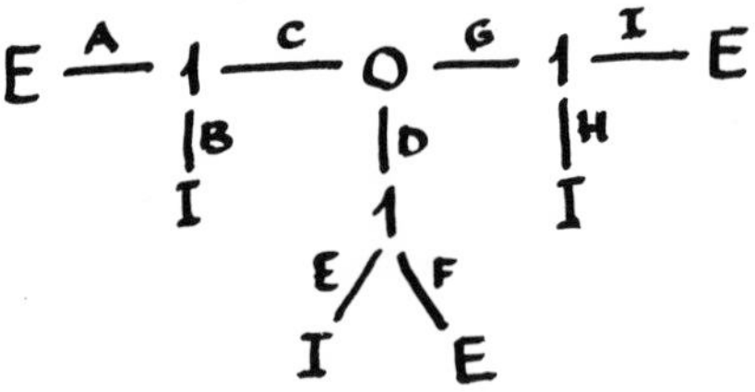

```
READY...

STRUCTURE

THE GRAPH, PLEASE...

E A, 1 A B C, I B, O C D G,
1 D E F, I E, E F,
1 G H I, I H, E I.

BØND H       IS IN A STATIC I FIELD.

CAUSALITY WAS NØT CØMPLETED.  PLEASE MØDIFY THE GRAPH.
```

(b)

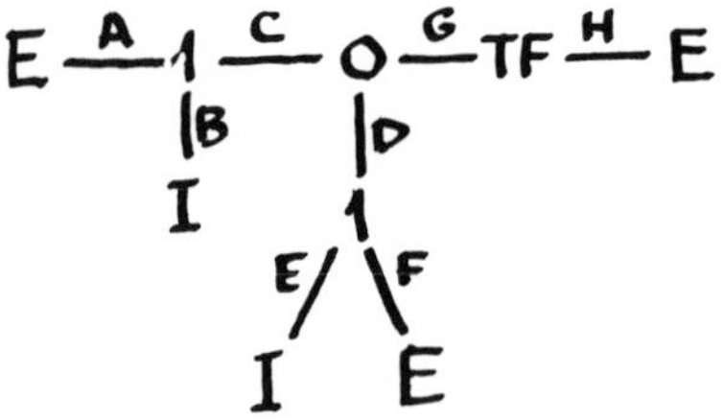

```
READY...

STRUCTURE

THE GRAPH, PLEASE...

E A, I B, 1 A B C, O C D G,
1 D E F, I E, E F, TF G H, E H.

 ST VBL  1 IS  FLØW  ØN IB
 ST VBL  2 IS  FLØW  ØN IE
```

(c)

Fig. 7-4 Some examples of error detection in ENPORT-1. (a) several graph errors, (b) causal conflict due to an implicit I-field, (c) acceptable equivalent graph for (b).

is ensured by bond activation, as shown in Fig. 7-5. The graph has three oscillators (C_A–I_B, C_E–I_F, and C_G–I_H), whose flows are measured by the 1-junctions and summed by the 0-junction. There is no back effect on any oscillator due to the effort, because each connecting bond (C, D, and I) has been activated. The new flow is imposed on a resistive load, which causes an effort (e_J) to arise. From this effort and the three independent flows the power demanded of each oscillator can be found. In ENPORT-1, activation of a bond is accomplished by suppressing one of the signals. In Fig. 7-5, the three efforts e_C, e_D, and e_I have been suppressed, leaving the three flows f_C, f_D, and f_I active.

Cyclic frequencies for the three oscillators are set by the parameter pair in the relation $\omega = 1/\sqrt{IC}$.

Thus,

$$\omega_1 = 1/\sqrt{I_B C_A} = 1/\sqrt{(1.)(1.)} = 1;$$

$$\omega_2 = 1/\sqrt{I_F C_E} = 1/\sqrt{(.33)(.33)} = 3;$$

$$\omega_3 = 1/\sqrt{I_H C_G} = 1/\sqrt{(.2)(.2)} = 5.$$

The relative phase and magnitude of each flow can be set by the two initial conditions on each oscillator: the effort on the C, and the flow on the I. In this case all the initial efforts are zero and the flows are chosen in the ratio (1:1/9:1/25). Thus,

$$f_B = -10. \quad , \quad e_A = 0.$$

$$f_F = 1.11 \quad , \quad e_E = 0.$$

$$f_H = -0.4 \quad , \quad e_G = 0.$$

The resistance was given a value of unity, so that the input flow and output effort have the same magnitude on bond J.

In Fig. 7-6(a) the effort on the resistance is plotted, indicating the approximately triangular nature of the flow source. A sampling interval of 0.25, about one fifth of the shortest period, was chosen. In order to allow a closer look at the quality of the signal, the sampling interval is cut by a factor of five, so that DT = 0.05. Then the first cycle is replotted in Fig. 7-6(b). This time the approximate nature of the signal is shown more clearly, being quite good in the smooth parts of the triangle but rounding off the sharp peaks where the signal "turns." Further frequency components could be added if it were desired to increase accuracy of the representation.

```
R ENPØRT
W 1044.0

READY...

STRUCTURE

THE GRAPH, PLEASE...

C A,I B,1 A B C,0 C D I J,R J,1 D E F,
C E,I F,1 G H I,C G,I H.

 ST VBL  1 IS EFFØRT ØN CA
 ST VBL  2 IS EFFØRT ØN CE
 ST VBL  3 IS EFFØRT ØN CG
 ST VBL  4 IS  FLØW  ØN IB
 ST VBL  5 IS  FLØW  ØN IF
 ST VBL  6 IS  FLØW  ØN IH

READY...

SUPPRESS

SUPPRESSED SIGNAL...    E
BØND...     C

SUPPRESSED SIGNAL...    E
BØND...     D

SUPPRESSED SIGNAL...    E
BØND...     I

SUPPRESSED SIGNAL...

READY...

PARAMETERS

CA   = 1.
CE   =  .33
CG   =  .2
IB   = 1.
IF   = .33
IH   =  .2
RJ   = 1.

READY...

INITIAL

  S1 =   0.
  S2 =   0.
  S3 =   0.
  S4 = -10.
  S5 =    1.11
  S6 =  -.4
```

C A I B 1 C C E 1 D 0 J R I F I C G 1 I H

. . . activate bonds C, D, and I

. . . oscillator frequencies are 1., 3., 5.

. . . initial flows in ratio 1: 1/9: 1/25

Fig. 7-5 Source modeling by activation—a triangle wave generator.

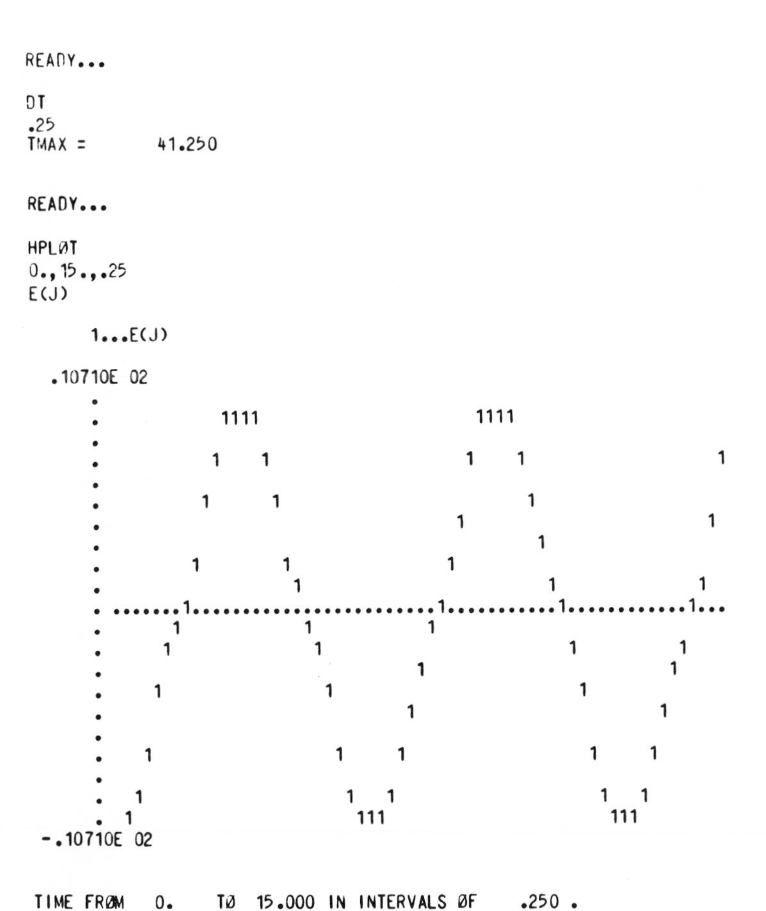

Fig. 7.6 Response of triangle wave generator of Fig. 7-5. (a) plot of several cycles.

```
READY...

DT
.10
TMAX =          16.500


READY...

HPLØT
0.,6.,.1
E(J)

        1...E(J)

   .10710E 02
      .
      .                       11111111
      .                     11        11
      .                    1            1
      .                   1              1
      .                  1                1
      .                 1                  1
      .                1                    1
      .               1                      1
      .             11                        11
      . ..............11..........................11.............
      .             11                            11
      .            1                                1
      .          11                                  1
      .         1                                     1
      .        1                                       1
      .       1                                         1
      .      1                                           1
      .     1                                             1
      .    1                                               11
      .  1111                                                11
  -.10710E 02

TIME FRØM   0.   TØ   6.000 IN INTERVALS ØF   .100 .
```

(b)

Fig. 7-6 Response of triangle wave generator of Fig. 7-5. (b) detailed plot of a single cycle.

One point to be made by this example is that every linear system with arbitrary forcing functions can be approximated by a closed system with active bonds at the cost of introducing additional state variables. In general, this method is not useful, because of the rapid growth in the size of the over-all system, but for certain sources (e.g., sinusoids) in studies where high accuracy in computed results is important, such system closure techniques may prove valuable. In addition, inspection of many physical source characteristics reveal that they are sometimes closer to the approximate signals generated by the modeling techniques cited than to the mathematically ideal functions used to represent them.

An interesting use of ENPORT-1 is in the simulation of time response of certain types of nonlinear systems. When a system can be represented conveniently by different linear systems in different regions of its state space, it is possible to examine its behavior by adjoining a sequence of suitable linear transients.

As an example we shall investigate the behavior of a common nonlinear mechanical system–the Coulomb-friction oscillator shown in Fig. 7-7(a). A bond graph model is shown in Fig. 7-7(b). The inertia and spring constant are assumed constant, and the friction characteristic is sketched in Fig. 7-7(c). Computational difficulty arises in part because the resistance is not unique in both directions, and in part because of the essential nonlinearity of the characteristic.

Basically, the system operates in one of two linear dynamic regions, depending upon the velocity. In each region the resistance imposes a *constant* friction force in a direction opposed to the velocity. A model that permits these conditions to be realized is given in Fig. 7-8. The power direction on bond B is from the source to the system, but the sign of the force is taken opposite to the velocity. Hence, the power is always into the source from the system. Thus the source dissipates energy. One final point in the model is that the steady state is reached whenever the velocity is zero and the spring force is less than the maximum friction force ($|\mu Mg|$). The basic strategy is to operate ENPORT-1 in time segments equal to about half a period of oscillation, locate the time at which the velocity reaches zero and check the spring force. Figure 7-9 shows a sequence of half cycles carried out for the values $M = 1$, $K = 1$, and $\mu Mg = 2$. The system was started with no velocity and 10. units of force in the spring. It is specified in Fig. 7.9(a). Figs. 7-9(b) and (c) show the first two half cycles of response. In the first half cycle the velocity reaches 0. at about 3.14 time units. The spring force is about minus six units. The initial conditions for the next half cycle are set accordingly, the sign of the friction force is changed, and the simulation run once more. Again a velocity zero is located in 3.14 more time units. This time the spring force is just less than the 2 units required for breakaway, and so equilibrium has been reached.

Further remarks about ENPORT-1

The over-all operation of ENPORT-1 is outlined in the flow chart of Fig. 7-10. In batch operation the flow of control would typically be cyclic, from top to bottom, and then repeat if conditions were to be changed. The

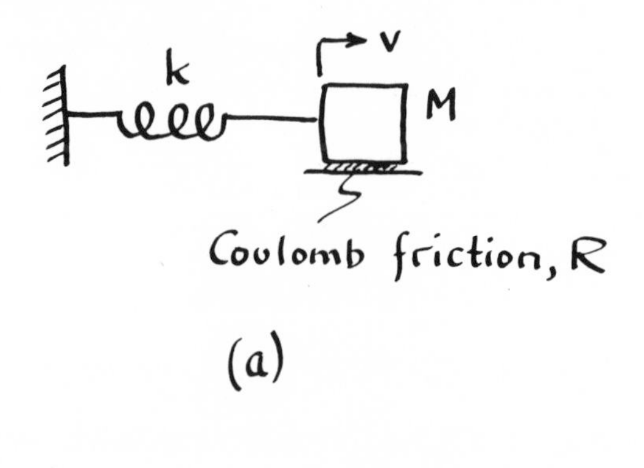

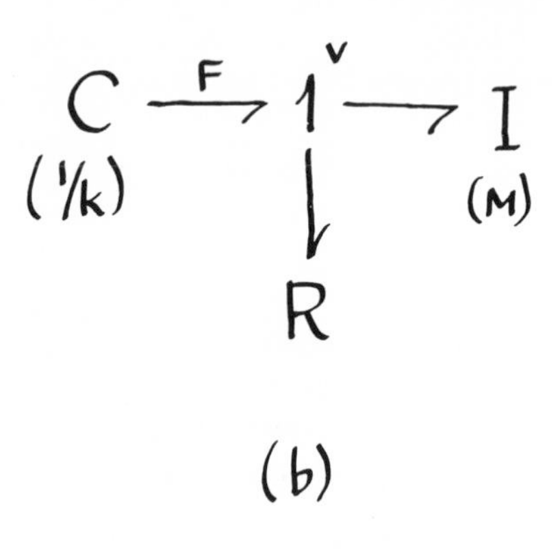

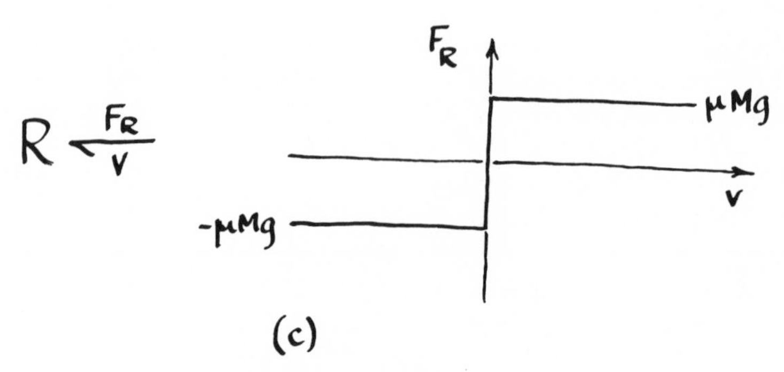

Fig. 7-7 A mechanical oscillator with Coulomb damping. (a) the mechanical schematic, (b) a bond graph model, (c) friction characteristic.

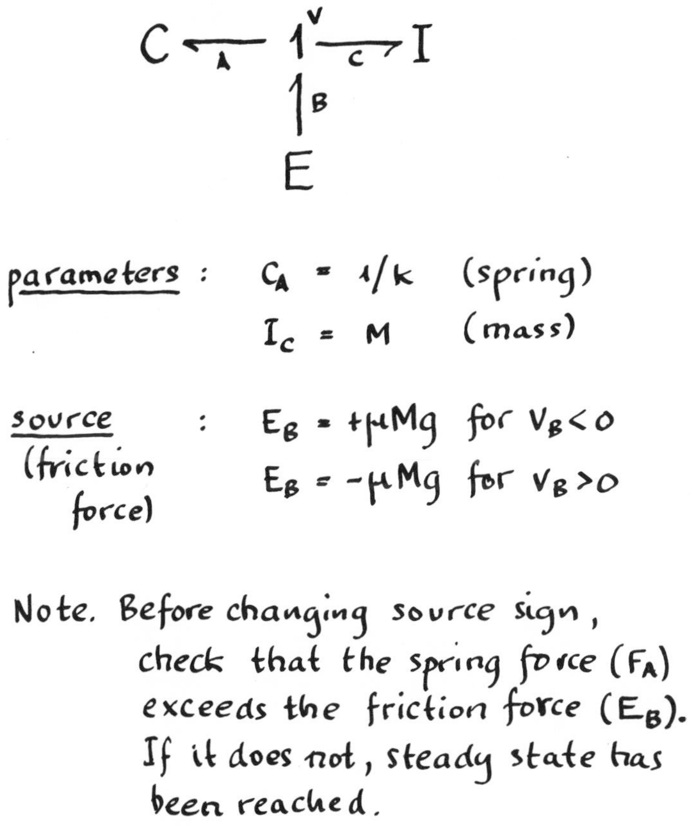

C ←A— 1^{v} —C→ I
|B
E

parameters : $C_A = 1/k$ (spring)
$I_C = M$ (mass)

source (friction force) : $E_B = +\mu Mg$ for $V_B < 0$
$E_B = -\mu Mg$ for $V_B > 0$

Note. Before changing source sign, check that the spring force (F_A) exceeds the friction force (E_B). If it does not, steady state has been reached.

Fig. 7-8 A bond graph model and simulation condition conditions for the system of Fig. 7-7.

input information for each operation or sequence of operations is indicated in the left column of the figure. The operations are indicated in the central column, and results available after each operation are shown in the right column. In interactive computing, a new input request (e.g., PAR for parameter modification) shifts control back up to the level indicated in the input column, after which descent begins once more. Thus, a change in DT requires that [M] and the state space results be recalculated, but not [A].

In ENPORT-1, all E and F sources except constant value ones (i.e., steps) must be represented in closed form, that is, by passive elements and active bonds. Therefore, all systems appear to be homogeneous. This method has certain advantages when the matrix exponential computing technique is used. One of the principal advantages of the method is that the roots of the the system need not be found, which is especially useful for systems having certain types of static fields among the energy elements (capacitances and inertances). In addition, it is possible to control the accuracy of the solution to any desired degree within machine tolerances.[3]

Extensions of the techniques used in ENPORT-1 will permit the simulation of certain classes of nonlinear systems in the next generation of ENPORT programs–ENPORT-2. In particular, nonlinear but bi-unique R, C, and I elements will be permitted, as well as arbitrary source characteristics. Some types of modulated 2-ports (MGY's, MTF's) will also be included.

Another very useful feature of ENPORT-1 is its ability to store and retrieve systems on which one has been working. Figure 7-11 shows the

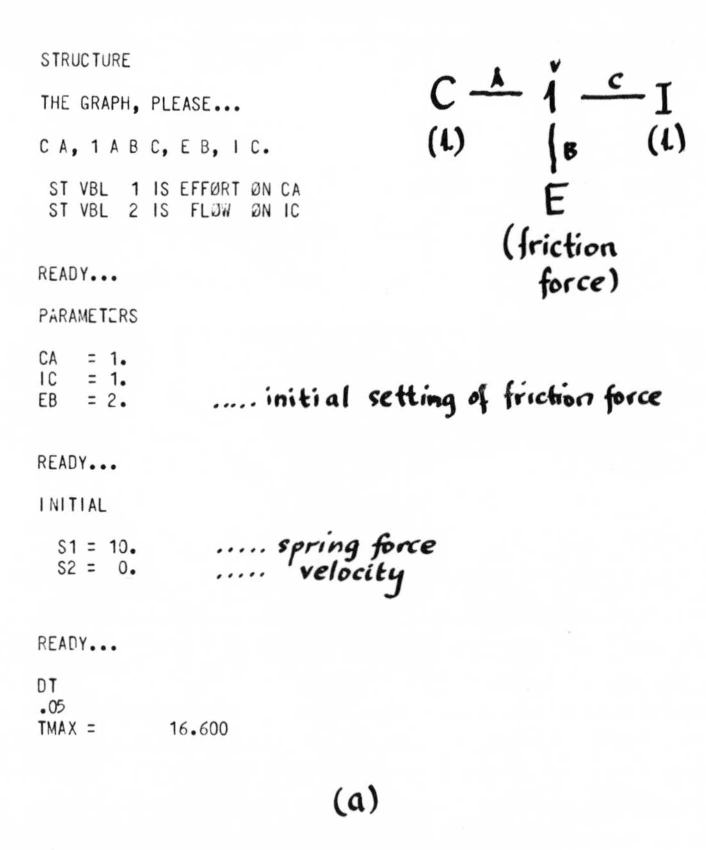

Fig. 7-9 **ENPORT-1 simulation of the Coulomb friction oscillator. (a) system specification**

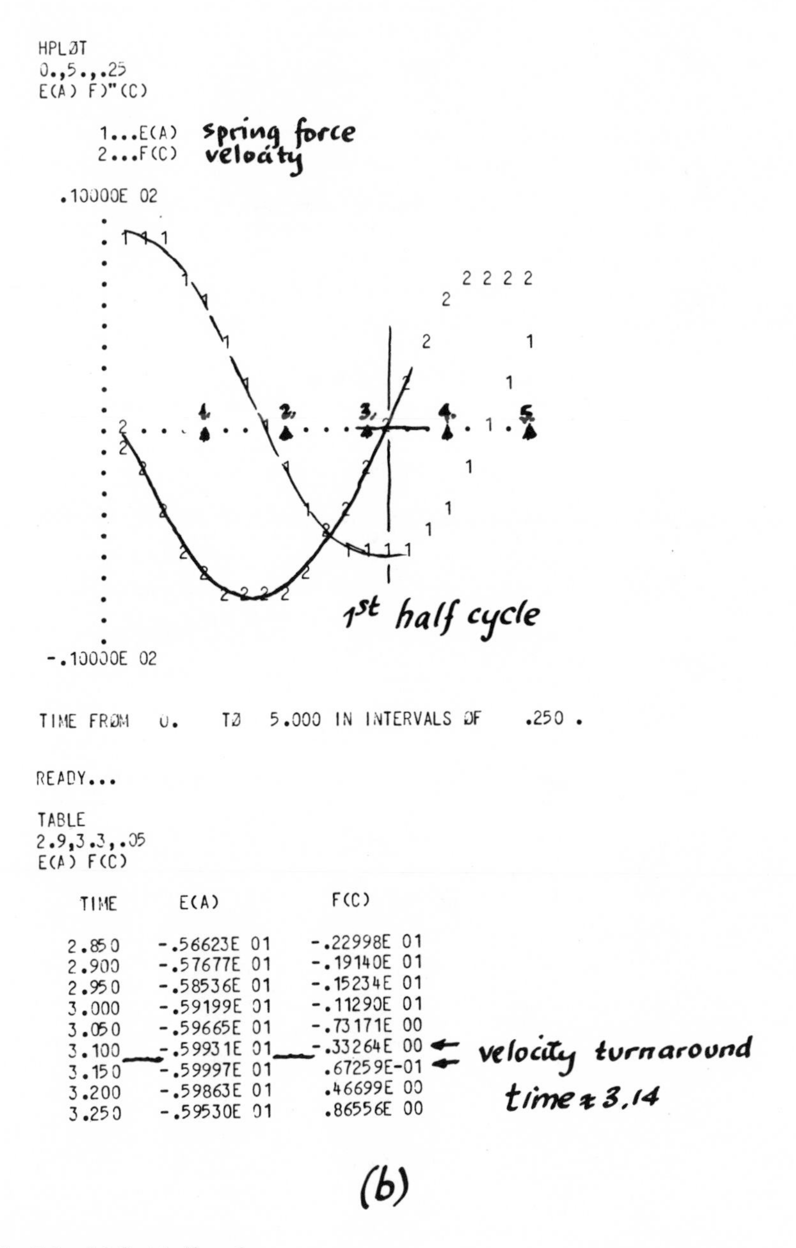

TIME	E(A)	F(C)
2.850	-.56623E 01	-.22998E 01
2.900	-.57677E 01	-.19140E 01
2.950	-.58536E 01	-.15234E 01
3.000	-.59199E 01	-.11290E 01
3.050	-.59665E 01	-.73171E 00
3.100	-.59931E 01	-.33264E 00
3.150	-.59997E 01	.67259E-01
3.200	-.59863E 01	.46699E 00
3.250	-.59530E 01	.86556E 00

Fig. 7-9 (b) first half cycle

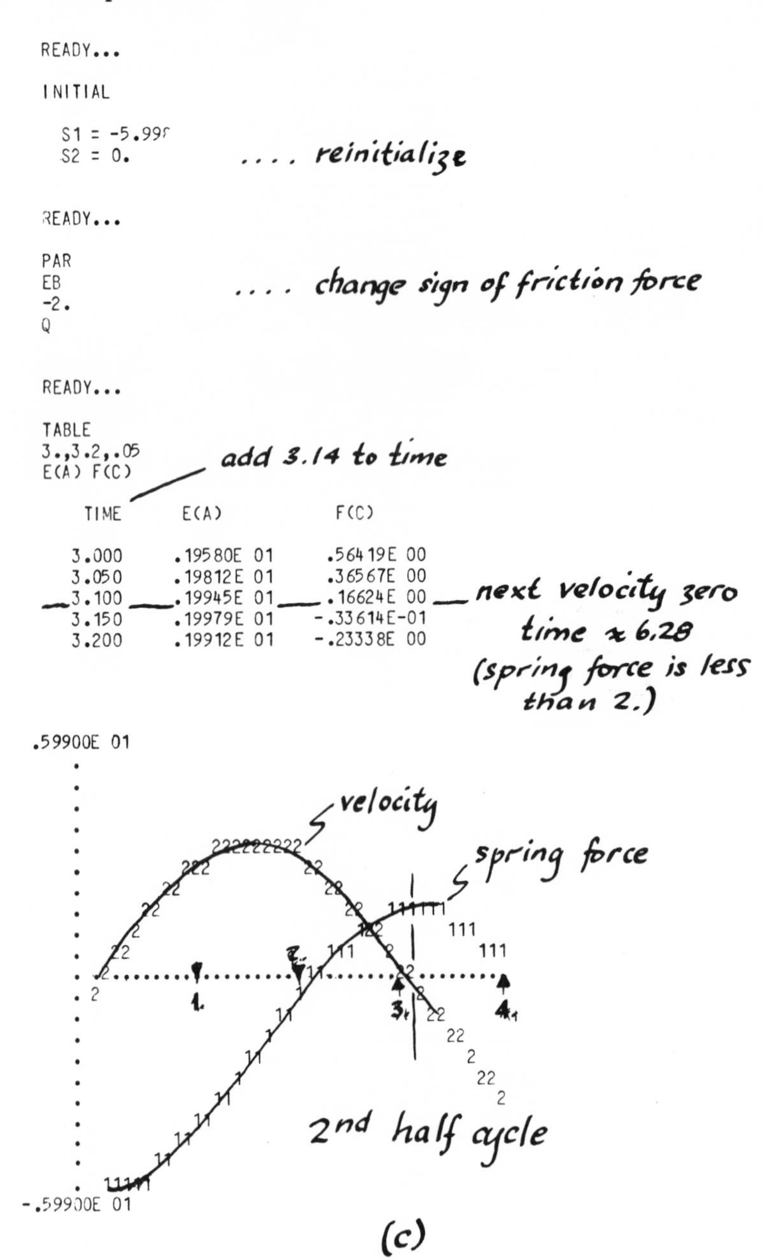

Fig 7-9 (c) second half cycle.

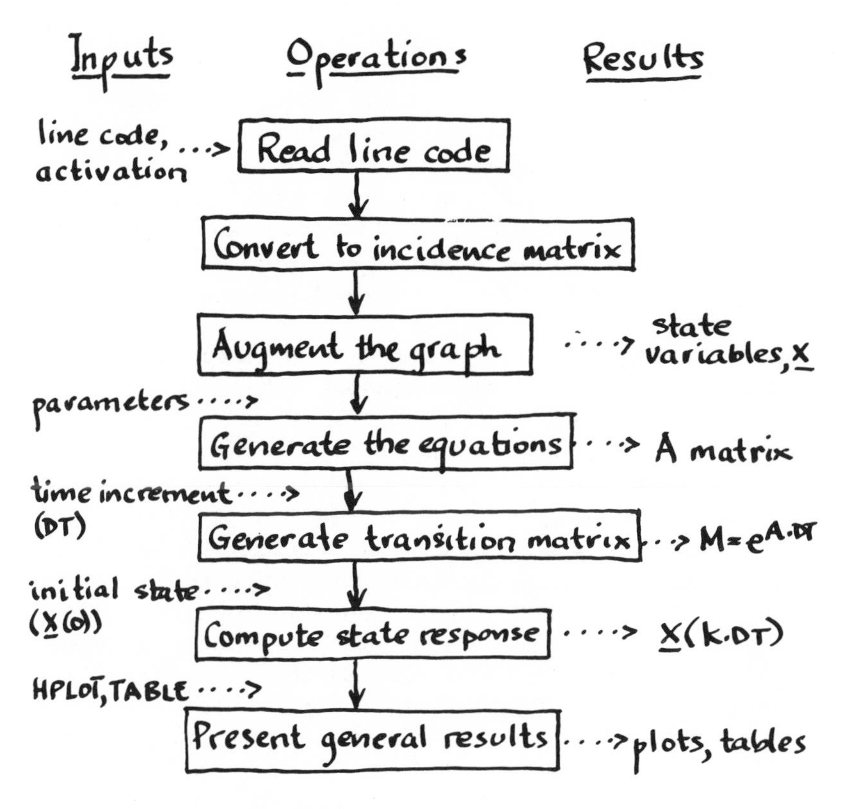

Fig. 7-10 A flow chart for ENPORT-1.

storage and retrieval process applied to the triangle wave generator system of Figs. 7-5 and 7-6. First a working "tape" number is set (in CTSS it is actually a file on the disk storage), and then the system has a remark line appended and is filed, in this case as record 1 on the tape. Subsequently [Fig. 7-11(b)], the tape contents are listed by remark line, and the stored contents of record 1 are examined. Finally, the triangle wave model (record 1) is brought into ENPORT-1 active status, and becomes the working system.

Engineering multiports

As indicated in the preceding section, ENPORT acts as an information expander or amplifier. The relatively succinct statements involved in specifying a system, bond graph, parameters, initial conditions, are transformed into the transient response of a large number of signals, efforts, flows, displacements, energies, over a broad range of time conditions and in a variety of display forms. Furthermore, a small variation in input information can lead to significant changes in the output information.

Such trends in the use of the computer as an assistant in managing information will be accelerated as systems being studied grow more complex and larger. In ENPORT-1 an engineer can file a system or component on which he has been working on "tape," identify it appropriately, and have it available the next time he wishes to retrieve it for further study. The information actually filed is kept to a minimum in order to conserve storage space (see Fig. 7-11). When the system is retrieved it is expanded internally to working form.

An important application of the storage and retrieval concept is in the construction of engineering component models, such as SHAFT 1 2, PUMP 1 2 3, and TRANSISTOR 1 2 3. These elements may be included as recognizable nodes in a bond graph, provided computable models have been stored for them previously. As an example of this concept a detailed model for a radar pedestal drive unit is retrieved, based on a very succinct bond graph of engineering components, as illustrated in Fig. 7-12. Fig. 7-12(a) shows the major components in schematic form. In Fig 7-12(b) a partitioning into multiports has been made. Notice that basic elements like E_S (supply voltage to the armature circuit) and E_C (command voltage to the field circuit) are compatible with elements like SHAFT and MOTOR.

The bond graph of 7-12(c) is assembled by replacing the engineering multiports by their stored equivalents. For example, the element SHAFT is replaced by a model (0-junction, capacitance) that allows for shaft compliance, but no inertia or dissipation. The element GEARS is replaced by the simple 2-port TF, indicating no losses or dynamics whatsoever.

```
SET TAPE                                          ....set working
TAPE NUMBER IS... 24641                               tape index

READY...

FILE                                              ....file the current
                                                      system
PLEASE ENTER A REMARK LINE...
12/21/67...TRIANGLE WAVE GENERATØR...RCR

FILED AS REC  1 ØF TAPE 24641 .
```

(a)

Fig. 7-11 Storage and retrieval of triangle wave generator system. (a) storing the system, (b) retrieval of the stored system.

```
READY...

SET TAPE                                        ....set working tape
TAPE NUMBER IS... 24641

READY...

LISTG                                           ....list stored systems

RECØRD  1
12/21/67...TRIANGLE WAVE GENERATØR...RCR

READY...

READ                                            .... scan the stored
RECØRD NUMBER IS..1                                    data

RECØRD  1
12/21/67...TRIANGLE WAVE GENERATØR...RCR

NB, NN, NSV, PLIST(1...9), KMAX, DT
 10 11  6  3  3  1  0  0  0  0  1  3   165  .1000

THE CØDE
C A,I B,1 A B C,0 C D I J,R J,1 D E F,
C E,I F,1 G H I,C G,I H.

CØDE FØR SIGNALS
 6 9 310 411 5

PARAMETERS
     1.00000      .33000      .20000      1.00000      .33000      .20000
     1.00000

INITIAL CØNDITIØNS
     0.           0.          0.        -10.00000     1.11000     -.40000

END ØF RECØRD  1 .

READY...

SET UP                                          ....retrieve and run
RECØRD NUMBER IS..1                                 the stored system

 ST VBL   1 IS EFFØRT ØN CA
 ST VBL   2 IS EFFØRT ØN CE
 ST VBL   3 IS EFFØRT ØN CG
 ST VBL   4 IS  FLØW  ØN IB
 ST VBL   5 IS  FLØW  ØN IF
 ST VBL   6 IS  FLØW  ØN IH
```

(b)

```
READY...
```

Extrapolation from the example of Fig. 7-12 makes it clear that much of the richness and utility of future ENPORT-like programs will come from the the set of predefined components that make up the allowable bond graph element set. Although the process of naming, storing, and retrieving components seems very straightforward (and it is), the ability to construct a hierarchy of subsystems "piggy-backed" on other subsystems is at the root of any powerful language or technique for growth. Modern electronics offers us a perfect example of this procedure put to sophisticated but broad-scale use. Where would modern electronic computing be but for the ability to use "logic circuits," and aggregates of them, in systems of increasing complexity? And serving as the underpinnings of the hierarchy there are a few key elements–resistors, transistors, diodes, capacitors–on which the whole is built. By analogy, based on an element set, such as (E, F, C, I, R, GY, TF, 0, and 1), we hope to see the growth of engineering multiport models as a major tool in simulation in the future.

A second phase of the ENPORT approach to multiport manipulation is the storage of a series of related models for a particular component. As a simple example consider a series of models for an electric motor, as shown in Fig. 7-13. The first bond graph shows the motor as a 3-port engineering component, MOTOR, having armature, field, and shaft ports. The conventional power directions are also shown, indicating electrical power in and mechanical shaft power out.

Depending upon the over-all system requirements for simulation purposes, MOTOR in Fig. 7-13 could be replaced by one of three computable models shown. The simplest model is the first, which treats the motor as an ideal energy converter. If more accurate steady-state data are desired and if the rest of the system is slow compared to the motor dynamics, a static model with losses can be used, shown as the second model. Notice how the second model has "grown" from the first. If the motor is part of a high performance servo loop, the motor dynamics may play an important part in over-all system behavior. They can be included, at least approximately, by use of the third model. Again, the dynamics can be introduced into the previous model in a constructive way. Clearly, the process of developing more accurate, but more complex, models of given components can be carried on indefinitely. (See, for example, reference 4 for a detailed study of rotating electrical machines.) The important point here is that each model is represented in a form compatible with other component models, so that they may be freely interchanged in assembling and simulating systems. Also, increasing the complexity of a model does not mean demolishing the previous model, but, typically, building on it in a rational way. It is worth emphasizing at this point that nonlinear and linear multiports may be treated alike at the graphical level.

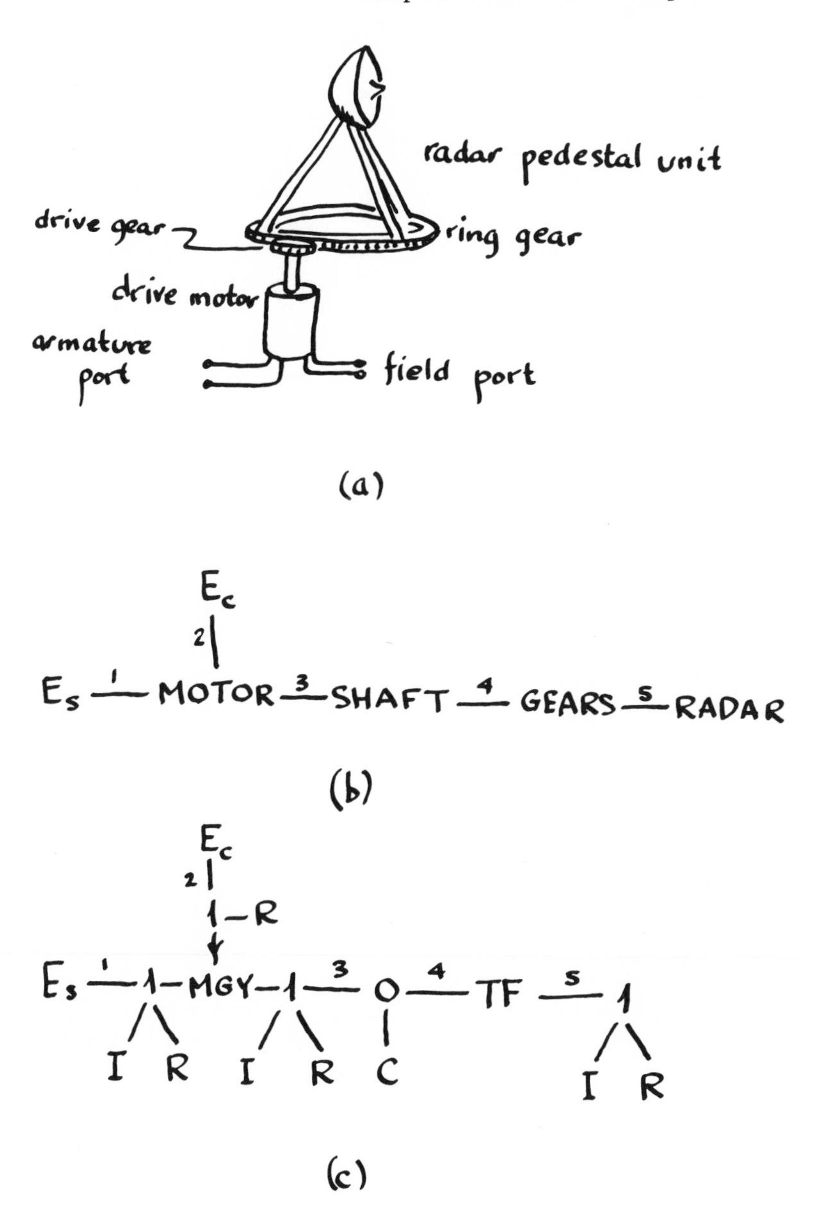

Fig. 7-12 **Bond graph model with engineering multiports. (a) schematic of radar pedestal drive system, (b) graph with engineering multiports, (c) detailed bond graph model.**

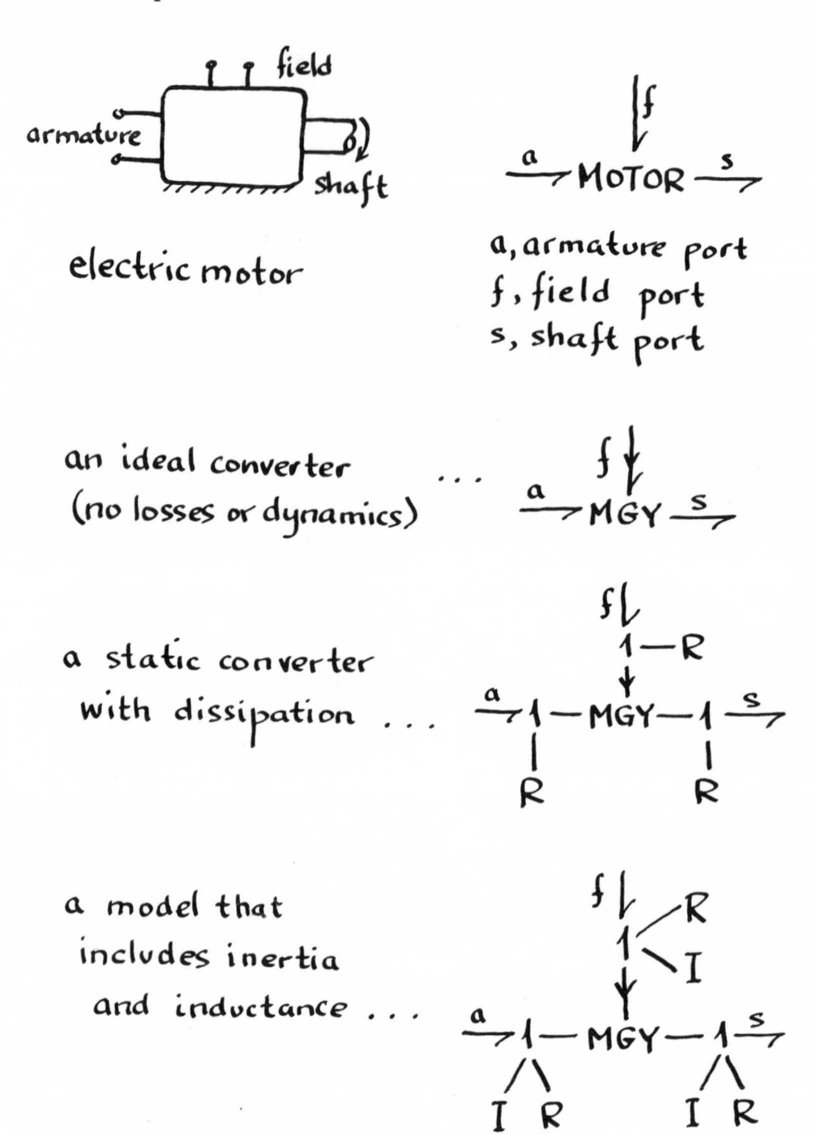

Fig. 7-13 A sequence of structural models for an electric motor.

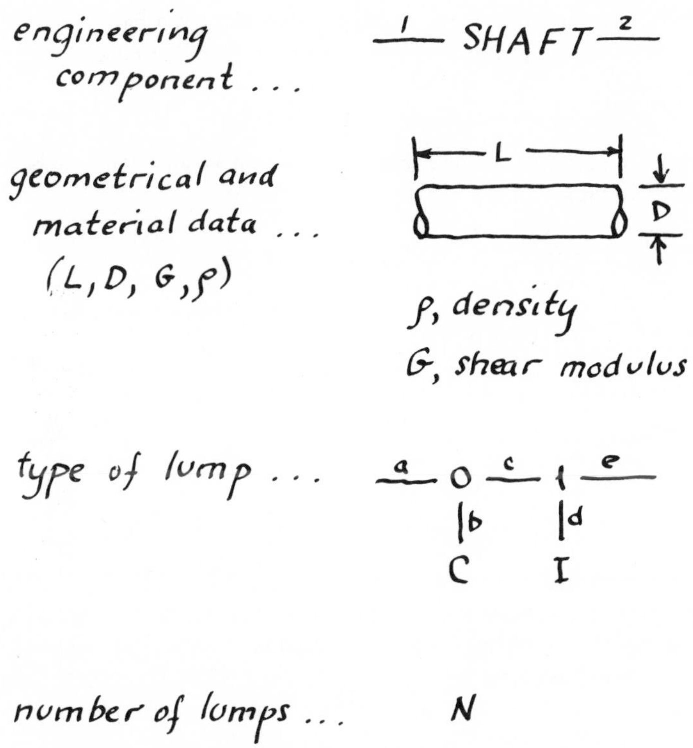

engineering component . . . — 1 — SHAFT — 2 —

geometrical and material data . . . (L, D, G, ρ) — L, D

ρ, density

G, shear modulus

type of lump . . . — a — 0 — c — 1 — e —; b — C; d — I

number of lumps . . . N

Fig. 7-14 Engineering and model data for a shaft in torsion.

One final comment on the subject of engineering multiports is that programs can be developed that allow the engineer to give data about a component in common engineering terms. The programs transform the data into the appropriate form for use with the particular model selected. (See reference 5 for some early efforts in this direction.) As a very simple example of this process we discuss the engineering description of a shaft and an associated lumped parameter bond graph model with its particular parameters. The engineer might like to specify, for a uniform shaft in a system, the type of "lump" to be used, the number of lumps, the geometry, and the material properties (Fig. 7-14). Thus the engineering specification for the uniform shaft in torsion consists of five numbers, L, D, G, ρ, and N, plus the line code (0, a b c, C b, 1 c d e, I d).

ENPORT, on the other hand, needs to relate the given data to the values of of C and I in the unit lump. This is done by storing the relations

$$c = \frac{32}{\pi D^4 C} \qquad \text{and} \qquad i = \frac{\pi}{32} D^5 \rho,$$

which give the capacitance and inertance per unit length. The lumped values of C and I become

$$C = \frac{cL}{N} = \frac{32L}{\pi D^4 GN} \qquad \text{and} \qquad I = \frac{iL}{N} = \frac{\pi D^4 \rho L}{32N} \cdot$$

Then a replacement of

$$\underset{(L,\, D,\, \rho,\, G,\, N)}{\overset{1}{\text{—}}\text{SHAFT}\overset{2}{\text{—}}} \qquad \text{by} \qquad \left[\begin{array}{ccccc} \text{—} & 0 & \text{—} & 1 & \text{—} \\ & | & & | & \\ & C & & I & \\ & (\frac{cL}{N}) & & (\frac{iL}{N}) & \end{array}\right]^N$$

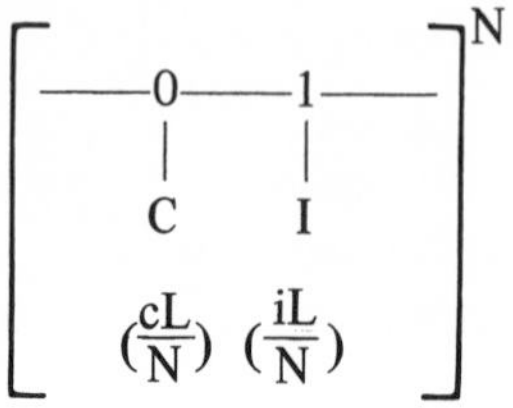

can be accomplished.

If one were to speculate a bit at this point, it might be to envision a computer catalog of engineering multiports, together with sets of computable models for them, available to anyone using the ENPORT system on any computer. As better models or new components are discovered they can be entered into the catalog, thus becoming available to all users. It might then be that much duplication of effort would be eliminated and the current state of sophistication with respect to a given component or set of phenomena will be much easier to discover than it is now. As some sort of goal in this direction one may cite the publication of algorithms in standard notation for digital computer procedures in the Communications of the Association for Computing Machinery.

7.2 Analog simulation

A principal use of analog computers is in the simulation of physical systems. Since the techniques associated with analog simulation, and particularly electronic analog simulation, are well known and well documented, we shall discuss here only the contribution to existing methods of the bond graph approach. In a sense, the possible contribution to analog computation resulting from the use of bond graphs may appear to be less spectacular than the contribution to digital simulation techniques using, for example, the ENPORT programs. This is because in analog computation many operations must be performed by human analysts or operators. (When many of these operations become automated, we would probably consider that a hybrid computer had evolved. Such machines will be discussed briefly in the next section.)

A rough listing of the steps involved in an analog computation might appear as follows:

1. Formation of a suitable quantitative model for the system.
2. Construction of a block diagram in which physical parameters appear.
3. Scaling of the physical variables and construction of a computing block diagram in which dimensionless parameters appear.
4. Setting up the computer, running the simulation with suitable input functions, initial conditions, and output recording apparatus.

Clearly, it is not until the latter stages of step 4 that the computer itself is capable of yielding any useful information. At this point some iteration through the listed steps typically occurs with changes in scaling constants and perhaps in the basic model itself being suggested by the results of the simulation.

It is primarily in the first three steps of an analog simulation that the bond graph techniques and concepts are useful. As we have tried to demonstrate in earlier parts of this book, the main thrust of the bond graph methods is in unifying the procedures for selecting a model of a physical system (step 1 above). In a more specific sense, Chapter 6 discussed methods for passing from a bond graph to the sort of block diagram required in step 2. In contrast to other, less disciplined, means of formulating physical-parameter block diagrams that are in common use, the method using the bond graph has the advantage that the parameters for individual physical elements remain distinct unless the block diagram is purposefully simplified. For many exploratory studies these distinctions are valuable, since the effects of changes in single physical parameters may be easily seen in the simulation without the need of repeated side calculations of the effects on several combined parameters of changes in the single physical parameter.

As we have shown, the aspect of bond graphs necessary for the construction of computable block diagrams is the explicit study of the causality that is possible within the bond graph formulation. Other methods of representing systems, such as circuit graphs, schematic diagrams, or equations, do not generally permit a study of the problems associated with the construction of a computable block diagram without an essentially trial-and-error attempt to set up such a diagram. With the bond graph formalism, the attempt to add causal strokes to the bonds will reveal problems caused by fields, noninvertible functions, and the like, at an early stage in the modeling process. As has been demonstrated, it is always possible to find a computable model of a system through the use of parasitic elements or algebraic reduction of fields, but without the explicit causal indications of bond graphs, the nature of the difficulties and the range of possibilities to circumvent such difficulties are often far from obvious. The existence of the ENPORT program gives evidence that the bond graph techniques can systematize those steps that in analog computation are carried out by pencil and paper manipulations and can be done efficiently by experienced personnel only.

A continuing difficulty in analog computation involves the scaling mentioned in step 3. This step is critical for high-order systems because of the limited dynamic range of analog computers; it is hard to systematize since the ranges of variables during the simulation are hard to predict. While bond graphs probably do not provide any unique contributions to the problem of scaling, it is interesting to note that an automatic scaling procedure may be based on a single run of a digital simulation.[6] Thus the use of a bond graph formulation and a digital simulation program such as ENPORT could solve scaling problems for a class of systems, with the bond graph serving to unify the system descriptions for both the analog and digital cases. Such an operation could prove useful in cases involving long running times such as, for example, in statistical studies of dynamic systems with stochastic inputs in which straight digital simulation would be very time-consuming but in which the analog setup might be rather complex. The use of both analog and digital simulation in this manner could be considered a sort of open loop hybrid computation.

7.3 Hybrid simulation

Until recently hybrid (digital-analog) simulation has meant that a configuration that was predominantly an analog computer had been modified or extended, to allow some digitally controlled elements as part of the circuitry. Also, extensive analog-to-digital and digital-to-analog data conversion has been used to work between the two types of simulation. In this section a hybrid computer is described which is predominantly digital in its nerve center but which "farms out" much of its ordinary simulation work to the analog part. Details are to be found in reference 7.

The computer simulates the time response of linear systems and presents the results in a form useful to a person studying system behavior. The basic plan is to use ENPORT-1 to run a trial simulation, on the basis of which it scales the necessary set-up data for an analog computer. ENPORT-1 then sends a minimum of set-up, control, and initialization data (through a teletype) to a special memory unit, which is coupled to an analog computer in such a way that the data held serve to wire and set the gains for the integrator units. Figure 7-15 shows the information flow among the major

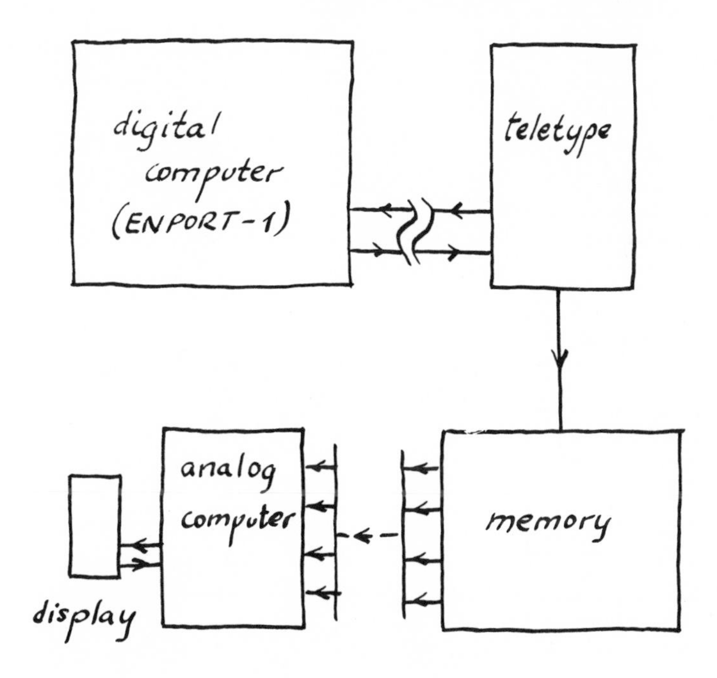

Fig. 7-15 Information flow among major hybrid components.

components. The teletype is useful as a decoder of the transmitted data into bit (or switch) form, so that the memory unit can be loaded. When the memory is in an appropriate state, each word corresponds to a gain in a prewired analog configuration. Under suitable relay control the analog computer results are displayed on an oscilloscope.

In order to understand the close coupling between the analog integrators and the memory, it is best to work backward (in terms of information flow) from the integrators to the memory. Each integrator is organized as shown in Fig. 7-16; there are four such units completely wired (i.e., each integrator output goes to all four integrator units as input). Figure 7-17 shows, in diagrammatic form, the over-all relation between the memory words that set the coefficients and the integrator units.

The integrator units are organized along the lines of the Philbrick K5-U Universal Linear Operator unit, which performs a scaling-summation-integration operation of a maximum of four inputs.[8] Instead of hand-set resistances for establishing the scaling coefficients, a set of digitally controlled "transconductors" is used. A functional diagram of a transconductor is shown in Fig. 7-18. One also notes, from that figure, that each memory word contains nine bits plus a sign. Each bit value is indicated by a light on the front panel of the memory unit. Since the memory words are

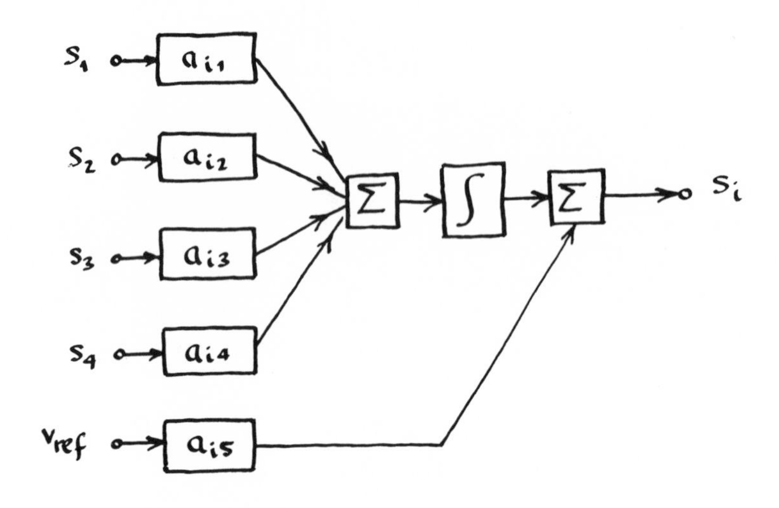

initial condition : $s_i(0) = a_{i5} \cdot V_{ref}$

integration form : $s_i(t) = s_i(0) + \int_0^t \sum_{j=1}^{4} a_{ij} \cdot s_j \cdot dt$

derivative form : $\dot{s}_i(t) = \sum_{j=1}^{4} a_{ij} \cdot s_j \; ; \; s_i(0)$

Fig. 7-16 Block diagram of a typical integrator unit.

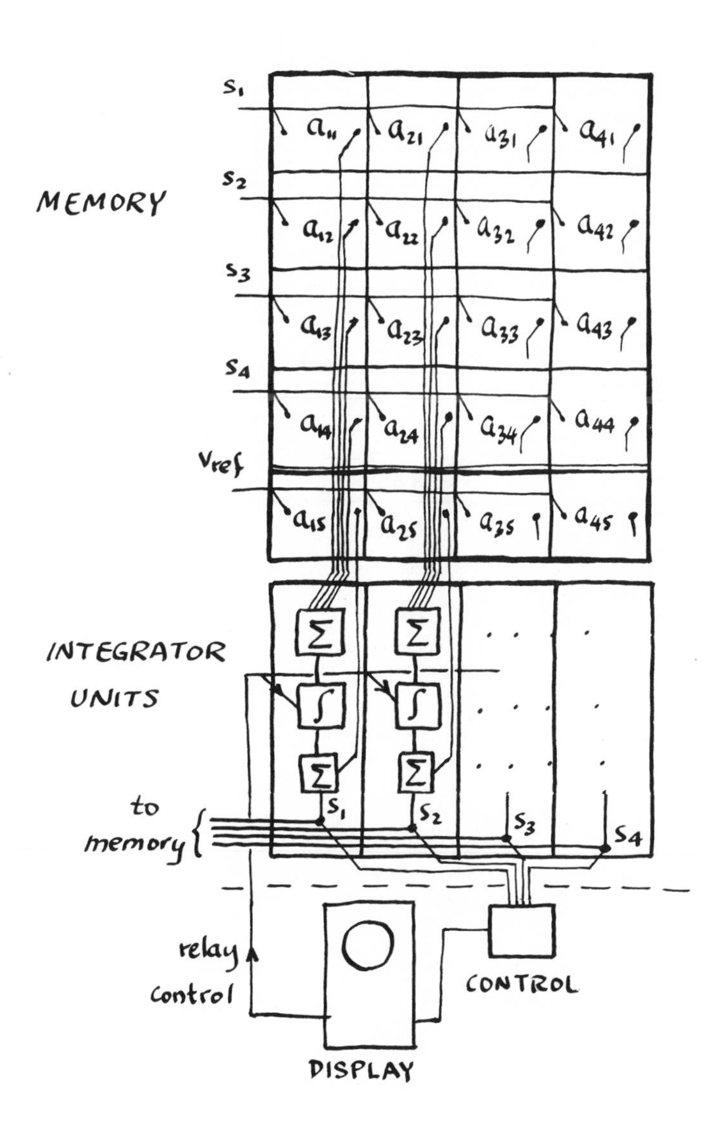

Fig. 7-17 Schematic of the analog computer and display.

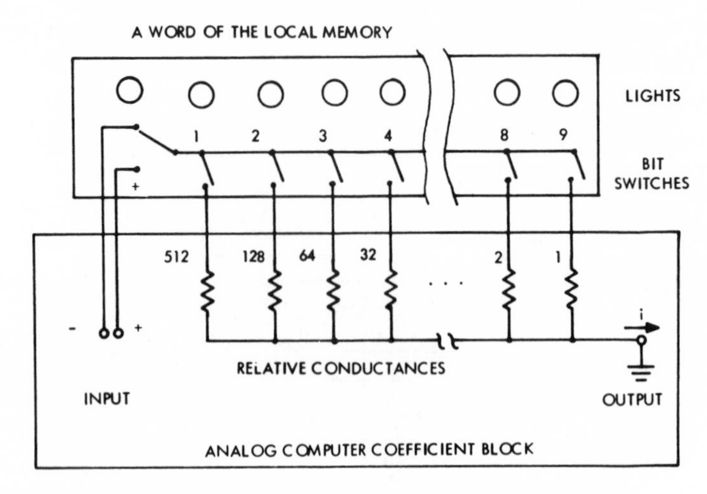

INPUT	DATA BITS	OUTPUT
VOLTAGE	SWITCH POSITIONS	CURRENT, i
s	0 000 000 000	0 s
s	1 000 000 001	-1 s
s	0 000 000 011	3 s
s	1 110 000 000	-768 s

Fig. 7-18 Technique used to set the coefficients.

spatially arranged in one-to-one correspondence with their use as matrix coefficients, the binary form of the coefficient array is displayed visually. This fact may be used to advantage in visually checking the memory and the display in rough form.

The actual information transferred from ENPORT-1 to the memory in order to conduct a simulation includes

(1) a set of control characters;
(2) a set of A-matrix coefficients, which contain both the structural and parametric information;
(3) a set of initial conditions for the simulation variables.

Having an analog computer under complete digital control presents certain advantages in generating time responses. Since ENPORT-1 is able to express any effort, flow, displacement, or momentum, in terms of a linear combina-

```
LOADGO MTEST TBIT
W 1008.5
 NEED BR      CLOCK
R 10.033+.833

USE BRCLOK
W 1008.9
EXECUTION.

'MEMORY' WILL LOAD, CLEAR, AND THEN LOAD MEMORY.
'CLEAR' WILL CLEAR MEMORY.
'RAMP12' WILL GENERATE RAMPS WITH INTEGRATORS 1 AND 2.
'RAMP34' WILL GENERATE RAMPS WITH INTEGRATORS 3 AND 4.
'SELF' WILL SET UP A FIRST ORDER SYSTEM FOR EACH INTEGRATOR.
'OSC12' WILL SET UP AN OSCILLATING SYSTEM WITH INTEGRATORS 1 AND 2.
'OSC34' WILL SET UP AN OSCILLATING SYSTEM WITH INTEGRATORS 3 AND 4.
'MEMO', WHERE 'O' IS AN INTEGER 1-6, WILL PERFORM THE MEMORY TEST
    ON ONE OF THE SIX VERTICAL WORD BLOCKS.
'CLEARO', WHERE 'O' IS AN INTEGER 1-6, WILL CLEAR ONE OF THE
    SIX VERTICAL WORD BLOCKS.


INITIAL CONDITIONS OF INTEGRATORS--
   INTEGRATOR       I.C
        1            +30
        2            +10
        3            -10
        4            -30


GO AHEAD..
```

Fig. 7-19 Test commands for the hybrid computer.

tion of the state variables, any set of these variables may be displayed by transforming the matrix of coefficients from A. That is,

given $\quad DX = AX$

and $\quad \mathbf{Y} = \mathbf{CX}$, where $\mathbf{C}$ is square,

then $\quad DY = \mathbf{CAC}^{-1}\mathbf{Y}$, and $\mathbf{Y}(0) = \mathbf{C}\cdot\mathbf{X}(0)$.

Also, as previously mentioned, automatic scaling is performed to ensure a set of signals that neither exceed the analog limits nor are too small to be useful. Another valuable dimension of flexibility is the ability to start the transients at any point in time (not necessarily at the zero point) and inspect a time range scaled to be maximum for the analog capabilities. The net effect has been described as "having a movable window with a rubber frame" which one can shift over the time responses.

A point of interest to those who have had to verify the working condition of an analog computer is the ease with which the equipment is checked. Figure 7-19 shows a set of commands that can be used to put the analog computer into a predetermined state. For example, typing 'RAMP12' should cause a pair of ramp signals to appear on the display, signal 1 starting at +30 and signal 2 at +10. Any deviation in a signal is attributable to its particular channel (i.e., coefficients and integrator) directly. The memory itself is visually checked by typing 'MEMORY'. This causes every word to be cleared (i.e., set to zero), then completely loaded (all lights on), and then cleared again. By simply typing a few of the commands it is possible to make a quick but accurate diagnosis of any malfunctions.

This small hybrid computer, built to test the organizational feasibility of the over-all plan, was used in a set of experiments in computer-assisted instruction in dynamic system behavior.[9] Some typical times for scaling and set-up (predominantly limited by the teletype transmission rate) were about four seconds for a second-order system and eight seconds for a closely coupled third-order system.

References

1. J. J. Clancy and M. S. Fineberg, "Digital Simulation Languages: A Critique and a Guide," *AFIPS Conf. Proc.*, v. 27, part 1, 1965 FJCC, pp. 23-36.
2. P. A. Crisman et al., *The Compatible Time-Sharing System, A Programmer's Guide,* The M.I.T. Press, Cambridge, Mass., 1963.
3. N. Leal-Cantu, *On the Simulation of Dynamic Systems with Lumped Parameters and Time Delays,* MAC-TR-45, Project MAC, M.I.T., Cambridge, Mass., Oct. 1967.
4. L. L. Evans, *Simulation Techniques for the Study of Non-linear Magnetic Field Engineering Systems,* Sc.D. Thesis, Dept. of Mechanical Engineering, M.I.T., Cambridge, Mass., August 1967.
5. E. R. Banks, *On the Simulation of Engineering Multiports,* M.Sc. Thesis, Dept. of Mechanical Engineering, M.I.T., Cambridge, Mass., Feb. 1968.
6. H. M. Paynter and J. Suez, "Automatic Digital Setup and Scaling of Analog Computers," *Trans. ISA,* v. 3, 1964, pp. 55-64.
7. R. C. Rosenberg et al., *A Low-cost Output Terminal for Time-shared Computers,* MAC-TR-38, Project MAC, M.I.T., Cambridge, Mass., March 1967.
8. *Philbrick Analog Applications Sheet SK5-U,* G. A. Philbrick Researches, Inc., Allied Drive, Dedham, Mass.
9. R. C. Rosenberg, *Computer-Aided Teaching of Dynamic System Behavior,* ESD-TR-66-260, Electronic Systems Division, U.S.A.F., Hanscom Field, Bedford, Mass., Nov. 1965.

INDEX